WOMAN'S WEEKLY
TREASURY
FOR 1984

"Treasury – a place where treasure is stored . . . a repository of information . . ." So says the dictionary. It sums up exactly the aims and ambitions of this little book. Within its pages we have collected all the ingredients that you enjoy week by week in Woman's Weekly magazine. There are 10 delightful romantic stories, knitting patterns for all the family, advice on fashion, beauty, travel and gardening, delicious recipes from our test kitchen . . . and many more of your favourite magazine's popular features.

**Spring, Summer, Autumn, Winter . . .
throughout the year, Woman's Weekly Treasury will be
your valued companion.**

SBN 85037-983-0

IPC Magazines Ltd., 1983

£2·25

WOMAN'S WEEKLY
TREASURY

THE FOUR SEASONS

FICTION

KNITTING

COOKERY

ENTS

TRAVEL

CRAFTS

GARDENING

BEAUTY AND FASHION

MISCELLANEOUS

YOU'LL FIND COLOUR ILLUSTRATIONS

SPRING

**Spring goeth all in white
Crowned with milk-white May**

Robert Bridges

BREAKING BUD

*All the green torrent of spring
Surging forth from this small sturdy bud;
All the great brotherhood
Of the green and growing earth,
Coming to birth
In this tiny focal point of it all:
Soft rainfall;
Wide meadows, great hills, deep woods,
Gardens everywhere,
In this stir of new life
Coming into leaf;
The whole of spring
In this miraculous, marvellous,
Tiny thing!*

Aileen E. Passmore

Good Morning, Good Breakfast

We all know that a really good breakfast makes all the difference to getting the best out of the day ahead. So whether you're on your own, you've a husband or family to feed, or are entertaining friends to 'brunch', here are some breakfast dishes to give you that top of the morning feeling all day long.

Liz Burn

BREAKFAST IN A HURRY

If a big cooked breakfast isn't possible, tuck into fruit juice, wholegrain cereal (especially home-made muesli mix served with fruit), lots of milk or yogurt, adding toast and marmalade if you're really hungry.

CRUNCHY MUESLI MIX

Makes 20 portions

1 lb. porridge or Jumbo oats
4 oz. wheatgerm
2 oz. demerara sugar
6 oz. sultanas
8 oz. toasted oat cereal
2 oz. bran
2 oz. toasted chopped hazelnuts or mixed nuts
$1/8$ level teaspoon salt
½ level teaspoon cinnamon, optional

Mix all the ingredients well together. Store in an airtight container until required. The muesli will keep in a dry place for 2 months.

To serve: Vary it day by day by adding fresh fruit such as sliced bananas, grapes, oranges, or fruit salad, and serve it with milk, plain yogurt or fruit juice.

WEEKDAY BREAKFASTS

If you and your children have got a long, busy and energetic day ahead it really is a good idea to have a cooked breakfast. Anything from the following will do:

TRADITIONAL BACON AND EGGS

For each person allow:

1-2 rashers back bacon
1 egg
½-1 tomato
A few mushrooms
A little oil or fat

Using a pair of scissors cut the rinds off the smoked bacon; if you prefer, rinds can be left on green or unsmoked bacon. Fry the rashers gently at first until some of the fat starts to flow then increase the heat slightly. Turn the rashers over to fry the second side, at the same time adding the wiped mushrooms and halved tomatoes with a little more fat or oil. Fry for 1-2 minutes, then carefully push to the side. Add a knob of fat and add the egg. Cook over a medium heat — the hotter the fat the more crispy the egg. Baste the yolk with fat during frying.

FAMILY FISH CAKES

Makes 6

1 lb. coley fillet or other white fish
1 lb. potatoes
4 tablespoons water and 4 tablespoons milk
Salt and pepper
1 level tablespoon freshly chopped parsley
A little seasoned flour
1 large egg, beaten
Browned breadcrumbs
Fat or oil for frying

Peel, cook and cream the potatoes.

Wipe the fish and put it into a shallow pan with the water and milk and a little seasoning. Bring the liquid to the boil, cover the pan then reduce the heat and poach the fish for about 15 minutes or until it is cooked. Drain it well then, using two forks, remove the skin and flake the coley. Mix the fish in a bowl with the creamed potatoes, parsley and plenty of seasoning. Divide the mixture into 6 equal portions and shape into about ½ inch thick flat cakes.

Put the flour, egg and breadcrumbs all on separate plates. Coat each fish cake in flour, egg and finally in breadcrumbs. Heat a little fat or oil in a frying pan and cook the fish cakes on both sides until golden brown and heated through.

More recipes overleaf

FRENCH TOAST

Serves 2

1 egg, size 2 or 3
2 tablespoons milk
A pinch each of salt and sugar
3 slices bread
Oil for frying
½ level teaspoon cinnamon
1-2 oz. sugar

Beat the egg with the milk, salt and sugar. Cut each slice of bread into 4, dip each piece into the egg mixture and fry gently in the oil until crisp and golden on both sides.

Mix the cinnamon and sugar together and use to sprinkle over the hot toast.

Serve with stewed apple or sausages.

BRUNCH

This meal combines the best of breakfast and lunch. It's a mid-morning meal, usually served at weekends for all the family or as an informal way of entertaining friends. It usually includes dishes there's never time to make on weekday mornings. A typical menu includes such things as: citrus cocktail; muesli with peaches and cream; grilled kippers or kedgeree; scrambled egg; croissants, toast, preserves; coffee.

Kedgeree, a good hot rice and fish main dish for Brunch with friends.

CITRUS COCKTAIL

Serves 4

3 grapefruit
3-4 oranges
Sugar to taste

Prepare the fruit: with a really sharp knife, cut a slice from the top and base of each fruit then work all the way round until it is completely free of peel and white pith. Hold the prepared fruit in your hand over the serving bowl to catch the juice, and cut into each segment in turn. Lift out the fruit sections and place in the bowl. Discard the centre membrane and any pips.

Add sugar to taste and leave for an hour or so, so that the sugar dissolves and forms some juice. Chill before serving.

KEDGEREE

Serves 3-4

1 lb. smoked haddock
Few sprigs parsley
½ bay leaf
1 lemon
Few peppercorns
2 oz. butter
1 small onion, peeled and finely chopped
6 oz. long grain rice
¾ pint fish liquor (see recipe)
Salt and pepper
3 eggs, size 3, hard-boiled

Rinse the haddock; cut into large pieces. Put in pan and add about 1 pint water just to cover. Add washed stalks of parsley—reserve tops for garnish—bay leaf, half the lemon cut in slices, and peppercorns. Bring to the boil. Cover with lid then remove pan from heat. Leave at the side of the cooker for about 15 minutes until the fish is cooked. Strain off cooking liquor and reserve ¾ pint for cooking rice.

Melt 1 oz. butter in pan, add the onion, cover with lid and cook gently for 5 minutes. Stir in rice and mix well with butter and onion; pour over fish stock, adding salt and pepper if necessary. Bring to boil, stir, cover pan with lid and simmer gently over a low heat for 15-20 minutes or until cooked and the water absorbed.

Remove skin and bones from fish. Break into flakes. Cut eggs into quarters, then, with a fork, fold these into the cooked rice. Add the rest of the butter cut in pieces and a little juice from the remaining lemon half.

Pile into hot serving dish. Sprinkle with snipped parsley and serve.

GRILLED KIPPERS

Allow 1 kipper per person. Cut off the heads neatly. Place skin side up on an oiled grill rack. Grill under a medium heat for 3-4 minutes. Turn over once half-way through the cooking.

If preferred, place the kippers in a jug or deep dish and pour on enough boiling water to cover and let them stand for 5 minutes before draining.

Serve with a knob of butter on top.

SCRAMBLED EGGS

Serves 4

6 eggs

6 tablespoons milk

Salt and pepper

1 oz. butter

Whisk the eggs, milk and salt and pepper together until well mixed.

Heat the butter in a non-stick pan, add the eggs, straining them in if preferred. Cook over a low heat, stirring most of the time with a wooden or non-stick spatula. Stir so that the egg cooks in large flakes. When the scrambled egg is thick and glossy but still moist spoon on to buttered toast or serve with fried mashed potato cakes.

Devilled Scrambled Egg: this adds a zippy flavour that adults will like. To the eggs add ¾ level teaspoon dry mustard and ½ teaspoon Worcestershire sauce. Cook as above.

CROISSANTS, ROLLS AND PRESERVES

Serve a basket of warm croissants and rolls with butter, marmalade and any other home-made preserve. Especially good are black cherry and apricot.

TEA AND COFFEE

I won't tell you how to make tea because everyone has her own way of making a cuppa.

Coffee: You can use the instant variety, but if like me you like the smell as well as the taste of freshly brewed coffee, here is the simplest way of making it:

You need an earthenware or china jug, boiling water and freshly ground medium coffee; here is the simplest way of making it: For each ½ pint of water allow a heaped tablespoon of coffee, but adjust the amount to suit your taste. Scald the pot by pouring boiling water in the bottom, swizzling it round then tipping it out. Then put in the coffee, add the boiling water and put on the lid, or cover with cling film. Leave for 5 minutes — cover with a cosy if you like. Stir once to settle the grounds, then serve with hot or cold milk.

Serve in large cups or mugs — it tastes better!

If Brunch is a party, set the mood with a perfect mid-morning drink, Bucks Fizz — one third fresh orange juice and the rest chilled champagne or sparkling white wine, mixed in the glass.

LEADING LADY

It's such a joy to see the classic jacket back in fashion, especially as it is a design so well suited to most figure-types, most age groups. Our smart Aran-style version is knitted in double moss stitch with trellis and cable panels and goes up to a size 46-inch bust.

Instructions in 7 sizes

Colour photo on page 20

Continued overleaf

This design will look good in almost any basic colour. Choose from crimson, blue, cactus, paprika, matelot, camel or dusk blue.

LEADING LADY Continued

MATERIALS: *Allow the following quantities in 50 g balls of Patons Capstan for Aran Knitting: 17 for 86 cm size; 18 for 91 cm size; 19 for 97 cm and 102 sizes; 20 for 107 cm size; 21 for 112 cm size; 22 for 117 cm size. For any one size: A pair each of No. 7 (4½ mm) and No. 9 (3¾ mm) knitting needles; a cable needle; 7 buttons.*

TENSION: *Work at a tension of 18 stitches and 25 rows to measure 10 x 10 cm, over the double moss stitch, using No. 7 (4½ mm) needles, to obtain measurements given below.*

ABBREVIATIONS: To be read before working: *K., knit plain; p., purl; st., stitch; tog., together; inc., increase (by working twice into next st.); dec., decrease (by taking 2 sts. tog.); s.s., stocking st. (k. on right side and p. on wrong side); d.m.st., double moss st.; cr. 2, cross 2 (slip next st. on to cable needle and leave at back of work, k.1, then k.1 from cable needle); tw. 2 lt., twist 2 left (slip next st. on to cable needle and leave at front of work, p.1, then k.1 from cable needle); tw. 2 rt., twist 2 right (slip next st. on to cable needle and leave at back of work, k.1, then p.1 from cable needle); c. 4, cable 4 (slip next 2 sts. on to cable needle and leave at back of work, k.2, then k.2 from cable needle); cr. 3, cross 3 (slip next 2 sts. on to cable*

needle and leave at back of work, k.1, slip p. st. from cable needle back on to left hand needle then bring cable needle to front of work, p. st. from left hand needle, then k.1 from cable needle); single rib is k.1 and p.1 alternately.

NOTE: *The instructions are given for the 86 cm (34 inch) size. Where they vary, work figures within first brackets for the 91 cm (36 inch) size; work figures within second brackets for the 97 cm (38 inch) size, and so on.*

THE BACK: With No. 7 (4½ mm) needles cast on 93 (97) (101) (105) (113) (117) (121) sts. and work in d.m.st. with panel pattern as follows: **1st row:** For d.m.st. * k.1, p.1; repeat from * 11 (12) (13) (14) (16) (17) (18) times, for panel k.4, p.1, k.1, p.3, ** cr. 2, p.3; repeat from ** 5 times, k.1, p.1, k.4, for d.m.st. * p.1, k.1; repeat from this * 11 (12) (13) (14) (16) (17) (18) times.

2nd row: For d.m.st. * p.1, k.1; repeat from * 11 (12) (13) (14) (16) (17) (18) times, for panel p.4, k.1, p.1, k.3, ** p.2, k.3; repeat from ** 5 times, p.1, k.1, p.4, for d.m.st. * k.1, p.1; repeat from this * 11 (12) (13) (14) (16) (17) (18) times.

3rd row: For d.m.st. * p.1, k.1; repeat from * 11 (12) (13) (14) (16) (17) (18) times, for panel k.4, p.1, ** tw. 2 lt., p.1, tw. 2 rt.; repeat from ** 6 times, p. 1, k.4, for d.m.st. * k.1, p.1; repeat from this * 11 (12) (13) (14) (16) (17) (18) times.

4th row: For d.m.st. * k.1, p.1; repeat from * 11 (12) (13) (14) (16) (17) (18) times, for panel p.4, k.2, ** p.1, k.1, p.1, k.2; repeat from ** 6 times, p.4, for d.m.st. * p.1, k.1; repeat from this * 11 (12) (13) (14) (16) (17) (18) times.

These 4 rows form the repeat of the d.m.st. at each end. Keeping continuity of the d.m.st. over 24 (26) (28) (30) (34) (36) (38) sts. at each end, continue working centre panel.

5th row: D.m.st. to panel, c.4, p.2, ** cr. 3, p.2; repeat from ** 6 times, c.4, d.m.st. to end.

6th row: D.m.st. to panel, p.4, k.2, ** p.1, k.1, p.1, k.2; repeat from ** 6 times, p.4, d.m.st. to end.

7th row: D.m.st. to panel, k.4, p.2, ** k.1, p.1, k.1, p.2; repeat from ** 6 times, k.4, d.m.st. to end.

8th row: As 6th row.

These 8 rows form the repeat of the 4-st. cable pattern at each end of centre panel. Working a cable over these 4 sts. every 8 rows from previous cable, continue remainder of panel.

MEASUREMENTS *in centimetres (and inches, in brackets)*				
To fit bust sizes	86 (34)	91 (36)	97 (38)	102 (40)
All round at underarms, fastened	94.5 (37¼)	98.5 (38¾)	103 (40½)	107.5 (42½)
Side seam	40 (15¾)	40 (15¾)	40 (15¾)	40 (15¾)
Length	62.5 (24½)	63.5 (25)	63.5 (25)	64 (25¼)
Sleeve seam	49 (19¼)	49 (19¼)	49 (19¼)	49 (19¼)

9th row: D.m.st. to panel, pattern 4, p.2, ** k.1, p.1, k.1, p.2; repeat from ** 6 times, pattern 4, d.m.st. to end.

10th row: D.m.st. to panel, pattern 4, k.2, ** p.1, k.1, p.1, k.2; repeat from ** 6 times, pattern 4, d.m.st. to end.

11th to 18th rows: Repeat 9th and 10th rows, 4 times.

19th row: D.m.st. to panel, pattern 4, p.2, ** cr. 3, p.2; repeat from ** 6 times, pattern 4, d.m.st. to end.

20th row: As 10th row.

21st row: D.m.st. to panel, pattern 4, p.1, ** tw. 2 rt., p.1, tw. 2 lt.; repeat from ** 6 times, p.1, pattern 4, d.m.st. to end.

22nd row: D.m.st. to panel, pattern 4, k.1, p.1, k.3, ** p.2, k.3; repeat from ** 5 times, p.1, k.1, pattern 4, d.m.st. to end.

These 22 rows form the repeat of the centre 37-st. pattern. Keeping continuity of d.m.st., cables and centre pattern, pattern a further 78 rows.

To shape armholes: Keeping continuity of pattern, dec. 1 st. each end of next row and the 6 (7) (8) (9) (11) (12) (13) following alternate rows —79 (81) (83) (85) (89) (91) (93) sts.

Pattern 23 (23) (21) (21) (17) (17) (15) rows.

To slope shoulders: Cast off 7 (5) (6) (6) (8) (6) (7) sts. at beginning of next 2 rows, then 6 (7) (7) (7) (7) (8) (8) sts. on the following 6 rows.

Cast off remaining 29 (29) (29) (31) (31) (31) (31) sts.

THE LEFT FRONT: With No. 7 (4½ mm) needles cast on 47 (49) (51) (53) (57) (59) (61) sts. and work in d.m.st. with panel pattern as follows: **1st row:** For d.m.st. * k.1, p.1; repeat from * 11 (12) (13) (14) (16) (17) (18) times, for panel k.4, p.1, k.1, ** p.3, cr. 2; repeat from ** twice, p.2.

2nd row: For panel k.2, ** p.2, k.3; repeat from ** twice, p.1, k.1, p.4, for d.m.st. * k.1, p.1; repeat from * to end.

3rd row: * P.1, k.1; repeat from * 11 (12) (13) (14) (16) (17) (18) times, k.4, p.1, tw. 2 lt., p.1, ** tw. 2 rt., tw. 2 lt., p.1; repeat from ** to end.

4th row: K.1, p.1, k.2, ** p.1, k.1, p.1, k.2; repeat from ** twice, p.4, * p.1, k.1; repeat from * to end.

These 4 rows set the position of the pattern and panel. Keeping continuity of pattern to match back, work a further 24 rows.

To divide for pocket opening: Next row: Pattern 8 (10) (12) (14) (18) (20) (22), turn and

leaving remaining sts. on a spare needle, work on these sts. for back half.

The back half: Work 1 row, then inc. and work in d.m.st. 1 st. at end of next row and the 13 following alternate rows —22 (24) (26) (28) (32) (34) (36) sts.

Break yarn and leave sts.

The front half: With right side facing, rejoin yarn to inner end of sts. on spare needle and dec. 1 st. at beginning of 3rd row and the 13 following alternate rows —25 sts.

Joining row: Pattern across these 25 sts. then pattern across sts. of back half —47 (49) (51) (53) (57) (59) (61) sts.

*** Pattern a further 42 rows

To shape armhole: Dec. 1 st. at *beginning*— read *end* here when working right front of next row and the 2 following alternate rows, work 1 row.

To continue shaping armhole and shape front edge: Dec. 1 st. at each end of next row and the 3 (4) (5) (6) (8) (9) (10) following alternate rows —36 sts.

Work 1 row, then dec. 1 st. at front edge only on next row and the 10 (9) (8) (8) (6) (5) (4) following alternate rows — 25 (26) (27) (27) (29) (30) (31) sts.

Pattern 1 (3) (3) (3) (3) (5) (5) row(s)— pattern 2 (4) (4) (4) (4) (6) (6) rows here when working right front.

To slope shoulder: Cast off 7 (5) (6) (6) (8) (6) (7) sts. at beginning of next row and 6 (7) (7) (7) (7) (8) (8) sts. on the 2 following alternate rows.

Work 1 row, then cast off remaining 6 (7) (7) (7) (7) (8) (8) sts.

THE RIGHT FRONT: With No. 7 (4½ mm) needles cast on 47 (49) (51) (53) (57) (59) (61) sts. and work in d.m.st. with panel pattern as follows: **1st row:** For panel p.2, ** cr. 2, p.3; repeat from ** twice, k.1, p.1, k.4, for d.m.st. * p.1, k.1; repeat from * to end.

2nd row: For d.m.st. * p.1, k.1; repeat from * 11 (12) (13) (14) (16) (17) (18) times, for panel p.4, k.1, p.1, ** k.3, p.2; repeat from ** twice, k.2.

3rd row: P.1, tw. 2 rt., ** tw. 2 lt., p.1, tw. 2 rt.; repeat from ** twice, p.1, k.4, * k.1, p.1; repeat from * to end.

4th row: * K.1, p.1; repeat from * 11 (12) (13) (14) (16) (17) (18) times, p.4, k.2, p.1, ** k.1, p.1, k.2, p.1; repeat from ** twice, k.1.

These 4 rows set the position of the pattern and panel. Keeping continuity of pattern to match back, work a further 24 rows.

To divide for pocket opening: Next row: Pattern 39, turn and leaving remaining sts. on a spare needle work on these sts. for front half.

The front half: Work 1 row, then dec. 1 st. at end of next row and the 13 following alternate rows —25 sts.

Break yarn and leave sts.

Continued overleaf

107	(42)	112	(44)	117	(46)
116.5	(45¾)	121	(47½)	125.5	(49½)
40	(15¾)	40	(15¾)	40	(15¾)
64	(25¼)	65	(25½)	65	(25½)
49	(19¼)	49	(19¼)	49	(19¼)

The back half: With right side facing rejoin yarn to inner end of sts. on spare needle and inc. 1 st. at beginning of 3rd row and the 13 following alternate rows — 22 (24) (26) (28) (32) (34) (36) sts.

Joining row: Pattern across these sts. then pattern across 25 sts. of front half — 47 (49) (51) (53) (57) (59) (61) sts.

Work as given for left front from *** to end, noting variations.

THE LEFT SLEEVE: With No. 9 (3¾ mm) needles cast on 49 (53) (53) (57) (57) (61) (61) sts. and, beginning odd-numbered rows with k.1 and even-numbered rows with p.1, work 30 rows in single rib.

Change to No. 7 (4½ mm) needles.

1st row: * K.1, p.1; repeat from * 5 (6) (6) (7) (7) (8) (8) times, for panel k.4, p.1, k.1, p.3, cr. 2, p.3, cr. 2, p.3, k.1, p.1, k.4, * p.1, k.1; repeat from this * 5 (6) (6) (7) (7) (8) (8) times.

2nd row: * P.1, k.1; repeat from * 5 (6) (6) (7) (7) (8) (8) times, p.4, k.1, p.1, k.3, p.2, k.3, p.2, k.3, p.1, k.1, p.4, * k.1, p.1; repeat from this * to end.

3rd row: * P.1, k.1; repeat from * 5 (6) (6) (7) (7) (8) (8) times, k.4, p.1, ** tw. 2 lt., p.1, tw. 2 rt.; repeat from ** twice, p.1, k.4, * k.1, p.1; repeat from this * to end.

4th row: * K.1, p.1; repeat from * 5 (6) (6) (7) (7) (8) (8) times, p.4, k.2, ** p.1, k.1, p.1, k.2; repeat from ** twice, p.4, * p.1, k.1; repeat from this * to end.

These 4 rows form the d.m.st. and set position of the pattern panel. Keeping continuity of the pattern to match back, working extra sts. into d.m.st. as they occur, inc. 1 st. each end of next row and the 12 following 8th rows — 75 (79) (79) (83) (83) (87) (87) sts.

Pattern a further 7 rows.

To shape sleeve top: Dec. 1 st. each end of next 24 (26) (26) (28) (28) (30) (30) rows — 27 sts.

For shoulder extension: Pattern 31 (31) (33) (33) (35) (35) (37) rows — read 32 (32) (34) (34) (36) (36) (38) rows here for right sleeve.

To shape for back neck extension: Cast off 8 sts. at beginning of next row, then dec. 1 st. at same edge on next row and the 7 following alternate rows — 11 sts.

Work 1 (1) (1) (3) (3) (3) (3) row(s).

Cast off.

THE RIGHT SLEEVE: Work as left sleeve, noting variation.

THE LEFT POCKET BACK: With No. 7 (4½ mm) needles cast on 22 sts. and s.s. 26 rows.

Dec. 1 st. at *beginning* — read *end* here when working right pocket back — of next row and the 13 following alternate rows.

Work 1 row then cast off remaining 8 sts.

THE RIGHT POCKET BACK: Work as left pocket back noting variation. Sew shaped row ends of pocket backs to shaped row ends of back half of pocket openings, then catch outer edges to wrong side.

THE POCKET RIBBINGS (2 alike): With right side facing, rejoin yarn and using No. 9 (3¾ mm) needles, pick up and k. 33 sts. from shaped row ends of front half of pocket openings and beginning with an even-numbered row, work 5 rows in single rib as given on sleeves.

THE BUTTON BORDER AND REVERS: With No. 9 (3¾ mm) needles cast on 11 sts. and work 114 rows in rib as given on sleeves.

To shape revers: Inc. 1 st. at *beginning* — read *end* here when working buttonhole border and revers — of next row and the 13 (14) (14) (15) (15) (16) (16) following alternate rows — 25 (26) (26) (27) (27) (28) (28) sts.

Work 1 row, then cast off in rib.

THE BUTTONHOLE BORDER AND REVERS: With No. 9 (3¾ mm) needles cast on 11 sts. and work 10 rows in rib as given on sleeves.

1st buttonhole row: Rib, 4, cast off 3, rib to end.

2nd buttonhole row: Rib to end, casting on 3 sts. over those cast off on previous row.

Rib 14 rows.

Repeat last 16 rows 5 times, then the 2 buttonhole rows again.

Rib 6 rows, then shape revers as on button border and revers, noting variation.

THE COLLAR: With No. 9 (3¾ mm) needles cast on 45 (45) (45) (49) (49) (49) (49) sts. and work 2 rows in rib as on sleeves.

Keep continuity of the rib and working extra sts. in rib as they occur, inc. 1 st. each end of next row and the 7 (7) (7) (8) (8) (8) (8) following alternate rows — 61 (61) (61) (67) (67) (67) (67) sts.

Rib 15 rows.

Cast off in rib.

TO MAKE UP THE JACKET: Press with a warm iron over a damp cloth. Join cast off edges of back neck extensions, and with end of this seam to centre back, sew straight row ends of extensions to shoulder slopings and neck edge of back. Sew shoulder slopings of fronts to straight row ends of shoulder extensions, then set in remainder of sleeves. Join side and sleeve seams. Sew front bands into place, setting revers shapings to front neck shaping with cast off edge level with shoulder seams. Sew cast-on edge of collar round neck, setting increases of collar to part of the cast off groups at top of revers. Sew row-ends of pocket ribbings to right side. Add buttons. Fold sleeve ribbings in half to right side.

WEDDING LISTS

A few helpful pointers from our fashion staff to bear in mind when planning clothes for a wedding

THE BRIDE Decide on your style of dress, and whether you are going to have a conventional white wedding dress or settle for something less formal, like a suit or dress and jacket. If you decide to have your outfit made, it's a good idea to go into a bridal department and try some styles on to give you an idea what suits you before you buy your pattern and fabric. If you are buying a dress, go to a reputable bridal specialist like Pronuptia who have branches throughout the country, and where you can buy literally everything you need, from bridesmaid's dresses to going-away outfits, all under one roof! If you wish to hire your dress or the bridegroom and best man want to hire or buy morning dress, he can do so from Young's of Wardour Street, London, W1 (who also have their own departments in Pronuptia shops) or from Moss Bros. of Bedford St., Covent Garden, London WC2. Write for detailed information. Pronuptia have now produced a booklet in conjunction with Elizabeth Arden entitled "Guide to Bridal Beauty" which is free to all their customers.

Mother-of-the-Bride/Guest Try to stick to an outfit that's fairly classic and that you will be able to get a lot of wear out of afterwards. Remember that classic things can always be dressed up with the aid of clever accessories. Don't buy something that is totally out of character for you; stick to a style you know suits you. It's always as well to bear in mind the wedding photographs and choose a good clear colour for your outfit that will show up well against the crowd, and again, stick to a colour that you know flatters you. Try and match up your hat to the colour of your

Photo courtesy Ellis Bridals

ensemble, and opt for shoes, bag and gloves in a toning colour. Any outfit looks so much more attractive with just a little thought and careful planning and if you've managed to match and tone your accessories to perfection, you can make an ordinary outfit look a million dollars!

RIBBON BOUQUETS

If you wish to make the ribbon flowers for the charming bouquets, slides and so on shown in colour on page 22, you can send for free instruction leaflets from: Eve Harlow, C. M. Offray & Son Ltd., Fir Tree Place, Church Road, Ashford, Middlesex TW15 2PH, enclosing a large, stamped self-addressed envelope and mentioning Woman's Weekly Treasury 1984.

13

To help get you
back into shape after
a little over-indulgence,
whilst giving you the
nourishment you need

DAY 1

On waking
Unsweetened lemon
juice, diluted

Breakfast
1 egg, boiled or poached, 1 slice of
wholemeal toast, lightly 'buttered' with
Outline margarine or similar
1 orange
1 cup of tea or coffee with milk (no sugar, but
you may use artificial sweeteners: this goes
for all cups of coffee and tea mentioned)

11 a.m.
One large glass of tomato juice

Lunch
Large helping of grilled fish
Large helping Brussels sprouts *or* carrots
1 slice wholemeal bread
An apple or a pear
Cup of coffee, with milk

4 p.m.
One cup of lemon tea

Dinner
2 generous slices of liver, grilled (or you could
braise it in ¼ pint beef stock, with herbs
Large portion of cauliflower or cabbage or
sprouts
A side salad of lettuce or white cabbage,
shredded and mixed with sliced cucumber,
carrots, tomatoes, radishes, green peppers,
dressed with 1 tablespoon vegetable oil and 1
tablespoon vinegar, plus any of your
favourite herbs
1 apple or pear, 1 cup of coffee

Evening
Cup of Bovril

DAY 2

On waking
Unsweetened lemon
juice, diluted

Breakfast
Muesli, consisting of 2 oz. raw porridge oats
mixed with 1 oz. each of brown sugar, raisins or
sultanas and chopped almonds or hazelnuts.
Serve with milk
Cup of tea or coffee

11 a.m.
Glass of tomato juice or cup of Bovril

Lunch
Bowl of any thin, clear soup
Omelette, made with 2 eggs (you can season it
with fresh herbs or add chopped mushroom to
it)
Green salad (lettuce, cucumber, celery, green
pepper)

An orange, cut into slices
Cup of coffee

4 p.m.
Cup of tea or coffee

Dinner
2 medium lamb chops, trimmed of fat, grilled
or baked
Large helping of any *two* of the following:
Brussels sprouts, peas, carrots, cauliflower,
string beans, cabbage (preferably fresh or
frozen, not tinned)
1 slice wholemeal bread, lightly 'buttered' with
Outline margarine or similar
1 apple or pear, or small bunch of grapes
Coffee

Evening
Cup of Bovril

 **DAY 3**

On waking
Unsweetened lemon juice, diluted

Breakfast
A carton of plain yogurt (empty it into a bowl) with 1 tablespoon of clear honey stirred in, and a few sultanas and chopped almonds, if liked
1 slice of wholemeal toast
Cup of tea or coffee

11 a.m.
Glass of unsweetened orange juice

Lunch
A bowl of any thin, clear soup
2 crispbreads, spread with slices of beef, corned beef, chicken or ham, plus lettuce, plus a tomato
1 apple or pear
Cup of coffee

4 p.m.
Cup of Bovril or lemon tea, no sugar

Dinner
2 generous pieces of grilled fish
Large helping of cabbage or sprouts or cauliflower, *plus* 2 medium boiled potatoes
1 apple or pear
Coffee

Evening
Cup of Bovril

 **DAY 4**

On waking
Unsweetened lemon juice, diluted

Breakfast
A slice of wholemeal toast, topped with 2 rashers of lean, grilled bacon; 4 or 5 grilled mushrooms
Coffee or tea

11 a.m.
An orange, cut into slices

Lunch
Bowl of any thin, clear soup
Up to 8 oz. cottage cheese, with chives or pineapple, if you like, plus a salad, containing as many of the following as you can muster: lettuce, cucumber, celery, radishes, tomatoes, green peppers, cauliflower florets, carrots
Slice of wholemeal bread *or* 2 crispbreads
Coffee

4 p.m.
Cup of Bovril or a glass of tomato juice

Dinner
2 grilled hamburgers, with onions, if liked (but *no* buns!)
Large helping of carrots
2 tomatoes, sliced and dressed with a little oil, vinegar and herbs
Apple or pear
Coffee

Evening
Tea or coffee, plus a piece of fresh fruit: grapes, apple, pear, melon

 **DAY 5**

On waking
Unsweetened lemon juice, diluted

Breakfast
Slice of wholemeal toast, spread with 1 oz. grated cheese and browned under the grill
An orange, sliced
Cup of tea or coffee

11 a.m.
Glass of tomato juice or vegetable cocktail

Lunch
A Scotch egg with a large mixed salad
Generous hunk of Edam cheese
An apple or a pear
Coffee

4 p.m.
Cup of lemon tea
A handful of dried apricots or figs

Dinner
A baked chicken joint *or* 4 oz. cooked chicken meat
1 medium potato (boiled)
Large helping carrots *and* sprouts
Apple or pear
Coffee

Evening
Tea or coffee

Don't forget that you can switch the order of the days, if you like—but don't switch individual meals (e.g., following the breakfast and dinner for Day 1, but taking the lunch from Day 5).

NOTE: *This is a 5-day diet—meant just for an occasional five days' worth, not longer. And if you have any health problems, always consult your doctor before embarking on a diet.*

Fair Cities

Each season brings its
special magic to these well-loved capitals

Vienna in midwinter — the Old Town, clustered round the Gothic magnificence of St. Stephen's Cathedral in snow-covered beauty, is immediately breathtaking, a Christmas card scene brought to life. Along the pedestrian-only Graben, the shops tempt with their displays of gorgeous furs, boots and elegant shoes, leatherware and the fine petit-point for which the Viennese are famous. The State Opera House programme is in full swing and the Vienna Philharmonic and Symphony Orchestras play to packed houses in this music-loving city where Beethoven and Mozart, Haydn, Schubert and Strauss all found inspiration.

In Demel's café-konditorei and in Sacher's Hotel, stalwart, well-upholstered ladies meet for coffee and slices of the rich chocolate cake called *sachertorte,* covered with thick cream. At the Spanish Riding School, some of the world's finest riders practise the proud art of classical horsemanship on their unique, white Lipizzaner stallions. The Hofburg, the splendid imperial palace of the Hapsburgs, under whose rule the Austrian Empire once stretched far and wide, is open to visitors and, in its medieval chapel, the Vienna Boys' Choir sings on Sundays. Out in the wine-growing village of Grinzing, on the edge of the Vienna Woods, the enormous fun of a Heuriger evening awaits — goulash soup, *backhendl,* the Viennese chicken speciality, *palatschinken,* delicious jam-filled pancakes and good wine, all to be enjoyed to the accompaniment of Viennese songs.

TULIPS, CANALS AND BARREL ORGANS
Spring brings flower beauty to the canal-crossed city of Amsterdam — the stalls and the floating market on the Singel are a mass of daffodils, tulips, narcissi and sweet-scented hyacinths, pink and white candles appear on the chestnut trees and the bare branches of the planes and sycamores that line the canal banks take on their cloaks of sharp, new green. The sun shines on gabled roofs and on the mellow stones of handsome patrician houses and countless little bridges. Glass-topped boats and barges ply the canal waters, carillons ring out from church belfries and men with weatherbeaten faces grind brightly-painted barrel organs on street corners.

In Wynand Fockink, favourite of the liqueur and gin tasting shops that date from the 16th century, customers sip heartwarming glasses of Half and Half, Tip van Bootz and Genever as they exchange the gossip of the day. Shoppers throng the Kalverstraat and the Leidsestraat and sightseers make for the Rijksmuseum to admire priceless paintings by Dutch Old Masters; for the house where little Anne Frank hid for two long years before being betrayed to the Nazis; for

Rembrandt's house in the old Jewish quarter; for the house known as Our Lord of the Attic, in whose secret upstairs room the once-persecuted Catholics practised their faith; for the old Béguinage off Spui — an oasis of peace in the midst of the city's bustle.

The glass-sheltered pavement cafés along the Damrak fill with coffee-drinkers. The wealth of restaurants invite the hungry to sample delectable Dutch specialities, including the Indonesian rice table feast. After dark, Amsterdam swings, the Leidseplein and the Rembrandtsplein the centres of its nightlife.

Athens in high summer — tourists scramble over the stones of the Acropolis, worn to glassy smoothness by sun and wind, rain and winter frost and by generations of sightseeing feet. The tongues of many nations rise as tour guides try bravely to capture the history of two thousand years in a few minutes, the intonations of their patter those of long familiarity. Bouzouki music, together with the mouthwatering smell of kebabs grilling over vine twigs, emerges from the tavernas of the Plaka, the old quarter that nestles on the lower slopes of the Acropolis. The frequent, high-pitched screeching of tyres tells the world that an Athenian driver is turning a corner. Shops tempt with painted icons, hand-embroidered dresses and blouses, pottery, goatskin rugs, sponges, woven bags and pleasing jewellery. Down in the colourful Microlimano, the one-time Turkish Harbour at Piraeus, the waterfront restaurants serve superb fresh-caught fish and plates of Greek salad topped with fetta cheese. In the main harbour, cruise-liners and the island ferries jostle for precious mooring space. And, as darkness falls, there can be few more memorable sights than moonlight shining on the pillared splendour of the Parthenon.

Rome, the Eternal City, in the lingering warmth of autumn — below the St. Angelo Bridge, crossed by thousands of pilgrims on their way to St. Peter's, the yellow Tiber trickles lazily, the first leaves begin to fall and scurry across the street to the wind's whim, a mellow sun bathes the walls of ancient palaces and churches. Visitors toss coins into the Trevi Fountain, cluster on the Spanish Steps, admire the overwhelming beauty of the Sistine chapel, Michelangelo's ceiling well worth the inevitable crick in the neck, shop along the Via Condotti and the Via Sistina, streets of infinite temptation, enjoy coffee or drinks at the pavement tables of Doney's or Harry's Bar along the fashionable Via Veneto, ride the length of the Via Appia Antica, the Way of Tombs, by horse-drawn carriage, wander through the incomparable gardens of the Villa D'Este at Tivoli, dine out in Trastevere, the picturesque old quarter.

*T*he twin spires of Vienna's neo-Gothic Votivkirche, built in thanksgiving for the failure of an assassination attempt on the life of Emperor Franz Joseph, stand in striking silhouette against the darkening sky as night falls on this beautiful city, a delight to explore at any season of the year.

18

F irm favourite with the menfolk — a fisherman rib sweater in three bold colours with comfortable raglan sleeves. (Instructions on page 34.) *Left:* Bags of bags . . . A zip-up holdall, roomy shoulder bag, plus a trio of smaller handbag cases — all to sew from quilted fabrics. See page 37.

*N*othing can beat the splendid British breakfast! Start the day well with something appetising and nourishing. A variety of suggestions starts on page 7. *Left:* This good-looking Aran-style jacket is at home in town or country. Instructions on page 9, comes in a wide range of sizes, too.

*F*or baby with love—a delightful set of bonnet, bootees, mitts and little matinée jacket in a pretty lacy stitch. (Instructions on page 41.) *Left:* Clever alternative to real flowers for that wedding bouquet or bridesmaid's posy—ribbon flowers! A lasting reminder, and simple to make from Offray's free leaflet (see page 13).

*S*pring sowings of vegetables under glass bring super summer crops. *Top left:* Stringless varieties of Runner Bean are easy to prepare. *Top right:* Peppers (Capsicums) may be harvested green or red. *Lower left:* Tasty Celery has almost no calories! *Lower right:* Pumpkin *Spirit*, fun to grow *(photo: Dobies Seeds)*.

YOUR GARDEN IN SPRING

With the lengthening days, plants are bursting into growth and it's "all systems go", says JOY SIMMONS

Gladioli corms, planted from March to May, will give a succession of blooms.

FLOWER GARDEN

Finish forking over perennial borders not later than March. During a mild spell, protective covering can be removed from the less hardy perennials.

Prepare the ground in readiness for Sweet Pea sowing towards the end of March and during early April. These delightful flowers can be grown in circles at the back of an herbaceous border, trained up a wigwam of sticks, or in the form of hedging where space is limited.

The spent blooms from Hydrangeas can be trimmed back to sound growth as soon as the new leaves begin to unfold after the frost.

Forsythia can be cut back after flowering.

In sheltered gardens Rose pruning can be carried out in February. In the north it is advisable to leave this job until March.

Apply a Rose fertiliser in April, lightly forking it into the soil surface. Where bushes suffered from black spot last season, spray with a fungicide when the new leaves appear.

Sprinkle slug pellets among rock plants and young perennial shoots or water them with a liquid slug killer.

Lawns should be raked free from matted growth now. Mowing can begin in March provided that the cutters are set high.

Where it appears necessary, you can apply a lawn weedkiller in April. This can take the form of a selective lawn weedkiller or, if you prefer, a weedkiller plus fertiliser.

Gladioli can be planted from March until the end of May, placing the corms 4 in. deep and 8 in. apart in rich, loamy soil.

KITCHEN GARDEN

Plant shallots from February to March, 10 in. apart with the tips just showing. Protect them from birds with Netlon.

At the end of February, given a mild spell, early Potatoes can be planted.

French Beans may be sown under cloches from mid-March onwards, or outdoor sowings can be made towards the end of April.

Sow Lettuces, Radishes, Onions, Leeks, Parsnips, Turnips and Broad Beans after the middle of March.

In easily worked soil, first early Peas may be sown in early March, and second early varieties from late March onwards.

Carrots can be sown at the end of March; Beetroots, Spinach, Cabbage and Brussels Sprouts in April.

Finish pruning Gooseberries and Apples in February. Apples should be sprayed against scab at bud burst and green cluster stages. Check for aphis, spraying with systemic insecticide.

Perennial herbs may be sown from March to May, and annual varieties during April and May.

Continued overleaf

25

GREENHOUSE

Scrub woodwork, staging, pots and pans, adding a dash of Jeyes Fluid to the water. Clean glass, removing algae.

Sow Lobelia, Geraniums (Pelargoniums), Dahlias, Heliotrope, fibrous-rooted Begonias, Antirrhinums, Phlox drummondii and Petunias in February and March at 15-18° C (60-65° F).

Tomatoes can also be sown if they are to grow on in a warm greenhouse.

Sow Aubergines, Peppers, Celery, Sweet Corn, Courgettes and Runner Beans in late March for transplanting outdoors later.

Sow Marrows and Pumpkins singly in 3 in. pots during April to plant out in May or June.

Space out seedlings in other boxes when large enough to handle.

Seeds can be raised in a propagator on a warm window-sill.

Plant out on a prepared site in late spring.

KEEPING HOUSE PLANTS HAPPY

Spring is a good time to repot most house plants, when they are starting into active growth. As a rule, however, they should only be repotted when the pot is full of roots. Many kinds can be propagated by root division.

Before removing them from their pots, water well. Use a good potting compost such as John Innes No. 1 or 2, or a proprietary soil-less (peat-based) compost. Never use garden soil.

Repot flowering plants into a pot that is only slightly larger, otherwise the roots and foliage will develop at the expense of flowers.

African Violets in particular flower better when pot-bound provided that the plants are fed regularly.

Large foliage plants which may not take kindly to repotting should have the top inch or two of soil replaced with potting compost.

Allow Cyclamen to dry off gradually after flowering. The corm can be repotted in July or August.

Pot-grown Primulas may be planted in a semi-shady spot outdoors after the frost. Lift them and repot them in a peat-based compost in September.

Keep a sharp look-out for pests. *Murphy's Systemic Insecticide* controls most pests, or insert a *Phostrogen Plant Pin* in the pot. However, these handy little pins are not suitable for all plants, so check before buying.

Left to right: African Violet, Chlorophytum, Geranium and Tradescantia.

Prelude to Spring

By Audrie Manley-Tucker

Her father had once said that in every life there came a
time of waiting — a brief span between the last frost and
the unfolding of the buds of spring. The past year had
been Rosemary's waiting time. Now she was ready to
turn her face to the sun — and her first love . . .

ROSEMARY WAS squatting on her heels in the Harlequin café, touching up the legs of chairs whose paint had been kicked and scuffed by last season's holidaymakers. It was a job she did every year for Meriel Adams who owned the café and the shop next-door, and who always took a month's holiday in March to prepare herself for a new season of holidaymakers. Not that Millwick Bay was ever flooded with visitors. A mile away, cars roared along the motorway towards Hampshire and Dorset, but some families turned off, year after year, to bump down the straggling lane that led to the small Sussex village by the sea.

The people who came to Millwick didn't care that there was no pier, no promenade, no amusements. They rented one of the small cottages along the bay, and their children played happily on the sands. Artists came to paint; dedicated sailing types bobbed up and down the bay in small boats.

There was only one street, with an assortment of houses — all of them old — plus a butcher's shop with a thatched porch. The shop was owned by Harry Brampton, who wore the same striped apron and straw hat that his grandfather had once worn, and chopped joints of meat on the same wooden block — no prepacked meat in Harry's shop, thank you!

There was a grocer's shop; a fish shop where the words *'Freshly caught'*, written on the window, were a statement of fact, not a doubtful boast; a cosy little pub called 'The Sailor's Arms' — a name on which many a ribald jest had been founded. There was nothing else, except the café and souvenir shop at the end of the bay.

The Harlequin was empty, except for the chairs being painted; from it a step beneath a wide arch led down into the shop next-door, where soon the shelves would be full of paperbacks for people to doze over on the beach. There would be a fresh supply of picture postcards on the revolving stand, and shellcraft souvenirs in the window; beachballs, sandals and shrimping nets would festoon the doorway that led to the beach.

Rosemary finished the yellow chair and stood it carefully on its sheet of newspaper to dry; she began on the red one, working with quick, neat strokes. She was a small, slim girl with a quiet face, blue eyes, and thick fair hair caught into a big tortoiseshell slide on her neck. She had an air of independence and self-sufficiency. Because she hated to be scruffy, even when she was working, her faded jeans were clean and uncreased, topped by a blue-and-white-checked blouse.

As she worked, she thought about the time of year, this no-man's-land between winter and spring. Today was a dreaming day, calm and windless, warm in the sunlight. A silky sea nudged small boats anchored in the bay, and spread fans of lacy foam along the curving shoreline.

Continued overleaf

ROSEMARY WAS neither happy nor sad, but calm, like the day, enjoying the rhythm of her painting. Her thoughts went backwards, not forwards, because the future held little meaning for her at the moment. No doubt it would shape itself in time, she thought tranquilly. It would be nice if people would leave her alone, though, instead of trying to push her this way and that, urging her into decisions she did not want to take. But it was very difficult to tell them all so, without hurting their feelings.

A shadow darkened the doorway and she looked up quickly. At first, she thought the man who stood there was a stranger. He was very tall, casually dressed in sweater and jeans; his hair was thick and black and curly, which gave him a slightly rakish air; his hazel eyes were full of laughter. A good-looking man, confident, self-assured, smiling down at her.

"We aren't open," she said quickly. "The season doesn't start until the beginning of next month."

"Pity," he said, with disarming candour. "I saw the open door and remembered that Meriel Adams used to make gorgeous sandwiches — the right kind, with more filling than bread — and her home-made cakes were something to remember."

"I've brought a flask of tea," she said. "There's plenty. You can have a cup, if you like."

"Are you sure? Well, that's kind of you," he said. "Thank you."

He would be used to people doing things for him, offering to supply anything he needed, she thought. She sat back on her heels, still holding the brush, as she studied him.

"Nothing changes here," he said, with great satisfaction. "I haven't been back in ten years, and it's still the same old Millwick. Isn't that wonderful?"

She stood up, and went across to the counter behind which the thick, white china cups hung on hooks. She took down two cups and poured tea into them, knowing he was still watching her.

"I had a marvellous holiday here, ten years ago," he told her. "The Fullers, my uncle and aunt, had three kids and they used to rent a cottage here every year. That year, I was with them for a month. The cottage is at the end of the street, the one that's nearly on the beach. Even the shutters are still the same colour — red. I'm staying there now."

CAREFULLY, ROSEMARY concentrated on pouring his tea so that she didn't spill it. He came and leant his arms companionably on the counter as she passed a cup across to him.

"Thank you," he said again, with great charm. "I promise to patronise your café for the rest of the time I'm here — two months."

"It isn't my café; it still belongs to Meriel Adams. I'm just getting it ready for her," she told him.

"I've already had a look around," he told her. "The butcher's hasn't changed; nor the little fish shop with the marble slab and the stuffed bird in the glass case. This place is a gem. Wonderful for a TV documentary on Unspoiled English Seaside Villages."

"No!" she said sharply. "Then hordes of people would come here."

"You'd hate that," he teased.

"Of course. It wouldn't be quiet and unspoiled any longer."

"Then I promise not even to consider it," he said firmly.

She poured her own cup of tea with great concentration, and studied it intently.

"The house opposite the cottage looks exactly the same," he told her. "It's big and shabby and Edwardian, with an overgrown garden. The man who lived there was called John Graham. He was a nice old boy — well, he wasn't that old, really. About fifty. He told me he'd got out of the rat race, retired early, to do the things he'd always wanted to do, like painting and fishing. He taught me how to fish, actually."

"He died last year," Rosemary said sedately.

"I'm sorry," he said regretfully. "He had a daughter. She was about twelve and her name was Rosie; a *fat* little girl, very solemn, and with a dreadful crush on me. She followed me everywhere. It was fearfully embarrassing. I got teased unmercifully. The more I tried to keep out of her way, the more she pursued me. She never said much; she was just *there*, looking at me all the time. She didn't go swimming or sailing or play with the other kids. Her father once said she was a loner. I wonder what happened to her?"

"She's still living in Bay House."

"You mean, she's still there?" he said in light-hearted dismay. "She'll be — let me see — about twenty-two, now."

"I shouldn't think she'd bother you," Rosemary told him. "She's pretty busy these days."

Something in the dryness of her voice bothered him.

"How well do you know her?" he asked.

Continued overleaf

"I've known her all my life," Rosemary told him tranquilly. "I have to get back to my painting. Excuse me."

"Do you live in Millwick?" he asked.

"Yes." She pushed back a straying tendril of hair and looked him straight in the eye. "I'm your nearest neighbour. I live at Bay House, Mr. Wilmot. No one calls me Rosie any more. I shed all the puppy fat a long time ago, and I also grew out of having crushes on big-headed seventeen-year-old schoolboys."

IF SHE had been furious, it would have been easier, Alec thought. It was her air of complete detachment about it all that made it worse.

"Oh, Lord, I am sorry!" he groaned. "I didn't recognise you."

"Of course you didn't," she said kindly.

"You look so different," he said. "I'd never have believed . . ."

"No." Her smile was still kind. She gave a small, dismissive nod and picked up her brush.

"Anyone can make a mistake," she assured him. "People change a lot in ten years, you know."

"Rosie . . ." he began desperately.

"Rosemary," she reminded him.

"Rosemary." He looked at her, dismayed. "That was a pretty awful *faux pas*, wasn't it?"

"People make them all the time," she pointed out, busy with her brush.

Her detachment was complete; she wanted to get on with the job but was too polite to tell him outright that he was wasting her time.

When she looked up, he had gone. She thought about him as she went on painting. She could still remember how she had felt, at twelve years old. He had dazzled her, like a bright being from another world. Good-looking and relaxed, he had been kind to her at first. Then he had started to suggest that there might be other things she'd like to do rather than keep tabs on him.

'I was a nuisance,' she reflected. 'I still remember the tight, painful feeling I had whenever I saw him. There's nothing quite like the awful agony of first love.'

When she had finished, Rosemary cleaned her brushes, put the cans away and locked up the shop. There was a chill in the evening air. The sea looked languid, as though it scarcely breathed, and she could see a ruffle of white clouds across the bay.

The telephone was ringing when she stepped into the hall. She knew it would be her cousin Meg, calling from Bristol.

"Rosemary, dear, it's bad for you to live alone in that great house. And Millwick is such a dead-end place . . ."

"I like them both, the house and Millwick," she said. "Stop worrying."

"We *all* worry," Meg said reproachfully.

That was true. Meg, Cousin Jane in London, Aunt Helen, various friends . . . And all Rosemary wanted was time to think, to gather herself together, find out what she wanted to do, what kind of person she really was. They would have thought she was mad if she had told them that. So she listened to Meg, and said she was fine, and why didn't Meg come down and see for herself one weekend?

AFTERWARDS SHE went into the big, old-fashioned kitchen and heated coffee, made an omelette, put fruit and cheese on a tray. She carried it into the conservatory, because she liked the view of the tanglewood garden from its long windows. There was an old wrought-iron table there, and a chair, and all around her were the ferns and plants her father had loved.

She had just finished her supper when she heard the knock at the front door. It was Alec, trying to look contrite and not doing it very well. He probably wasn't used to contrition, she decided.

"Look . . ." he began.

"Would you like to come in and have a drink?" she asked.

"Actually, I was going to suggest we could walk down to 'The Sailor's Arms'."

"It gets very crowded on a Saturday night," she told him.

He stepped into the hall and followed her into the big sitting-room with its old-fashioned chairs, long rows of books, and paintings of ships and seas and flying gulls that all bore John Graham's signature on them.

"There was a tree at the bottom of the garden," Alec said, nodding towards the conservatory, and the view beyond it. "It was a wild fuchsia, covered with red tassels. It was the prettiest thing I ever saw."

"It's still there, only it's too early for the flowers yet," she said.

"The lily pool? The apple tree?"

"All still there." She smiled, handing him a glass of sherry. "Do you want to look?"

In the last of the light they wandered down the garden, carrying their drinks, which made the situation seem easy and relaxed. He looked at the little twisted tree and nodded with satisfaction; he watched the fish flick lazily through the water.

When they went indoors, she switched on the lamp and sat down in one of the deep armchairs. She had taken the tortoiseshell slide from her hair and let it fall, thick and shining, over her shoulders. She wasn't beautiful, nor even pretty; it was the quality of stillness about her that made her so attractive, an air of being completely in possession of herself. Her skin was faintly tanned because she lived all the year by the sea; the hand holding the glass was square and capable-looking.

"You must miss your father very much," he said.

"Yes. He was good company. He had so many things to talk about, because he was interested in so much." She nodded towards the books. "Sometimes, he would tap on my bedroom door very early in the morning, and bring me a mug of tea. I always knew what that meant. He wanted me to get up and dress and come out and study the stars — 'before they went down the sky', as he said. Sometimes I'd sit out there and shiver, even with my duffel coat on, but he was always so pleased I'd come — and I learned quite a lot."

ALEC SAID reminiscently: "He said once that your mother left him because she didn't want to live in a place like this; she loved London and a social life."

"Yes," Rosemary replied. "After the divorce, she married and went to America. I wrote to her when Father died, and she wrote back and said how sorry she was, and that she had married again. That was all. I didn't answer; there didn't seem anything to say."

"Will you stay here?" he asked.

"I don't know. Perhaps. Sometimes I feel as though my father isn't dead at all, and that I'm just keeping the house tidy until he comes back."

"I shall call you Rosie," he said suddenly. "It suits you."

She smiled, with gentle amusement.

"I'm not twelve years old," she murmured, "not any more."

"Indeed you aren't," he agreed. "What happened in the last ten years?"

"Nothing very much. I went to Italy, because my father thought I ought to study all the art treasures of the world. We went to France just because he wanted to go there. And we went to Spain because I wanted to see the Easter Fair at Seville. I left school and learned to be a secretary. It isn't particularly exciting, but I like it. I see your name sometimes on TV. I remember your telling my father it was what you wanted to do."

"It isn't all that glamorous," he said. "It's mostly hard slog, being one of a team researching facts, and hammering out programmes. But, yes, I like it. I like living in London, being in the heart of things. I've got two months all to myself, the first break since last summer. I thought of going to Greece, and then, suddenly, I remembered Millwick and how I'd enjoyed myself here all those years ago. Isn't that odd?"

She nodded and offered to refill his glass, but he said he hadn't unpacked yet and stood up, so tall that he seemed to fill the room, bringing it to life suddenly.

It was quiet when he had gone. She washed the glasses and her supper things, and thought about him, just a little.

THE NEXT day was Sunday. In the morning she went to the little village church, and then she came home, changed into her working clothes and went down to the café to finish Meriel's chairs, and bring back the flowered curtains to wash. The sun was still warm and a few hardy souls were swimming from the beach. Coming back from Meriel's, she saw Alec walking to the cottage in his swimming trunks.

On Monday morning she drove a mile up the winding lane, then two miles along the motorway before turning off into Melworth. It was a fair-sized town, brisk and busy. There were three estate agents in Melworth, but Banham's was the largest and had been there longest. Rosemary had been Henry Banham's secretary for three years.

Later that day, Alec went into Melworth to buy the odds and ends he had forgotten to bring with him. Passing Banham's, he stopped to look idly at the photographs of the desirable properties decorating the windows, and so saw Rosemary walk across the outer office to speak to a client. He stared at her in disbelief. Her hair was fastened into a smooth knot; she wore an expensive-looking silk shirt and a narrow, dark skirt and high-heeled shoes. She looked crisp, efficient, well-groomed. Not the sort of girl he would dare to call 'Rosie'.

Continued overleaf

When the client had gone, he tapped on the glass. She looked out, saw him and smiled, before she went back to the inner sanctum where Mr. Banham spent most of his days.

She didn't come home until very late that night. Alec, sitting in the window of the scarlet-shuttered cottage, saw her turn into the short drive with its straggling border of rhododendron bushes.

It was none of his business how she passed her time, he reminded himself.

She was in when he went across next evening, and he felt as though he was on familiar ground when he saw her wearing jeans and shirt, her hair loose. This girl had some link, no matter how slight, with the twelve-year-old Rosie whose youthful adoration had been very flattering.

"Let's go out to supper," he said.

"Oh, Alec, I'm sorry, I can't," she told him, shaking her head. "We're having an Arts and Crafts Exhibition on Saturday, and I'm busy finishing a piece of work."

"You were home late last night," he said accusingly.

"I went out to dinner with Mr. Banham," she said.

"Oh?" His eyebrows went up disapprovingly. Rosemary smiled.

"With Mr. Banham *and* his wife. It was my birthday, and they always take me out to a meal then. Isn't that kind of them?"

"Very," he said shortly.

He went away, with the briefest of good nights.

The next evening, she found Alec sitting by the gate when she reached home.

"I can cook," he told her belligerently.

"Yes?" she replied, with polite surprise.

"Cooking for one is ridiculous. I've made a beautiful curry, and a special pineapple dessert. I didn't have time to write out a menu, but I laid the table for two, just in case."

She looked thoughtfully at him, and realised, surprised, that under that charm he was unsure of himself, and unsure of her reactions.

"I need ten minutes," she said.

H E HAD laid the table in the window; lit a small, rose-shaded lamp. He left one of the windows unlatched because the night was surprisingly warm, and they could hear the sound of the sea as it crept up the beach.

He opened a bottle of wine. The curry was good; so was the dessert.

"You're a better cook than I am," she told him. "My father liked his cooking very plain. I'm not much of a gardener, either. I look at it, and think that I should do something or get someone in to put it tidy, but I never do anything about it."

"Why?" he asked bluntly.

"When my father was alive, we didn't bother. And now —" She frowned. "It seems a bit pointless. Everyone is trying to make me decide what to do with my life. I suppose they're right, and I should do something."

"Like what?"

"Sell the house and go round the world; get myself a marvellous, exciting job somewhere. Take life in big gulps, not little sips." She laughed, and he thought what a pretty sound it was.

"Chris accused me of sipping at life. I was nineteen, and we were in love. Well — *I* was. I thought he felt the same. We had that odd, old-fashioned thing called an 'understanding'. Then he suddenly told me one day that he was giving up his studies to go abroad, out to the Far East, to join some kind of commune.

"It was his way of finding himself, realising his personality potential, so he said. I told him it was a marvellous idea, and he said he thought so, too. Only *he* meant it — and I didn't. I missed him horribly for six months, hated him for the next six, and finally decided that as he hadn't written, he wasn't going to come back."

Alec didn't laugh, he merely said: "Your father once told me there was a time of waiting somewhere in everyone's life. It's like the time between winter and spring, when the brief, cold days are almost over and the lovely, warm days aren't here yet. 'The time between the frost and the bud unfolding,' that was the way he put it."

"How long is the waiting time?" she asked ruefully.

"Longer for some people than others," he told her.

O N THURSDAY evening, she went to the café and hung the clean curtains for Meriel. On Friday, she was busy helping to get the hall ready for the Arts and Crafts Exhibition. She was bone-tired when she arrived home, and crawled into bed.

The Exhibition always attracted a crowd of people, because all the work was done locally by

THE ROBIN FAMILY

**The little
Robins hear
the cuckoos'
song a
little early . . .**

THE FIRST
SIGN OF SPRING ?

"LISTEN!" whispered Rosemary Robin, stopping suddenly as she and her brother and cousin were walking through the Woodlands on their way to school.

Roley and Richard obediently stopped and listened.

"Cuckoo! Cuckoo!" came the call. "Cuckoo! Cockoo!"

"Oh, lovely," squeaked Richard. "The cuckoos have come."

"If we looked carefully, might we see one?" asked Roley.

Rosemary looked a little doubtful. "Cuckoos are *very* shy."

Very carefully the three little Robins crept towards a large hawthorn bush, for that was where the sound seemed to be coming from. But just then, from behind a beech tree, the voice of another cuckoo made them jump.

"Why, there are two of them!" cried Rosemary.

Suddenly there was a burst of laughter, and who should appear but Donald Dormouse and Freddy Frog. Donald from behind the hawthorn bush, and Freddy from behind the beech tree.

"April fool!" they cried. "Caught you, didn't we!"

amateurs. When Alec went into the hall, it was full of people. There were wood carvings, paintings, corn dollies, collage pictures, shellcraft, patchwork quilts and a host of other things. The articles looked professional, even if the hands that had created them were amateur. The proceeds from the sale were to go towards maintaining a minibus for the old people of Millwick and Melworth, so the announcement said.

He saw Rosemary at the back of the hall. She wore skirt and sweater, and looked about sixteen. Then he saw the picture she had painted.

It was a tree; a thin, young, rather dejected-looking tree, without any leaves on it. It was standing alone in the centre of a field. The sky behind it was cloudy and there was nothing else, just the tree, the bare field, the horizon . . . and a small red 'Not For Sale' star stuck in one corner.

He went straight across to Rosemary.

"Fifty pounds!" he said loudly.

She looked confused. Those near enough to hear him looked intrigued and delighted.

"It's not for sale," she pointed out.

"I know, but you can't refuse an offer like that. Think what it costs to maintain a minibus these days. All right then, seventy-five pounds!"

The interest around deepened, and so did the colour in Rosemary's cheeks. She was the centre of interest and speculation and felt the eye of the Committee Chairman fixed sternly upon her. Seventy-five pounds! Think what it cost to maintain a minibus . . .

"Of course," said Rosemary, with a bright smile. The Chairman breathed a sigh of relief.

Rosemary pleaded a headache and went home early. She showered and then put on the caftan she had bought after Chris had left her — to cheer herself up, to make believe she was glamorous and beautiful, not just Rosemary Graham, once fat, now thin, still solemn little Rosie who never knew what to say to people nor how to hide her feelings.

Continued overleaf

The caftan was of fine, silk chiffon, multi-coloured as though an artist's palette had been laid against the material. It floated airily around her, light and delicate, as she went downstairs. She had worn it only once, feeling foolish in it. Her father had said she wasn't ready for it yet; that you had to wear a dress like that with an air of knowing you were special.

S HE WAITED for fully ten seconds before she went to answer his knock. Then she opened the door wide, and stood there with the porch light shining down upon the delicate, many-coloured caftan.

Alec had the painting under his arm. He stared down at her, and said softly: "Rosie! Oh, Rosie, you look beautiful!"

"I don't make good curry," she reminded him, "but there's a chicken casserole I put in the oven before I left this morning, and ice-cream in the freezer."

"It sounds like a feast," he told her.

She poured drinks in the sitting-room, with hands that shook only a little. He didn't take his eyes from her as she handed him his glass.

"I brought your picture back," he told her.

"It's yours; you paid for it," she reminded him.

"No." His voice was gentle. "I gave a donation to the minibus funds. It's a good picture; it says a lot about you."

"Keep it," she said. Her smile was warm. She didn't look self-sufficient, like the girl who had sat painting the chairs; nor coolly elegant like the woman in Mr. Banham's office. She looked vulnerable and there was a tentative offer of friendship in her smile.

"I was thinking," she said slowly "about my father telling you there was a time of waiting; epilogue to winter, prelude to spring. He was quite right. I don't know, yet, what I want to do, how I want to begin . . ."

"You have all the time in the world," he told her. "Don't let's rush things. Let's take our time. After all, I've only just met you, Rosie."

Looking at him, she was aware of a new emotion; a tenderness for him, deep within her, because he looked somehow unsure, like a young man making his first ever overtures to a girl.

"So take your time," he was saying. "You don't know, yet, what there is to discover. You might find out that you could learn to like living in a noisy city instead of by the sea, for instance. You just might. You never know."

"You never know," she agreed softly.

THE END

© *Audrie Manley-Tucker, 1983*

ON EASY LINES

Three striking colours for a handsome fisherman rib sweater, with easy turtle neck and fully-fashioned raglan shaping, all calculated to make it a favourite with the menfolk

Instructions in 4 sizes

Colour photo on page 19

MATERIALS: *Allow the following quantities in 40 g balls of Argyll Ferndale D.K.: 8 white, 4 red and 2 navy for the 97 cm size; 9 white, 4 red and 2 navy for the 102 cm size; 9 white, 5 red and 2 navy for the 107 cm size; 10 white, 5 red and 2 navy for the 112 cm size. For any one size: A pair each of No. 9 (3¾ mm) and No. 10 (3¼ mm) knitting needles.*

TENSION: *Work at a tension of 17 stitches and 41 rows to measure 10 x 10 cm over the pattern, using No. 9 (3¾ mm) needles to obtain the measurements given opposite.*

ABBREVIATIONS: To be read before working: *K., knit plain; p., purl; st., stitch; tog., together; dec., decrease (by working 2 sts. tog.); inc., increase (by working twice into same st.); s.s., stocking st. (k. on the right side and p. on the wrong side); k. 1d., k. 1 down (k. into next st. one row below st. on left hand needle); nil, meaning nothing is worked here for this size; dec. R., decrease right (slip into next st. 1 row below, slip next st., slip into next st. 1 row below, then place last 3 loops back onto left handed needle, k. these 3 tog., then pass the 1st 2 slip loops over); dec. L., decrease left (slip into next st. 1 row below, slip next st., slip into next st. 1 row below, then place last 5 loops back onto left hand needle and k. all 5 loops tog.); w., white; n., navy; r., red.*

NOTE: *The instructions are given for the 97 cm (38 inch) size. Where they vary work the figures within the first brackets for the 102 cm (40 inch) size; work figures within second brackets for the 107 cm (42 inch) size, and so on.*

Really attractive co-ordinating colours might be cinnamon/pine forest/coriander; cranberry/larkspur/pampas or hazelnut/bullrush/pampas.

THE BACK: With No. 10 (3¼ mm) needles and w. cast on 87 (91) (99) (103) sts. and work in rib as follows:

1st row: P.1, * k.1, p.1; repeat from * to end.

2nd row: K.1, * p.1, k.1; repeat from * to end.

Repeat the last 2 rows, 9 times more.

Change to No. 9 (3¾ mm) needles and work the 2-row pattern as follows:

1st row: P.1, * k. 1d., p.1; repeat from * to end.

2nd row: K.1, * p.1, k. 1d.; repeat from * to end.

Pattern a further 12 rows.

Join in r. and pattern 16 rows.

Join in n. and pattern 6 rows.

Pattern 24 rows in w.

The last 46 rows form the stripe pattern.

Pattern a further 116 rows.

To shape the raglan armholes: Keeping continuity of the pattern, cast off 6 sts. at the beginning of each of the next 2 rows.

Next row: Pattern 5, dec. R., pattern until 8 sts. remain, dec. L., pattern 5.

Pattern 9 rows. **

Repeat the last 10 rows, 8 (6) (4) (3) times more — 39 (51) (67) (75) sts.

Next row: Pattern 5, dec. R., pattern until 8 sts. remain, dec. L., pattern 5.

Pattern 7 rows.

Repeat the last 8 rows, 1 (4) (7) (9) time(s), then the 1st of these rows again — 27 (27) (31) (31) sts.

Work 1 row.

Leave these sts. on a spare needle.

THE FRONT: Work as given for back to **.

Repeat the last 10 rows, 5 (5) (4) (3) times, then the first of these rows again — 47 (51) (63) (71) sts.

For the 97 cm and 102 cm sizes only: To divide for neck: Next row: Pattern 18 (20) and leave these sts. on a spare needle for right half neck, pattern 11 and leave these sts. on a st. holder, pattern to end and work on these 18 (20) sts. for left half neck.

The left half neck: Pattern 2 rows.

For the 97 cm size only: Dec. 1 st. at neck edge on the next row and the following 4th row, then on the 4 following 6th rows, *at the same time,* dec. 1 st. at armhole edge as before on the 7th of these rows and the 2 following 10th rows — 6 sts.

*** Pattern 5 rows — pattern 1 row here when working 107 cm and 112 cm sizes.

Next row: Pattern 2, dec. R., pattern 1 — read pattern 1, dec. L., pattern 2 here when working right half neck.

Pattern 7 rows.

Next row: Pattern 1, dec. R. — read dec. L., pattern 1 here when working right half neck — 2 sts.

Continued overleaf

MEASUREMENTS *in centimetres (and inches, in brackets)*								
To fit chest sizes	97	(38)	102	(40)	107	(42)	112	(44)
All round at underarms	102	(40¼)	107	(42)	116.5	(45¾)	121	(47¾)
Side seam	47.5	(18¾)	47.5	(18¾)	47.5	(18¾)	47.5	(18¾)
Length	74.5	(29¼)	75.5	(29½)	76.5	(30)	78.5	(30¾)
Sleeve seam	53	(21)	53	(21)	53	(21)	53	(21)

The left half neck: Pattern 2 rows.

Dec. 1 st. at neck edge on the next row and the following 4th row, then on the 5 following 6th rows, *at the same time*, dec. 1 st. at armhole edge as before on the 5th of these rows and the 3 following 8th rows—6 sts.

Work as given for the 97 cm size from *** to end, noting variation.

The right half neck: With the right side of work facing, rejoin yarn to inner edge of the 18 (20) (21) (21) sts. left on spare needle and work as given for left half neck, noting variations.

THE SLEEVES (both alike): With No. 10 (3¼ mm) needles and w. cast on 43 (47) (47) (51) sts. and work 20 rows in rib as given on back.

Change to No. 9 (3¾ mm) needles and work 6 rows in pattern as given on back beginning with the 13th row of the 46-row stripe pattern.

Maintaining continuity of the pattern, taking extra sts. into pattern as they occur, inc. 1 st. at each end of the next row and the 9 following 16th rows—63 (67) (67) (71) sts.

Pattern a further 45 rows.

To shape the raglan sleeve top: Cast off 6 sts. at the beginning of each of the next 2 rows.

Next row: Pattern 5, dec. R., pattern until 8 sts. remain, dec. L., pattern 5.

Pattern 11 rows.

Repeat the last 12 rows, 7 (4) (6) (4) times more.

Next row: Pattern 5, dec. R., pattern until 8 sts. remain, dec. L., pattern 5.

Pattern 9 rows.

Repeat the last 10 rows, nil (4) (2) (5) times—15 sts.

Next row: Pattern 3, dec. R., pattern until 6 sts. remain, dec. L., pattern 3—11 sts.

Work 1 row.

Leave these sts. on a spare needle.

THE NECKBAND: First join right raglan seams, then left sleeve to front only. With right side of work facing, using No. 10 (3¼ mm) needles and w., k. across the 11 sts. of left sleeve, pick up and k. 29 (31) (30) (30) sts. down left side of neck, k. across the 11 (11) (13) (13) sts. at centre front, pick up and k. 29 (31) (30) (30) sts. up right side of neck, k. across the 11 sts. of right sleeve, then finally, k. across the 27 (27) (31) (31) sts. at back neck, decreasing 1 st. at the end of these sts. — 117 (121) (125) (125) sts.

K.1 row, then beginning with a k. row, s.s. 2 rows.

Work 38 rows in rib as given on back.

Cast off loosely in rib.

TO MAKE UP THE SWEATER: Do not press. Join remaining raglan seam, continuing seam across neckband. Join side and sleeve seams, taking care to match stripe pattern. Fold neckband in half to wrong side and slip st. down.

ON EASY LINES
Continued

Pattern 1 row. Work 2 tog. and fasten off.

For the 102 cm size only: Dec. 1 st. at neck edge on the next row and the following 4th row, then on the 4 following 6th rows, *at the same time*, dec. 1 st. at armhole edge as before on the 7th of these rows, then on the 3 following 8th rows—6 sts.

Pattern 2 rows.

Work as given for 97 cm size from *** to end.

For the 107 cm size and 112 cm sizes only: Pattern 7 rows.

Next row: Pattern 5, dec. R., pattern until 8 sts. remain, dec. L., pattern 5.

Repeat the last 8 rows, 1 (3) time(s)—55 sts.

To divide for neck: Next row: Pattern 21 and leave these sts. on a spare needle for right half neck, pattern 13 and leave these sts. on a st. holder, pattern to end and work on these 21 sts. for left half neck.

TRAVEL IN STYLE

Designed for short trips where you don't need a hefty suitcase – this pretty, lightweight set of travel bags to make. You can see them in colour on page 18.

WE MADE all these bags from Liberty ready-quilted Tana lawn, which has a plain lining. A lining is not absolutely necessary for the toilet and cosmetic bags as they are lined with plastic, but for the other three items choose a 'double-sided', ready-quilted fabric. (Laura Ashley also make ready-quilted fabric using two contrasting prints.)

Lay out the pattern pieces squarely on the fabric so that the quilting lines are always running diagonally across each pattern piece.

When machining through several layers of quilted fabric, reduce the top thread tension and increase the stitch length.

For binding the edges with bias binding, follow the method shown on page 39, first machining it to the right side then folding it round and slipstitching it to the wrong side. Don't be tempted just to sandwich the raw edges inside the binding and machine through all layers; even if you tack them first, you'll still find it difficult to stop the binding from slipping and you'll achieve a very uneven finish that will spoil the appearance of the bag.

HOLDALL

Finished size is approximately 66 (at widest point x 39 cm (26 x 15½ in.)

You will need: 1.40 m (1½ yd.) of ready-quilted floral fabric 91 cm (36 in.) wide; 40 cm (½ yd.) of ready-quilted, plain fabric 91 cm (36 in.) wide for the handles; 7.20 m (8 yd.) of matching bias binding 2.5 cm (1 in.) wide; 55 cm zip; matching thread; metric graph paper ruled with 2 cm squares.

To make the holdall: First scale up the patterns overleaf, copying them square by square on to graph paper. Using the scaled-up patterns, cut one front, one back, one inside pocket, one large outside pocket and one small outside pocket from floral fabric. Also cut a strip 135 x 13 cm (53 x 5⅛ in.) for the gusset and two strips each 53 x 7.5 cm (21 x 3 in.) for the zip pieces.

Bind the upper edge of each of the two outside pockets (see 'Binding'): Machine binding to the
Continued overleaf

right side of the fabric, fold it round to the wrong side and slipstitch in place. Lay the smaller pocket over the larger one, right sides uppermost and aligning the side and lower edges. Tack together round these edges. Divide smaller pocket into two down the centre with a line of machining taken through both pocket pieces.

Lay joined pockets centrally on bag front, aligning lower edges (see pattern for position). Pin and tack in place.

Bind top, straight edge of inside pocket as before. Place inside pocket to back piece with wrong sides facing and matching side and lower edges. Pin, then tack round raw edges. If you wish, divide the pocket into two sections with a line of machining taken through both layers, as for the small outside pocket.

Bind both short ends of the gusset as before. Then, starting 2 cm (¾ in.) down from one top corner of the bag back, pin the gusset to the back with wrong sides facing. Continue right round the back piece, finishing 2 cm (¾ in.) below the other corner. Tack, then machine close to the raw edges. Repeat with the bag front and the other edge of the gusset.

Now bind both these edges with bias binding, starting at the top corners each time. Always machine binding to bag front or back, then fold it round the raw edges and slipstitch neatly to the gusset (see 'Binding').

For the handles cut and join strips of plain quilted fabric 9 cm (3½ in.) wide to make **one** piece 325 cm (128 in.) long. Fold strip in half down the length with right sides facing and pin, then machine 1 cm (⅜ in.) from the long raw edges. Turn through to right side. Press strip with seam centred down back (see diagram 1). Turn in the raw edges at one end of the strip and slip the other end inside it. Slipstitch neatly together to join strip into one continuous piece.

Taking slipstitched seam as one end, fold handle strip double and mark each end with a pin. Pin handles to bag with the two marker pins centred on the gusset in line with the outer edges of the pockets on each side (see diagram 2).

With these points fixed, pin handles to bag front, covering the raw edges of the pockets. Start pinning 1 cm (⅜ in.) away from the bound edge and make sure you have the wrong side of the handles (i.e. the side with the seam) facing the bag. Finish pinning 5 cm (2 in.) above the top edge of the large pocket on each side.

Pin handles to back of bag in the same way, making sure that the inside pocket is left free. Tack handles in place along pinned lines, then machine close to the edge of the handles. To reinforce handles, machine 'crosses' (see diagram 3) at the top and base of the machined sections of the handles on the front and back of the bag. **Note:** The handles are left free underneath the gusset.

We also strengthened the tops of the handles by doubling each one back on itself and machining close to the edge all round (see diagram 4).

Bind both short ends of each zip piece with bias binding. Also bind the two long edges (one on each piece) to which the zip will be joined, turning in the raw edges of the binding at each end to neaten.

Neaten both ends of the zip with tabs made from small pieces of bias binding sewn on by hand (see diagram 5). Tack, then machine zip between the bound edges of the two zip pieces, using a zipper foot on the sewing machine (see diagram 5).

Pin raw edges of the zip pieces to top, raw edges of bag, wrong sides facing. Tack, then machine close to raw edges. Then bind these edges with bias binding, as before, turning in the short raw ends of the binding to neaten (see diagram 5).

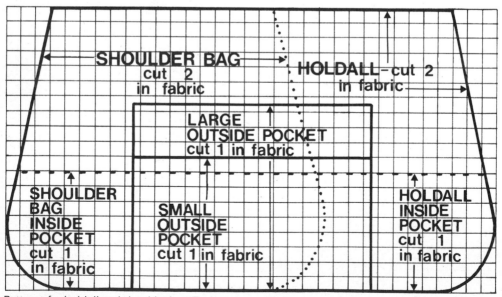

Patterns for holdall and shoulder bag. Each square = 2 cm.

BINDING

Open out one edge of binding. Place this edge of the binding to the quilted fabric, right sides facing and aligning raw edges. Tack, then machine along binding fold line. Fold binding round to wrong side and slipstitch neatly in place.

Where ends of binding meet, overlap them, turn in the raw edge of the upper piece and slipstitch ends together neatly.

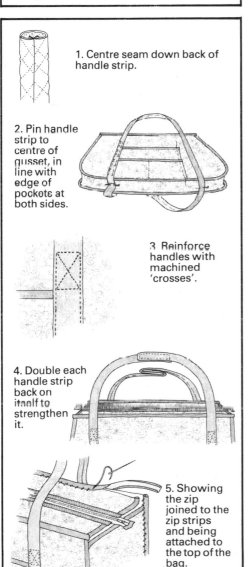

1. Centre seam down back of handle strip.

2. Pin handle strip to centre of gusset, in line with edge of pockets at both sides.

3. Reinforce handles with machined 'crosses'.

4. Double each handle strip back on itself to strengthen it.

5. Showing the zip joined to the zip strips and being attached to the top of the bag.

SHOULDER BAG

Finished size is approximately 41 (at widest point) x 38 cm (16 x 15 in.).

You will need: 90 cm. (1 yd.) of ready-quilted, lined floral fabric 91 cm (36 in.) wide; 30 cm (⅜ yd.) of ready-quilted, plain fabric for handles; 3.70 m (4 yd.) of matching bias binding 2.5 cm (1 in.) wide; 35 cm zip; matching thread; metric graph paper ruled with 2 cm squares.

To make the shoulder bag: Scale up the patterns on page 38 copying them square by square on to metric graph paper. Using the scaled up patterns, cut one front, one back and one inside pocket from floral fabric. Also cut two strips each 58 x 10 cm (23 x 4 in.) for the gusset and two strips each 31 x 5 cm (12¼ x 2 in.) for the zip pieces. For handles cut and join strips of plain, quilted fabric 9 cm (3½ in.) wide to make **two** pieces each 132 cm (52 in.) long.

Make up the handles as for the holdall, turning in the short raw ends to neaten. Pin, then tack one handle to the bag front and one to the bag back, positioning the ends 9 cm (3½ in.) up from the lower edge and 19 cm (7½ in.) apart. Machine close to the edges of each handle, stopping 4 cm (1½ in.) from the top edge. Reinforce handles with machined 'crosses' as before. (It is not necessary, however, to strengthen the tops of the handles by making them double thickness as for the holdall.)

Bind top edge of inside pocket as for holdall and tack to wrong side of back piece. Join gusset strips, taking a 2 cm (¾ in.) seam. Neaten raw edges of seam and press open. Join front and back to gusset and bind edges as for holdall. Make up zip strip and complete as for holdall.

Continued overleaf

TOILET BAG
& COSMETIC BAG

The toilet bag and cosmetic bag are made in exactly the same way, using the appropriate patterns. Finished size of toilet bag is approximately 30.5 x 22 cm (12 x 8¾ in.). Finished size of cosmetic bag is approximately 21 x 15 cm (8¼ x 6 in.).

You will need: 50 cm (⅝ yd.) of ready-quilted fabric and plastic lining 91 cm (36 in.) wide; 4.50 m (4⅞ yd.) of matching bias binding 2.5 cm (1 in.) wide; 4 large press studs; matching thread; metric graph paper ruled with 2 cm squares.

To make the bags: Scale up the appropriate pattern pieces on to metric graph paper, as before. Cut one front and one back piece from quilted fabric and plastic lining. Also cut a gusset strip from fabric and lining measuring 64 x 8.5 cm (25 x 3¼ in.) for the toilet bag, 41 x 6.5 cm (16 x 2½ in.) for the cosmetic bag.

Place front lining piece to wrong side of bag front. Tack close to the edge all round, then bind top, straight edge as for holdall. **Note:** As it is not possible to slipstitch the binding to the plastic lining, machine the binding to the wrong (lining side), then fold round and slipstitch neatly to the right side. Tack gusset lining to gusset and bind the short edges in the same way. Place back lining to wrong side of back and tack all round.

Pin gusset to front with wrong sides facing. Tack, then machine close to raw edges. Pin back of bag to remaining long edge of gusset, aligning lower edges and leaving top flap free. Tack, then machine as before. Bind the raw edges as for the holdall, binding the back and flap with one piece of binding and the front with another.

Sew halves of two press studs inside the flap and the other halves to the front of the bag to close. Make a bow from a 20 cm (8 in.) length of bias binding, folded in half lengthways, and sew to front of flap.

SPECTACLE CASE

Finished size of spectacle case (closed) is approximately 21 x 15 cm (8¼ x 6 in.). It can be made from oddments of quilted fabric left over from the toilet and cosmetic bags plus 1 m (1⅛ yd.) of bias binding 2.5 cm (1 in.) wide and a large press stud.

To make the case: Scale up the pattern pieces on to metric graph paper as before. Cut one front and one back from quilted fabric only. Bind the top, straight edge of the front piece.

Place front to back, wrong sides facing, and aligning lower edges. Tack together close to the edge then bind all round with one piece of binding. Sew on a press stud and a bias binding bow as for the toilet and cosmetic bags.

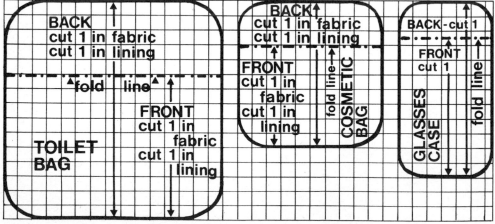

Patterns for toilet and cosmetic bags and spectacle case. Each square = 2 cm.

BABY LOVE

For the newest member of the family,
a delightful matinée jacket in a lacy diamond pattern,
with matching bonnet, mitts and bootees

From birth to 6 months
Colour photo on page 23

MATERIALS: *6-20 g balls of Sirdar Snuggly 3 ply: 3 small buttons for matinee jacket; 1 metre of ½ inch ribbon for bonnet; 2 metres narrow ribbon for matinee jacket, mitts and bootees; a pair of No. 13 (2¼ mm) knitting needles.*

TENSION AND MEASUREMENTS: *Worked at a tension of 40 stitches and 51 rows to measure 10 x 10 cm, over the pattern, using No. 13 (2¼ mm) needles, the matinee jacket will fit a 41 to 46 cm (16 to 18 inch) chest size; side seam, 14 cm (5½ inches); sleeve seam, 11 cm (4½ inches).*

ABBREVIATIONS: To be read before working: K., *knit plain;* **p.,** *purl;* **st.,** *stitch; tog., together; k.2 tog.b., k.2 tog. through back of sts.; sl., slip; inc., increase (by working twice into same st.); dec., decrease (by working 2 sts. tog.); g.st., garter st. (k. plain on every row); y.fwd., yarn forward to make a st.; p.2 s.s.o., pass 2 slipped sts. over; s.s., stocking st. (k. on the right side and p. on the wrong side).*

MATINEE JACKET

THE BACK AND FRONTS (worked in one piece to armholes): With No. 13 (2¼ mm) needles cast on 279 sts. and g.st 10 rows.

Work the 16-row pattern as follows:

1st row: K.7, k.2 tog., k.2, y.fwd., k.2 tog.b., y.fwd., k.1, y.fwd., k.2 tog., y.fwd., k.2, * sl.2 k.wise, k.1, p.2 s.s.o., k.2, y.fwd., k.2 tog.b., y.fwd., k.1, y.fwd., k.2 tog., y.fwd., k.2; repeat from * until 9 sts. remain, k.2 tog.b., k.7.

2nd and every alternate row: K.5, p. until 5 sts. remain, k.5.

3rd row: K.7, k.2 tog., k.1, y.fwd., k.2 tog., y.fwd., k.3, y.fwd., k.2 tog.b., y.twd., k.1, * sl.2 k.wise, k.1, p.2 s.s.o., k.1, y.fwd., k.2 tog., y.fwd., k.3, y.fwd., k.2 tog.b., y.fwd., k.1; repeat from * until 9 sts. remain, k.2 tog.b., k.7.

5th row: K.7, k.2 tog., y.fwd., k.2 tog., y.fwd., k.5, y.fwd., k.2 tog.b., y.fwd., * sl.2 k.wise, k.1, p.2 s.s.o., y.fwd., k.2 tog., y.fwd., k.5, y.fwd., k.2 tog.b., y.fwd.; repeat from * until 9 sts. remain, k.2 tog.b., k.7.

7th row: K.8, * y.fwd., k.2 tog., y.fwd., k.2, sl.2 k.wise, k.1, p.2 s.s.o., k.2, y.fwd., k.2 tog.b., y.fwd., k.1; repeat from * until 7 sts. remain, k.7.

9th row: As 7th row.

11th row: K.9, * y.fwd., k.2 tog.b., y.fwd., k.1, sl.2 k.wise, k.1, p.2 s.s.o., k.1, y.fwd., k.2 tog., y.fwd., k.3; repeat from * until 6 sts. remain, k.6.

13th row: K.10, * y.fwd., k.2 tog.b., y.fwd., sl.2 k.wise, k.1, p.2 s.s.o., y.fwd., k.2 tog., y.fwd., k.5; repeat from * until 5 sts. remain, k.5.

15th row: As 1st row.

Continued overleaf

41

Delicate baby shades in this soft machine-washable yarn include: petal pink, angelica, lemon, ice green and white.

right front, k.2, then k.3 tog. 28 times, k.2 tog., k.1 across right sleeve, k.1, then k.2 tog. 66 times, k.1 across back, k.2, then k.3 tog. 28 times, k.2 tog., k.1 across left sleeve, then k.2 tog. 33 times, k.6 across left front — 210 sts.

Next row: All k.

Next (buttonhole) row: K.2, k.2 tog., y.fwd., k. to end.

G.st. 7 rows.

Next (dec.) row: K.19, * k.2 tog., k.2 tog., k.10; repeat from * until 23 sts. remain, k.2 tog., k.2 tog., k.19 — 184 sts.

G.st. 7 rows.

Next (dec.) row: K.18, * k.2 tog., k.2 tog., k.8; repeat from * until 22 sts. remain, k.2 tog., k.2 tog., k.18 — 158 sts.

G.st. 1 row.

Work the buttonhole row again, then g.st. 3 rows.

Next (dec.) row: K.17, * k.2 tog., k.2 tog., k.6; repeat from * until 21 sts. remain, k.2 tog., k.2 tog., k.17 — 132 sts.

G.st. 5 rows.

Next (dec.) row: K.16, * k.2 tog., k.2 tog., k.4; repeat from * until 20 sts. remain, k.2 tog., k.2 tog., k.16 — 106 sts.

G.st. 3 rows.

Next (dec.) row: K.15, * k.2 tog., k.2 tog., k.2; repeat from * until 19 sts. remain, k.2 tog., k.15 — 80 sts.

G.st. 1 row, then work the buttonhole row again.

G.st. 1 row.

Next (slot) row: K.6, * y.fwd., k.2 tog., k.4; repeat from * until 8 sts. remain, y.fwd., k.2 tog., k.6.

G.st. 2 rows.

Cast off.

TO MAKE UP THE MATINEE JACKET: Join tiny underarm seams sewing the last 8 row ends of sleeves to shaped row ends of armhole shaping. Thread ribbon through slot row and secure each end of slot row on the inside. Add buttons.

BOOTEES

TO MAKE (2 alike): With No. 13 (2¼ mm) needles cast on 53 sts.

G.st. 10 rows.

Work 15 rows in pattern as given on back and fronts of matinee jacket, omitting the 5 g.st. edge sts. at either side of back and fronts.

Next (dec.) row: P.4, * p.2 tog., p.5; repeat from * to end — 46 sts.

G.st. 2 rows.

BABY LOVE *Continued*

16th row: K.5, p. until 5 sts. remain, k.5.

Repeat the last 16 rows twice, then the first 15 of these rows again.

To divide for back and fronts: Next row: Pattern 72 and leave these sts. on a spare needle for left front, pattern 135 and leave these sts. on a spare needle for back, pattern to end and work on these 72 sts. for right front.

The right front: Pattern 8 rows and leave these sts. on a st. holder.

The back: With right side of work facing, rejoin yarn to the 135 sts. left on spare needle and work 8 rows in pattern, decreasing 1 st. in the centre of the last of these rows — 134 sts. Leave these sts. on a spare needle.

The left front: With right side of work facing, rejoin yarn to the 72 sts. left on spare needle and work as given for right front.

THE SLEEVES (both alike): With No. 13 (2¼ mm) needles cast on 46 sts. and g.st. 9 rows.

Next (inc.) row: K.1, * inc.; repeat from * until 2 sts. remain, k.2 — 89 sts.

Work 56 rows in pattern as given on back and fronts, omitting the 5 g.st. edge sts. on either side of back and fronts.

Leave these sts. on a spare needle.

THE YOKE: With right side of work facing, rejoin yarn and k.6, then k.2 tog. 33 times across

Next (slot) row: K.2, * y.fwd., k.2 tog.; repeat from * to end.

K.1 row. **

To divide for instep: Next row: K.29, turn leaving remaining 17 sts. on a safety pin for left side.

Next row: K.12, turn leaving remaining 17 sts. on a safety pin for right side.

On these 12 sts., g.st. 20 rows, then break off yarn.

With right side of work facing, sl. the 17 sts. from right side safety pin onto needle, rejoin yarn, then pick up and k.13 sts. from row ends at right side of instep, k. the 12 instep sts., pick up and k.13 sts. from row ends at left side of instep, then k. the 17 sts. from left side safety pin — 72 sts.

G.st. 9 rows.

To shape the sole: 1st row: K.2 tog., k.31, k.2 tog., k.2, k.2 tog., k.31, k.2 tog. — 68 sts.

2nd and every alternate row: All k.

3rd row: K.2 tog., k.29, k.2 tog., k.2, k.2 tog., k.29, k.2 tog. — 64 sts.

5th row: K.2 tog., k.27, k.2 tog., k.2, k.2 tog., k.27, k.2 tog. — 60 sts.

6th row: All k. Cast off.

TO MAKE UP THE BOOTEES: Join back seam and underfoot seam. Thread ribbon through slot row, bringing ends out to tie at front.

THE MITTS

TO MAKE: Work as given for bootees to **.

G.st. 20 rows.

To shape the top: 1st row: * K.4, k.2 tog.; repeat from * until 4 sts. remain, k.4 — 39 sts.

2nd and every alternate row: All k.

3rd row: * K.3, k.2 tog.; repeat from * until 4 sts. remain, k.4 — 32 sts.

5th row: * K.2, k.2 tog.; repeat from * to end — 24 sts.

7th row: * K.1, k.2 tog.; repeat from * to end — 16 sts.

9th row: * K.2 tog.; repeat from * to end — 8 sts.

Break off yarn leaving a long end, thread this through remaining sts., draw up tightly and secure.

TO MAKE UP THE MITTS: Join side seam. Thread ribbon through slot row, bringing ends out to tie.

THE BONNET

TO MAKE: With No. 13 (2¼ mm) needles cast on 123 sts. and g.st. 10 rows.

Work 39 rows in pattern as given on back and fronts of matinee jacket.

K.1 row.

Beginning with a k. row, s.s. 4 rows.

Next (picot) row: K.1, * y.fwd., k.2 tog.; repeat from * to end.

Beginning with a p. row, s.s. 4 rows.

K.1 row, decreasing 3 sts. evenly across this row — 120 sts.

To shape the crown: 1st row: * K.10, k.2 tog.; repeat from * to end — 110 sts.

2nd and every alternate row: All p.

3rd row: * K.9, k.2 tog.; repeat from * to end — 100 sts.

5th row: * K.8, k.2 tog.; repeat from * to end — 90 sts.

7th row: * K.7, k.2 tog.; repeat from * to end — 80 sts.

9th row: * K.6, k.2 tog.; repeat from * to end — 70 sts.

Continue in this way decreasing 10 sts. on every alternate row as before, working 1 st. less between each dec. until 20 sts. remain.

Next row: * K.2 tog.; repeat from * to end — 10 sts.

Break off yarn leaving a long end, thread this through remaining sts., draw up tightly and secure.

TO MAKE UP THE BONNET: Fold at picot row, then catch together at ridge st. each side of s.s. Join back seam for 2.5 cm (1 inch). Sew on ribbon.

Love in a Garden

by Kate Taylor

Keeping her nursery garden going was the most important thing in Philly's life. Her independence was everything to her. But can any of us get by without a little help from our friends?

PHILLY'S HANDS were small and neat, like Philly herself, and exactly right for the task she was absorbed in this morning. It was still early, but already there was a pale sunlight which warmed the greenhouse, and the potting compost, and Philly's fingers as they moved among the tiny seedlings. She enjoyed working in the greenhouse; she loved the delicate miniature plants, the good, clean smell of the soil, the sunlit silence. Though, indeed, she loved the outside work as well, and in fact anything and everything about the Manor House Nurseries, Proprietors: Philippa Forbes and Elizabeth Harper, Dip. Hort.

A car door banged shut nearby and Philly glanced at her watch. Bess was late this morning. It had been her weekend off, but she was normally back long before this. Rapid footsteps pattered along the path outside and the door rattled open. Bess shot in, pink of face and breathless, long black hair fluttering about her shoulders.

"Sorry I'm late, Philly. But listen, I've got news! Tom and I are getting married!"

"Oh, Bess, that's marvellous. Congratulations! I'm so happy for you." Philly hugged her friend joyfully. "Not that it's much of a surprise, you know — we've all been expecting it for weeks! But it's splendid news all the same. Have you fixed a date yet?"

Bess took a deep breath and said, "Yes — well — that's why I'm so late. We've been going over and over it, but there's no way out." She sat down on a bag of peat and looked up at Philly.

"I didn't tell you, but Tom applied for this new university post back in the winter — so long ago that I'd forgotten all about it. And then he suddenly heard on Saturday that he's got it. And it's abroad — in Australia, actually — and we go next month. Early next month."

Philly said quickly, "Golly, Australia! It's a long way." Not that it mattered twopence how far Bess went; what mattered was her going at all, and so soon.

"Yes, it is a long way," Bess said. "Oh, Philly, I'm so sorry. What will you do?"

"Good heavens, I'll be all right." Philly went over to the tap with a vast watering can. "There's always Samson," she shouted, as the water clanged into it. "We'll have to upgrade him!" She came back and sprinkled the seedlings she'd been planting out. "Now, come on. What about you and Tom and Australia? Gorgeous climate for growing things! Where exactly is it you're going?"

SHE MANAGED very well until her mother made her usual weekly phone call that evening, and then it was an enormous relief to be quite honest about what had happened.

"Well, yes, you're quite right, Mother, it is a blow. I expect I'll work something out when I've had time to think about things calmly, but just at the moment I haven't the slightest idea what I'm going to do. But I am very happy for Bess, absolutely delighted, and I'm not going to fuss now and spoil things for her."

"You wouldn't think of selling up, I suppose?" Mrs. Forbes ventured.

"No." Philly hoped she sounded resolute rather than desperate. "You know how I love this place, Mother. I hated it when you and Dad sold the house and moved away, but hanging on to the cottage and the kitchen garden was a fine idea, and it's been great fun setting up the nursery. Did I tell you

Continued overleaf

44

we've got a foot in at the hotel? Bess met the new owner recently and had a talk with him about supplying stuff, and we're hoping to hear from him quite soon. We're all set to make great progress, if only I can keep going," she finished with a sigh.

"What about looking round for someone to take Bess's place?"

"It's a possibility," Philly said, "though the problem is paying them. Bess settled for a minimum salary, you know, like me, for the sake of future prospects, but I don't know if anyone else will."

She sat up late that night, making lists. 'First things first,' she thought. That meant tomato plants; they must be dealt with immediately. Then the lettuces — all those rows of early lettuces under glass, all at different stages. She must keep them going, whatever happened, especially if the hotel order came off. There was all the heavy outside work to get on with, too. She would get Samson along tomorrow and see if he could put in some extra hours when Bess went. She sighed heavily. An intuitive gardener and a splendid worker was Alexander Meredith Samson, totally devoted to the Manor House Nurseries and the ladies who ran it, but he had a major problem, and that was his age. He was only fourteen, and so his hours available for work were limited.

Children need love, especially when they
do not deserve it.
Harold Hulbert

BESS'S RUSHED wedding plans steamed ahead, and a month later it was all over. Bess and her Tom were on the other side of the world. Philly had turned down all the best man's repeated invitations to dinner here, or a theatre there, and had put her wedding hat back in its box. And this afternoon she stood at the back door of the cottage and watched a small, dogged figure making its way along the garden towards her, head down against the thumping rain.

"Hi, Samson," she called as he came near.

He joined her at the doorway, throwing his satchel of books through into the kitchen. "What's first, Miss?"

"Muck," said Philly. "There's that last load the farm delivered. Can you get it all carted down and stacked against the bottom wall? You can use the buggy."

Samson departed into the rain with a gleam in his eye, the buggy being a miniature tractor which was the light of his life, and Philly returned to sorting her seed potatoes. Then she went over to the greenhouses and packed her prime lettuces, first into plastic bags and then into trays, ready to be collected. The hotel was taking its first batch today. Then she went back to the house to make some tea. As she filled the kettle she caught sight of herself in the little mirror beside the sink and burst out laughing.

Her normally trim golden-brown hair stood out spikily round her face like a sunflower head, and there were thick, muddy streaks on her forehead. There was more mud on her jersey and dungarees. "What a mess you look!" she said aloud, and then jumped as she heard a sharp rap at the back door, and the sound of a throat being cleared.

"Excuse me, I was looking for Miss Forbes. Is she anywhere about?"

Philly swung round in some confusion and found the doorway filled by a large, unknown man. Afterwards she thought she remembered black curling hair and cool grey eyes, but all she took in now was his extreme elegance. He was wearing an immaculate dark suit and a shirt so gleaming white that she instinctively took a step backwards. She found herself saying wildly and foolishly, "Er — well — er — I'm not sure where she is just now. Can I give her a message?"

The vision frowned slightly. "It's about the lettuces for the hotel. I've come to pick up today's batch, and I really wanted to see her about some further orders because we haven't actually met yet. Ask her to phone me later on, will you? The name's Greenwood."

"Yes, I'll tell her," Philly said in a strangled voice, and directed him over to the greenhouses to pick up the lettuces.

The rain relented during the night and she spent the next morning preparing ground and sowing seed, grateful both for the damp soil and for the warmth of the sun on her back. The phone was ringing as she came trudging up to the back door at lunch-time. A man's voice asked crisply for Miss Forbes. "David Greenwood here. I left a message asking you to ring, but you didn't. What about these lettuces?"

"What do you mean?" Philly's voice rose in consternation. "Is anything wrong?"

"Good Lord, no. They're fine," he said, and Philly sent up a silent prayer of thanks. "But I do need to see you," he went on, "to talk about future supplies and the whole question of terms. The trouble is, finding a suitable time. Could I come up later on this evening, some time after nine perhaps? Would that be all right?"

46

PHILLY SAID that would be fine and put the phone down, wishing fervently that she hadn't been such a fool yesterday. He was bound to recognise her, and what would he think? Just when it was so important, too, that she should impress him as competent and business-like, and a reliable supplier of first-class lettuces.

By nine she had changed into clean trousers and her only silk shirt, and a log fire was crackling in the hearth of her little sitting-room. She was just putting coffee cups ready on a tray when David Greenwood arrived, presenting himself at the back door as he had on his previous visit.

"Hello, Miss Forbes," he said, and Philly jumped this time too because he didn't look like the same man at all, now totally transformed by faded corduroy trousers and a thick, pale jersey featuring a family of woolly sheep. He said, "Miss Forbes?" again, looked at her in some perplexity, frowned, and then very slowly began to smile.

"That was you yesterday," he said, not accusingly at all but with vast amusement. Philly felt suddenly greatly relieved and beamed at him. "Yes, it was me," she said. "I do apologise." She picked up the tray and led the way through to the sitting-room. "Silly of me," she said as they sat down, "but I was so very dirty. And you were so very clean," she added as an afterthought.

"Ah well, that was my hotel-manager-on-duty outfit. Just a uniform really."

"Like my muddy dungarees," Philly said. "That's my gardener-on-duty uniform."

"It suited you," he assured her, taking the coffee cup she was handing him. "And how many of you are there? Gardeners on duty, I mean?"

Philly reflected. "One-and-a-quarter on weekdays, and two most Saturdays and Sundays. The quarter is Samson, you see, because he's still at school and can't do more than two hours or so, except at the weekend." She leant forward to put more wood on the fire. David Greenwood watched the firelight's glow flickering across her small face and said, "You mean there's just you? To do all this? But I don't understand—I met a Miss Harper last month, what happened to her?"

SO PHILLY explained cheerfully about Bess and Tom, and Tom's new job, and then found herself going right back to the beginning of things. She told him how she and Bess had met at college and been close friends ever since. Bess had gone into teaching but her heart wasn't in it. "And I was mouldering away in an office, longing to get my hands on a spade again," Philly said with great feeling, "so when the chance came to set up the nursery, we both jumped at it. It seemed meant to happen, if you see what I mean."

David said he knew exactly what she meant, and told her how well they had done. He only had to look around, he said warmly, to see how well-run the place was. Philly went pink with pleasure.

"I'm so glad you think so," she said, then allowed herself a small sigh. "Yes, it was all going beautifully until this happened."

"Meaning Tom Whatever-his-name is? And falling in love, to use a nice old-fashioned term?" Philly nodded, and David said quietly, "It does happen to people, you know. Quite a lot." He paused for a second, his eyes on her face, and then added, "Sometimes very quickly indeed. Out of the blue."

"Yes, well," Philly said, unaccountably flustered, "it's just been a bit inconvenient, that's all. Not that I can't cope," she added firmly, remembering in the nick of time that she was talking to a customer. "It's going to mean a lot more work, obviously, but I think I'll be able to manage—for the time being, anyway."

"You can't," he said gently. "It's too much."

THE PART of Philly that was always tired these days was grateful for his concern, and acknowledged that he was probably right. But the other, stubborn, part was insisting that she'd taken on something that was very important to her, that she'd never thought it would be easy, and that this man, beguiling though he was, was here to talk about business. Her role was supposed to be that of capable gardener and manager. She sat up straight, picked up the notebook she had ready beside her, and said, "Let's talk about the lettuces." David murmured something flippant about 'cabbages and kings', but Philly ignored this and proceeded to give him a concise but detailed account of what she thought the nursery could provide over the summer months, complete with quantities, dates and approximate prices.

David listened carefully, and with growing respect, and when she'd finished he said, "That's great! Just what we need." There was real enthusiasm in his voice. "I've always maintained that a local source of fresh fruit and vegetables makes all the difference to hotel catering. If you really can supply all that, I'll be eternally grateful. And the house plants, too; you'll provide them and undertake to keep an eye on them from time to time as well?" Philly had thrown that extra in at the last minute and now privately regretted it, but she wasn't going to say so. "Oh, yes," she said. "No trouble at all. I'll try and fit in a quick visit once a week."

"I've got a good idea," David said. "If they're ready by Saturday, bring the plants up to the hotel in

Continued overleaf

the evening and we'll have dinner. Have to be late-ish I'm afraid, when I'm free. About eight-thirty?" Philly said that would be lovely, then yawned cavernously. David laughed and got to his feet. Philly got up, too, and said contritely, "I'm so sorry. It must be the fire. Thank you for coming." Then she yawned again. This time they both laughed, and David made his farewells and departed.

SATURDAY EVENING turned out to be very pleasant indeed. It was refreshing to wear a dress again after her routine shirts and trousers, and David was very entertaining to be with. The food was good — much better than she remembered from previous occasions — and she said so unreservedly. "Thank you," David said solemnly. "Have some more salad; I can thoroughly recommend it."

The wine was good, too, though Philly broached it with caution; she seemed to carry tiredness around with her like a lead weight these days, and sometimes it threatened to overwhelm her completely if she sat back and relaxed. Two glasses, she thought, and she'd probably fall asleep, snoring.

She had been quite determined beforehand that she wouldn't talk about the nursery too much, but David showed such interest in it that by the time they had reached the coffee stage she had forgotten her resolution and was talking at length about the garden and all it meant to her. She talked about preparing land, and nourishing it; about seed-time and harvest; the whole reassuring business of working with the seasons in orderly progression — reassuring because there was relatively little room for argument or doubt. "There's almost always a right time to do things, you see," she said.

David said, "Yes, I know. 'A time to sow and a time to reap'." He stirred his coffee and went on watching the bright face opposite him.

There were primroses in a tiny pot on the table between them, and Philly touched a petal lightly with one finger. "And in the end," she said, "it's still a miracle, the whole thing. I mean, I know with my head what happens to the seed in the ground, but it's still a totally marvellous process, life going on repeating itself, over and over again."

She stopped suddenly, and there was a little silence between them, very comfortable and easy. Then he said, "I've never had a garden, or even wanted one. But I'm beginning to see why I might, some day." There was another pause, and then he went on abruptly, "Look here, whatever happens you've got to keep that place going."

"Oh, I know," Philly said with sleepy fervour, and then broke off suddenly because a sizable yawn was welling up and it would take all her strength to subdue it. She pressed a hand tightly over her mouth and tried very hard to listen to David, who was leaning forward with a purposeful look on his face.

"I've been giving this quite a bit of thought," he was saying. "I hope you don't think I'm interfering or anything like that, but it occurs to me that there are one or two ways . . ." He broke off abruptly. "Philly, wake up!"

Philly jumped, and said defensively, "I am awake!" Then the yawn won — enormously and devastatingly — and David threw back his head and laughed.

A few late diners glanced their way with curiosity and some envy, and Philly wailed, "Oh, David, I'm so sorry! I am listening. It's just that I'm so tired by the end of the day, and in the evenings I get sleepy. I can't help it." She stared at him, wide-eyed and apologetic.

"Come on," he said, "I'll take you home. You can't drive like this." Philly accepted meekly and was glad she had, for by the time they got back to the cottage she was nodding with drowsiness and barely able to say thank you and good night. As David's car roared off into the darkness, she fell into bed and dreamt of running through endless avenues of giant primroses, pursued by monstrous lettuces.

PHILLY LIKED Monday. You could begin all over again on Monday. Especially a Monday morning in spring, like this one: the air soft and dampish from overnight rain; the clouds still pearly grey but tinged with pale blue. She worked hard all morning in the benevolent sunshine, planting the last of the potatoes, and came wandering up to the house at midday, well-pleased with her efforts. That was another big task out of the way. The scent of narcissi reached her from the tubs under the kitchen window as she leaned against the wall and began to wriggle her boots off. It was then that she noticed the envelope sticking out from under the back door. She lined the boots up and took the envelope into the kitchen with her, staring at the unfamiliar writing as she tore it open. There was a single sheet of paper inside.

"*Dear Miss Filly*," she read, "*very sorry but my Alec cannot come and help you after School today. He has broke his leg. He come off his bike last night after Youth Club and Dr. says it is a bad one and he will likely not get back to School this term. I am getting his Dad to leave this on his way to work because Alec is worried about you and the Garden. He says to say he is very sorry. Yours truly, Mrs. Samson."* And there was a P.S. *"He says to tell you it does not hurt very much, and will you come and write your name on the plaster?"*

Philly read the note a second time, then sank down into an ancient wicker chair and laid the note carefully on the table beside her, smoothing it with her earthy fingers. Slowly, she put her head down on Mrs. Samson's neat, round writing and burst into tears. She cried hard for several minutes, and when at last the tears stopped flowing she sat up and blew her nose fiercely.

"That's quite enough of that, Philly Forbes!" she said aloud. "It's not the end of the world, or anything like it."

A sound from outside made her glance out of the window just in time to see the hotel van drawing to a halt in the yard. David's burly figure emerged, and Philly caught her breath. Just for a second she hesitated, but it was only for a second, and then she was out of the door and in the yard, racing towards him.

David appeared gratified at this reception and obligingly wrapped both arms around her in a comforting manner, so that Philly's face lay against his chest. "What is it?" he said, looking down at the top of her head. "What's happened?" Philly kept her face where it was, quite overcome by her own temerity. Her answer was muffled somewhat by his shirt, but Samson's name and something about a broken leg were audible, and David nodded as the situation became clear. "Well, that's rotten luck for both of you. But, Philly, my love, don't cry!" He gave her a gentle shake. "We'll work something out, truly we will."

P HILLY REMAINED quite still for an instant, wondering if he really had said what she thought he'd said, and then she lifted her head and looked up at him. David bent his head, and kissed her tear-stained cheek, and then unfolded his arms and took her by the hand instead. "Come on," he said. "Let's go in and make some tea, and see what we can sort out."

Back in the kitchen, he made her sit down while he poked about and found mugs and milk, and made a pot of tea. Then he drew up another chair and sat down beside her.

"Listen, Philly, I've got a plan. As a matter of fact, it's been on my mind for some days now. I very nearly put it to you on Saturday evening, only you fell asleep on me before I could start." Here Philly managed a weak giggle. "So in a way it's nothing to do with poor old Samson's broken leg, except that it's brought matters to crisis point a bit sooner. It seems to me that what the nursery needs is to be taken into partnership with another concern—like the hotel, for instance. The hotel needs fresh fruit and vegetables and the nursery needs financial backing, so why don't we run the two together?"

Life is like playing a violin solo in public and learning
the instrument as one goes on.

Samuel Butler

Philly stared at him, aware of faint stirrings of relief and hope, and a growing spark of excitement as well. She said cautiously, "But would it still be mine, David? You can't imagine how I feel about the place."

"Yes, I can." David smiled. "You told me, remember?" He took the mug away from her and clasped her hands in his. "You'd still be in complete charge in every way, I promise you. But for a start, the hotel would be able to help with paying for extra staff, and that's your main problem solved straight away."

Philly sat staring at their clasped hands and thought about not having to keep going every single moment of every day, of perhaps having time to read a book again, or go for a walk. She glanced up at David's watchful face and smiled. "It sounds wonderful—just wonderful," she said.

He sighed with relief and said, "Yes, well, I think so too. We'll have to go into all the legal ins and outs and see exactly what's involved, of course, but if you're happy with the idea, I think we should go right ahead." He let go of her hands and went over to the window. He stood looking out for a moment, and then turned to smile across at her. "There are all kinds of partnerships, you know. Business and personal; short-term and long-term. It's only fair to say that what I have in mind is both business and personal, and totally permanent. Dear Philly."

The kitchen was bright with noonday sunshine, and Philly felt golden with excitement and hope. Laughter welled up inside her. "Tell you what," she said, "let's *both* go and write our names on Samson's plaster!"

THE END

©*Kate Taylor, 1983*

49

SUMMER

It is very quiet here; it is quiet
In the deep pause of summer,
Before the gathering of fruit.

Richard Church

SUMMER SONG

And through each mellow timeless day,
On summer beaches so serene,
By lisping waves small children play.
And in the wood when night descends,
Beneath a crescent moon so frail,
Above all other sound transcends
The love song of the nightingale.

Kay Worne

Ices, sorbets and long, cool drinks.

Refreshing concoctions to laze in the sun with; ices to make yourself or to buy and dress up in delightful ways. Roll on, heat wave!

Colour photo on page 75

POINTS ABOUT ICES

Here are a few general points to remember before you begin making your own ice-creams:

Freezing reduces the sweetness, so mixtures should taste a little over-sweet before they are frozen.

If you have space, it is advisable to freeze ice-cream in small containers, so the mixture will freeze more quickly and be smoother as a result (slow freezing means the formation of large ice crystals, which is what you want to avoid).

Most ice-cream mixtures are beaten when half-frozen, i.e. when mushy. This is to crush up large ice crystals and improve the texture. Gelatine is often added to less rich mixtures as this helps to keep large ice crystals from forming during freezing.

Once the ice-cream has frozen, turn the fridge dial back to its normal setting.

Never leave ice-cream in the freezing compartment until the last moment, but transfer it to the main part of the fridge for about half an hour before serving.

CUSTARD ICE-CREAM

Makes 2½-3 pints

| 1½ pints milk |
| 1 oz. custard powder |
| 4 oz. sugar |
| 2 large eggs, size 2, separated |
| 1 teaspoon vanilla essence |
| ½ pint whipping or double cream |

Set the fridge dial at maximum freezing temperature.

Heat 1¼ pints milk. Mix the egg yolks, sugar and custard powder to a smooth cream with a ¼ pint cold milk in a large bowl, then stir in the hot milk. Return the custard to the pan and gradually bring to the boil, stirring all the time, until it has thickened. Remove from the heat and stir in the vanilla essence. Wet a piece of greaseproof paper with water then press it down on to the surface of the custard – this prevents a skin from forming.

Leave the custard until it is quite cold. Whisk the egg whites until stiff but not dry. Fold the lightly whipped cream and egg whites into the cold custard.

Pour the ice-cream mixture either into a 3 pint plastic or foil container or three 1 pint containers. Freeze until firm in the ice-making compartment of the fridge, or a freezer. Return fridge dial to its normal setting.

Serve in scoopfuls with fruit and wafers

Melon Ice-Cream: Scoop out the flesh from a 1½ lb. ripe melon and chop very finely, or purée. Fold into the custard together with the cream and egg whites. Continue as above.

RASPBERRY SORBET

Serves 4

| ½ lb. fresh or frozen raspberries |
| Two 5 oz. cartons natural yogurt |
| 1 tablespoon lemon juice |
| 2 level teaspoons gelatine |
| Liquid sweetener to taste |
| 2 egg whites, size 2 or 3 |

Sieve the half-thawed raspberries or mash and sieve the fresh ones. Mix the fruit purée together with the yogurt and lemon juice. Dissolve gelatine in 2 tablespoons hot water then add the sweetener to taste and stir into fruit mixture.

Whisk egg whites until stiff then fold carefully into fruit mixture. Pour into a deep container and freeze.

To serve: thaw for a short time in the fridge to bring out the flavour.

More recipes overleaf

Tart yet sweet –
Rhubarb Sorbet.

Lemon-Ice
Cream is
made with
condensed
milk.

ICES . . . COOL DRINKS . . . *Continued*

RHUBARB SORBET

Makes 1½-2 pints

1 lb. rhubarb
4 oz. sugar
½ pint water plus 1 tablespoon
2 teaspoons lemon juice
Rose pink colouring (optional)
2 large egg whites (size 2)

Set the fridge dial at maximum freezing temperature.

Wash and trim the rhubarb. Cut into small chunks and simmer with the 1 tablespoon water until very soft. Remove from the heat and purée in a blender or through a sieve.

Make a sugar syrup: dissolve the sugar in ½ pint water in a small pan over a gentle heat then bring to the boil and boil gently for 10 minutes. Add the syrup to the rhubarb, stir in the lemon juice and a few drops of colouring if required. Pour into a 2½ pint container or smaller ones and freeze until 'mushy' in the ice-making compartment or freezer.

Whisk the egg whites until stiff but not dry. Transfer the rhubarb mush to a cold bowl and beat it quickly with a rotary whisk to break up any large ice crystals. Quickly, but carefully, fold the egg whites evenly through the rhubarb then pour it back into the container and freeze until firm but still of a slightly soft texture. Return fridge dial to its normal setting.

Serve with rolled wafers, if liked.

LEMON-CREAM ICE

Makes 2-2½ pints

1 level teaspoon gelatine
¼ pint water
3 lemons
2 large eggs, size 2, separated
1 large can (14 oz.) sweetened condensed milk

Set the fridge dial to maximum freezing temperature.

Stir the gelatine in the water in a small pan and heat to dissolve; leave to cool.

Finely grate the lemon rind; squeeze and strain the juice and make up to ½ pint with water. Beat the rind, juice, condensed milk and egg yolks together with a rotary whisk or wooden spoon, until well mixed. Stir in the gelatine.

Pour the mixture into a 3 pint container and put into the ice-making compartment of the fridge or freezer and freeze until it is 'mushy'. (Because of the sweetness of the condensed milk, this mixture will take at least 4 hours to freeze.)

Whisk the egg whites until stiff but not dry. Transfer the lemon mixture to a cold bowl and, with a rotary whisk, beat for about 30 seconds until the mixture is smooth but still very cold. Quickly and carefully fold the egg whites evenly through the lemon then return it to the container and freeze until firm.

Once the ice-cream has frozen, return the fridge dial to its normal setting.

Serve with slices of lemon, if liked.

CHOCOLATE ICE-CREAM

Makes 2½-3 pints

3 oz. plain chocolate
½ pint milk
2 large eggs, size 2, separated
4 oz. sugar
1 large can (14.5 oz.) evaporated milk, chilled

Set the fridge dial to its maximum freezing temperature.

Melt the chocolate with the milk over a low heat – it does not matter if the chocolate does not dissolve smoothly as chocolate bits in the ice-cream make a pleasant contrast of textures.

Beat the egg yolks and sugar together in a basin until creamy. Gradually stir in the hot chocolate milk, return to the heat and, stirring all the time, cook over a low heat until the custard thickens – it should coat the back of a wooden spoon. Remove from heat and leave to become cold, stirring occasionally.

Whisk the evaporated milk for about 7 minutes until it is thick and leaves a trail when the whisk is lifted out. Fold in the chocolate custard, pour into a 3½ pint container or smaller ones, and freeze until it is 'mushy'.

Whisk the egg whites until stiff but not dry. Whisk the chocolate mush in the container to break up any large ice crystals. Fold in the egg whites until evenly mixed. Return the ice-cream to the freezer and freeze until firm, then turn the fridge dial to its normal setting.

Serve the ice-cream topped with nuts, grated chocolate or a chocolate mint cream.

Kids' favourite – Chocolate Ice-Cream.

SERVE WITH . . .

Bought ice-cream can be served in a variety of ways: with a sauce or fruit for a sundae; with a sprinkling of tiny sweets as a treat for a small child; topped with crunchy biscuit crumbs; as a filling for a flan. Here are a few ideas.

NUTTY CHOCOLATE TOPPING

Serves 4-6

2 oz. plain chocolate

3 level tablespoons peanut butter

3 tablespoons milk

2 level tablespoons icing sugar

1-2 level tablespoons chopped mixed nuts

Stir all the ingredients together in a pan over a low heat until they are well mixed. Serve hot or cold.

Nutty Chocolate Topping for flavour.

TROPICAL TOPPING

Serves 4

3 tablespoons golden syrup

1 oz. sultanas

The grated rind and juice of ½ orange

4 glacé cherries, sliced

½ oz. angelica cut into diamonds

½ teaspoon rum essence

Heat the syrup, sultanas, orange rind and juice gently in a small pan for 2 to 3 minutes to plump up the sultanas. Remove from the heat and stir in the cherries, angelica and the rum essence.

Serve warm over vanilla ice-cream.

Party trick – add Tropical Topping.

More recipes overleaf

Fancy Ice Cakes from family block.

ICES . . . COOL DRINKS . . . *Continued*

FANCY ICE CAKES

Makes 6

6 wafer biscuits
2½ fl. oz. double cream
1 level tablespoon drinking chocolate
Family block of cream or white ice-cream
An icing bag with star pipe attached

Cut 3 wafers in half, 1½ wafers into 6 triangles and the rest into 9 fingers.

Whisk the cream and drinking chocolate together until thick, then spoon into the icing bag. Remove the ice-cream from the freezing compartment and cut it into 6 small blocks. Place each one on half a wafer. Working quickly decorate the top of each one with rosettes of chocolate cream. Place wafer triangles and fingers in position and serve immediately.

STRAWBERRY-FILLED SWEET CHEESE CRUST

Serves 6

2 oz. cream cheese
1 oz. melted margarine
4 oz. digestive biscuits, crushed
1 family block strawberry ice-cream
¼ lb. fresh or canned strawberries
An 8 inch pie plate

Beat the cream cheese until soft then gradually beat in the melted margarine.

Stir in the crushed biscuit crumbs then press the mixture round the base and sides of an 8 inch pie plate. Leave in a cool place for half an hour.

When ready to serve, fill the flan with scoopfuls of ice-cream and cleaned, halved strawberries.

Serve immediately.

Note: Other good flavour combinations to try are chocolate ice-cream with sliced bananas or pears, or vanilla ice-cream with sliced oranges or peaches, or with fresh or canned fruit salad.

MORE QUICK AND EASY WAYS WITH ICES

1. *Sweet Creams:* as a special treat, sprinkle a child's favourite small sweets over the top of an ice-cream cornet.

2. *Hot and Cold Tartlets:* heat bought pastry cases in the oven. Quickly fill with ice-cream and drizzle warm raspberry jam or sweetened purée over the top. It's a little messy but absolutely delicious!

3. *Fruity Flans:* a) Spread base of flan with fruit purée or lemon curd and top with scoopfuls of ice-cream. Sprinkle nuts or crushed biscuit crumbs over the top.
b) Fill flan with sliced fresh or canned fruit, top with ice-cream and coat with chocolate or other flavoured sauce.

4. *Meringues:* just before serving, fill meringue halves or baskets with ice-cream and top with bought or home-made sauce.

5. *Delectable Sponge Desserts:* ice-cream makes a delicious topping to a trifle instead of the usual cream.
Sponge sandwich cakes turn into a gorgeous gâteau when the layers are spread with either jam or fruit and topped with slices of ice-cream.

6. *Ice-Cream Drinks;* add a scoop of ice-cream to a glass of fizzy lemonade, ginger beer or your favourite fruit juice or cordial made up with a little less water than usual. For a milk shake, beat a scoopful of flavoured ice-cream into cold milk.

COOL DRINKS

There are lots of occasions – parties, weddings, festive winter evenings or just long hot days in summer – which call for a drink that is a little bit more special.

WHITE WINE CUP

Serves 12

1 bottle (28 fl. oz.) dry white wine, chilled
1 bottle (35.2 fl. oz.) lemonade
¼ pint dry sherry
1 level tablespoon sugar
4 inch piece cucumber, washed
1 small orange, washed
1 small, red-skinned apple, washed
16 ice cubes
Cocktail sticks

Pour the wine, lemonade, sherry and sugar into a large jug.

Dice the cucumber and slice the orange. Cut the orange slices into small pieces; cut the apple into quarters, core and dice. Spear pieces of fruit and cucumber together on cocktail sticks and add to the cup with the ice cubes just before serving.

HOME-MADE SANGRIA

For about 30 glasses

Two 28 fl. oz. bottles red wine, chilled

Two 1½ litre bottles lemonade, chilled

¼ pint brandy

A few strawberries, sliced

Ice cubes

Mix together the red wine, lemonade and brandy. Pour into large jugs and float a few sliced strawberries on top. Put an ice cube into each glass before pouring in the Sangria.

STILL LEMONADE

Makes about 6 glasses

3 large lemons

About 6 oz. sugar

1½-2 pints boiling water

Wash the lemons and with a vegetable peeler pare off the rind thinly. Put the rind and sugar into a large bowl or heatproof jug and pour on the boiling water. Leave to cool, stirring occasionally. Add the lemon juice. Strain and serve chilled.

ICED TEA

Make a pot of your favourite tea, but brew it twice as strong as usual.

Fill glasses one third full of crushed ice then pour the tea – straining if necessary – over. Sweeten to taste and put a slice of lemon into each glass. Chill and serve. Chilling immediately after brewing helps retain the flavour.

Chilled Coffee Milk – easy to make.

CHILLED COFFEE MILK

Chill some creamy milk until very cold. Stir in Camp Coffee essence to taste – allowing about 2-3 teaspoonfuls per person. Chill the coffee milk until required. Serve in glasses.

FRESH ORANGE JUICE

Makes about 6 glasses

2 oranges

1 large lemon

Sugar to taste

Wash the fruit then roughly chop. Quarter fill the goblet of a blender with fruit pieces then pour on sufficient cold water to just over half-fill the goblet. Switch the machine on for a quick count of 10. Strain the juice into a bowl. Repeat with the rest of the fruit. Sweeten the juice to taste. Chill and serve.

Sensational! Cider and Orange Cup.

CIDER AND ORANGE CUP

Makes about 15 glasses

1 carton frozen orange juice

1 pint cold water

Two 8.5 fl. oz. bottles tonic water, chilled

Two 1 litre bottles cider

Pour the orange juice and water into a large jug or bowl. Stir until the orange juice has thawed. Stir in the tonic water and cider. Serve immediately.

APPLE AND ORANGE QUENCHER

Makes about 6 glasses

25 fl. oz. apple juice

Grated rind of 1 orange

Juice of 3 oranges

Juice of ½ lemon

Combine all the ingredients and serve chilled.

The Real Story of Cinderella

By Rosemary Suttill

Mrs. Pringle had got it all wrong. It was
certainly true that my name was Cindy, that I had a stepmother
and stepsisters, and that the family dog was called
Button. But that's where the similarity with the fairy
tale ended — or so I thought . . .

I BECAME Cindy the day after my fifth birthday. Everyone seemed to give me presents. Smelly stuff for the bath. Maybe a doll or a toy. Perhaps both. I think that was the year I was given my first bracelet. And the story of Cinderella.

Mum read it to me that night in bed and I changed my name the next morning. Cynthia I am really, but from that moment on I never answered to anything but Cindy. Well, hardly ever!

Mum died when I was ten, and soon after that Dad asked for a transfer away from the area.

Later on, Dad married again. Steppy I called her — her real name's Stephanie — and I was quite pleased with the joke at the time. She's a super cook, really top quality, and she made our home a lot more comfortable. We used to rush round looking for dinner money and the other sock all the time before she came. Not any more though.

Steppy didn't mind sharing Dad with me, either, and I was really glad about that. It was just him and me for such a long time. Then Steppy and Dad had twins! Super little girl twins, and I didn't spend nearly so much time with Dad after that.

Zoe and Vonnie they were called. Totally identical, unless you looked at their knees. Zoe had a birthmark on one kneecap, and that was the only way you could tell them apart. When the pair of them started crawling around we made sure they had the cleanest knees in the neighbourhood. There was just no other way to tell which was which.

Steppy and Dad made it clear I could live with them as long as I wanted, and I was pretty pleased about that. We were such a happy family and I adored all that marvellous cooking.

Right through university I used to look forward to coming home for vacations. Of course, I did other things as well. Travelled a bit, and found I enjoyed that, or stayed with friends. But home was where I really liked to be, playing with the twins or learning at least some of the dishes Steppy produced with such ease.

The summer I finished at university was beautiful — long hot days in which to laze around or mess about in the garden. We all developed glorious tans.

ONE AFTERNOON the vicar's wife, Mrs. Pringle, arrived for tea. There was something she wanted to discuss with Steppy; garden fêtes or the kiddies' home, most probably. Steppy had said we had to have tea in the garden. We'd have it under the big striped umbrella.

So, while she was fiddling with the spring clip, I loaded up a tray and was half-way across the hall when the door bell rang. Mrs. Pringle. Steppy says she's really very kind and agreeable; just rather too conscious of her position. Whenever she sees me, though, she seems to have a special straight-line-mouth, disapproving face switched on in seconds.

Continued overleaf

"Cindy, my dear girl, whatever are you doing with that tray?"

Well, it was obvious what I was doing, balancing it on one knee while I held open the door for her.

"Can I help? Really?"

"That's very sweet of you, Mrs. Pringle. Perhaps you could shut the front door."

To be honest, I'd overloaded the tray a bit and I wasn't too happy about the balance so I hurried out through the French windows and set the tray down on the garden table.

Behind me, Mrs. Pringle was muttering something about 'Such a weight, and in this heat,' so I knew she was disapproving of me for overloading the tray. Well, some people are just walking accidents looking for somewhere to happen. I'm a lot better than I used to be, but the twins are handier than me any day.

It's a joke in the family. If I'm all set to do something more than usually foolish, like pump out the washing machine when the hose is still clipped round the back, or pile a chair on a table to fix a light bulb, the family will yell: "Cindy!" and I'll stop and think about it.

Steppy had managed the umbrella, so the twins set out the food while I gathered up some chairs, and Mrs. Pringle buttonholed Steppy about making toys or cakes or whatever it was she wanted.

The tea was quite a spread. We hadn't bothered much for lunch, even with the twins on holiday; it was just too hot. One thing I can manage in the kitchen is sandwiches. I'd made grated cheese ones, cucumber ones, sardine ones, and put frilly lettuce all round the plates as well.

Steppy had made the cakes, of course. One was a toothsome chocolate affair, and the other was a lemon sponge with gorgeous feather icing, and chopped almonds round the sides.

"What delicious sandwiches," said Mrs. Pringle. No one tended to compliment Steppy on her cakes. It was stating the obvious a bit and, anyway, if you started you soon ran out of adjectives.

"Cindy made them," Steppy put in for me. "She arranged all of this," she said, waving the jug of orange at the table. Which was a kind thing to say because I'd only organised the twins putting out pickles and jams while I buttered the bread and kept Zoe's fingers out of the chocolate spread.

There went Mrs. Pringle with that straight-line-mouth, sour-puss face again. "I'm surprised to see Cindy so much at home still," she said. "Most girls would be out in the world. I can see she's very useful to you."

I thought she meant I should be working, bringing in some money for my keep. "The *Evening Press* has taken me on for a couple of months," I offered. "Until I start the journalism course."

"We like having Cindy here," protested Zoe. "She helps Vonnie and me an awful lot." That came out rather sharply because Zoe always thinks attack is the best method of defence.

"That will do, Zoe," said Steppy and Zoe wisely piped down, though she still looked mutinous. I decided to leave Mrs. Pringle to Steppy and went back to the kitchen for fresh supplies of squash.

To be without some of the things you want is an
indispensable part of happiness.

Bertrand Russell

The twice-weekly *Evening Press* (I think after a bit of string-pulling from Dad) had agreed to let me work with them for a couple of months. I hoped to pick up a lot of practical experience and have some fun at the same time.

After a couple of days I discovered the *Press* didn't really know what to do with me, and as I wasn't interested in making tea I arranged my own programme, spending some time in each department (and no doubt getting in everyone's way). When things were really slack I hoisted my own portable on to a vacant table corner and attempted items of my own. I even enjoyed typing '*By our junior correspondent, Cindy Duke.*' It was great fun.

APART FROM the people I've mentioned, we had another member of the family: Button, the Jack Russell. He's Dad's dog, really, but he allows anyone to take him out for a walk.

So there Button and I were, one Saturday afternoon, on our way to the local shops, basket on wheels trailing behind us. The weather had broken. A summer rainstorm had revived the roses and brought back the springiness to the cricket field. Steppy had taken the twins to a swimming gala, and Dad was doing careful things with one of his clematis.

Mrs. Pringle was out in her garden, exchanging remarks with a neighbour.

"Good afternoon, Cindy. Shopping again?"

"It's all right, Mrs. Pringle. I'm not blueing my savings in Fay's," I joked.

"I never imagined you were," she replied quietly. At that moment Button spotted the vicarage one-eyed feline. I could feel the static travelling along the lead. "Have to rush, Mrs. Pringle," I said.

I filled the basket with vital things. Bones for Button; slug pellets for Dad from the incredibly cramped, amazingly well-stocked chemist; and, while I was there, a new frosted-pink lipstick for me.

We took the long route home: up the track by the wood, round the back of the church and across the cricket field. I didn't really have on the right shoes for the mud, but Button hadn't had a decent walk for a couple of days because of the storm.

I don't know if there are nightingales in that wood. I know there's an owl, woodpeckers are often at work, and I've seen a wren. There are bluebells and cowslips in the spring, their delicate colours having a perfect foil in the dark old trees towering over them.

Disaster struck half-way across the field. The wheel came off the wretched basket. Pulling it over a fallen branch, I must have dislodged something.

Button came fussing round, putting his nose in the way. It was really irritating. I couldn't start to think how I'd carry that unwieldy basket home. I'd have everyone staring at me. To make matters worse, all of a sudden there was someone coming towards me. I really didn't want any Good Samaritans. I'd have been much happier left to work it out for myself. This chap was all done up in a smart suit, too. Not the usual wear for people round here on Saturdays.

"Having a spot of trouble?" he said. "Let's have a look."

So there we were, bending anxiously over this ridiculous basket as though it were some Grand Prix vehicle with laurel wreaths at stake. Naturally I had to start giggling — it was all so absurd — and then I choked trying to smother it. I didn't want to seem rude.

"You've lost the split pin," he explained (whatever *that* was), and then he glanced up at me and I could see he was trying not to smile, but there was amusement dancing in his eyes anyway. "I can fix it for you with a piece of string, or even a hair grip." He was grinning quite openly now, and I didn't feel at all bad at being caught in a spot.

I put up my hand to the large slide that keeps my hair more or less organised. I wasn't keen to sacrifice it, but if he could really mend the basket . . .

"Ah, here's some string round one of these parcels," he said, and the wheel was fixed in no time.

"That should see you home," he said. "Not far to go, have you?"

"Thank you so much." Should I shake hands? "We're only just round the corner."

"Well, I expect I'll see you about then," he remarked. "Goodbye."

I WAS babysitting that night. Steppy and Dad were going to a bridge supper. Steppy doesn't care for bridge too much but she goes along because Dad enjoys it. She works off her ill-feeling on the car (she's the world's worst driver, I have to admit it), and comes home all sweetness and light again.

I was fixing the supper for the twins and me. This meant popping the casserole Steppy had made from the freezer into the microwave oven and setting the dials. I managed it.

Later, when I went up to check the twins' teeth, the pair of them were in top teasing form. Zoe started with a steady stream of requests about the curtains. Open, closed, just a little bit open, and then it was the pandas. The pandas on the curtains, that is. "I want to make sure they can all reach the bamboo shoots," she said.

"Listen," I said, as I tucked in her sheet, "only real pandas eat bamboo shoots. Real pandas are shy, retiring creatures and they'd all have been scared away long ago. Stop chattering."

Vonnie decided I needed some riddles. She tried out three elephant ones in quick succession, but I knew them all from school. "One more," I said.

"Don't know any more," she said, thinking furiously. I was at the bottom of the stairs before she yelled triumphantly, "What's bright red and goes at 140 miles an hour?"

'An E-type carrot,' I thought. "A goldfish with the cat behind it," I called. "Good night."

Through the open door I could hear Steppy bring the big estate leaping from the garage. She found reverse at the third attempt and pulled up at the door in a spattering of gravel.

"George," she yelled, and hooted at the same time. Button slunk under the sofa and I sympathised. It was a terrific relief the day I passed my test and didn't have to ask Steppy to drive me any more.

Dad appeared with his shirt agape, and three ties across one arm. He ducked down to talk to Steppy through the car window. "What do you think?" he asked anxiously. "This Paisley thing or the plain red? Or shall I wear a blue shirt and this tie?" He held out a knitted navy object that Aunt Jane had bought him from some sale of work. As far as I know he's never worn it and Steppy's threatened to give it away more than once. Honestly, he's hopeless.

"For heaven's sake," said Steppy, "it's a bridge party. They'll be looking at their cards, not at your tie." Finally Dad *was* ready. The car door slammed, the gravel spurted again, and Steppy missed the gatepost by a coat of paint and a deep breath.

Upstairs, the twins were playing Ring-a-Roses. "We're going to play bri-idge, we're going to play bri-idge."

"Bed."

Continued overleaf

"Story. 'Cinderella.' Go on. Please." I never could resist two pairs of blue eyes at their most beseeching. So I read them 'Cinderella,' and they were fairly asleep before the glass slipper fitted its rightful owner.

Downstairs, I was absentminded with the dishwasher, crocheted three more patches for my new waistcoat before I realised I'd mixed up the colours, and found my usually favourite TV programme so dull I switched the hero off in mid-sentence.

It was all Prince Charming's fault, pitching up like that; totally unexpected, totally right. Of all the chaps I'd met at university, there hadn't been one I could imagine sweeping me out of the fairy tale to the land of Happy Ever After.

I don't mean I was looking for a Prince, Precisely, or anyone particularly wealthy. I'd have liked to find someone good-looking, with a pleasant personality. Someone I could respect, but feel on equal terms with.

The car brakes squeaked, jerking me out of the day-dream. Just as well. I was an educated female, with a course in journalism and a successful career as a foreign correspondent ahead! No time for reveries or, I guiltily realised, for conjuring up visions of the smartly dressed man who'd assisted in the matter of the shopping basket.

"Good party?" I asked, tucking away the crochet.

"The usual people," said Steppy. "The Perrys have invited us all on Thursday. Their wedding anniversary! The twins are invited, too, and we can bundle them upstairs with the Perrys' mob after supper. They might even behave themselves," she said ruefully. "It's to be a buffet supper and dance. They've invited the new doctor along, too. He's joining their panel. The Perrys say he's charming, quite charming."

I WAS sitting, hunched up and lop-sided. I was flying! Taking off and bumping back to earth, downhill through a sea of mud. I was in the basket on wheels! Mud flew up ahead, clinging to my face, cold and sticky. Button raced along beside me. I could see his face turned towards me as he ran. *He* handed me a steering wheel. "That should see you home," he said.

I guided myself somehow into the woodland path. I only had one wheel! Ahead was the tree trunk across the path. I had to stop! I tugged desperately at the basket handle. I didn't stop. I rolled even faster. Suddenly, two magnificent elephants appeared, hauling at the tree. They had the twins' faces. They came swinging down the path towards me. I braced myself for the collision and as I did so I saw Mrs. Pringle peering down from one of the elephants, ringing the church bell.

There was no feeling of impact, yet I knew we had collided. Twins, Mrs. Pringle, Button, myself and the basket were all cast slowly skywards in amazing cartwheels of revolving heads and limbs. Gravity was totally defied. We were all as trim and orderly as at a church service. Upside down, Mrs. Pringle had maintained her grasp of the church bell and continued to ring it insistently.

I FOUND myself awake, lying spreadeagled across the bed. The alarm was winding itself down beside my ear and the twins were peering round the door, caution wrestling with amazement.

"Gosh, your alarm's been ringing for years."

"Sorry." I reached groggily for the clock. "I had a dream. You turned into elephants."

I had to have a second cup of coffee at breakfast. That dream had left me distinctly shattered. Steppy and I had the kitchen to ourselves.

"Cindy," she started carefully, "don't think I'm rude, but what do you plan to wear on Thursday?" I hadn't considered it yet. "Why not buy something really summery for the evening?" She pressed some notes into my hand. "I owe you that for babysitting," she said. "Mrs. Pringle was right. Most girls would be off and away."

"Mrs. Pringle . . ." I tapped the end of my nose meaningfully.

"Well, never mind about that," said Steppy hastily, forgetting I was grown-up and she didn't have to hide her smile. "Fay's has some lovely things just now. Why don't you look in on Tuesday?" That was my afternoon off.

I liked Fay's Fashions. It was a neat little shop tucked into the corner of the square. Fay had converted the shop from the ground floor of her house, and with the roof jutting low over the entry there was an impression of entering a cool grotto. Fay herself always wore light fluttery garments, and wafted rather than walked about like an ordinary mortal. Whenever she came to rest for a moment, her clothes floated to stillness like a butterfly's wings.

After long, enjoyable rummaging, I picked a dress in several shades of green, all swirled together, with deep, pleated frills at the neck and hem.

Fay was enthusiastic, prinking out the frills and checking the length. "You could wear it for

THE ROBIN FAMILY

A PROBLEM WITH HOMEWORK

. . . and Roley wonders if he will ever have time to practise for Sports Day

ROSEMARY ROBIN was in the garden of Tree Stump House, trying to skip up to a hundred. It would soon be Sports Day at Miss Owl's School and she was hoping to be first in the Skipping Contest, so as soon as she had finished her homework, she had hurried outside to practise. Roley could hear her chirping "forty-eight. forty-nine, fifty . . ." in the distance.

It was very disturbing for he had not finished his homework and he was working on a sum that just would *not* come out right.

Roley wanted so badly to go outside and practise for Sports Day too. 'It seems unfair that grown-ups are more anxious for you to do well at sums and things rather than win prizes on Sports Day,' he thought, beginning to feel quite dejected and sorry for himself.

Then Mr. Robin came into the room. He had begun to wonder why his son was taking so long with his homework.

"I just can't get this sum to work out," said Roley. "I think it is too difficult for me and my brain is getting tired."

"Perhaps your brain is not working," said his father with a smile. "Let me see if I can help."

And he explained the problem so clearly that Roley wondered why he had thought it difficult. So in a very short time he too was out in the garden with Rosemary.

daytime or evening. Put your hair up as well. That would look *really* elegant."

The twins snooped in the bag, naturally, and of course I had to show Steppy. Everyone was most admiring. "Hold it up against you, let's see." And "Can you twirl round in it? It's smashing."

Dad said it looked very attractive, and green always had suited me. All in all I should have felt happy and enthusiastic at the idea of wearing it to a properly organised party, instead of the casual student 'bring a bottle' gatherings.

Instead, I felt depressed, dispirited, and almost inclined to plead a thundery headache, except that there was no thunder to be had.

I felt brighter after a shower, though. The dress fitted perfectly, the new lipstick was dreamy, and with ten minutes to spare (the twins had needed no hurrying for once) I remembered Fay's advice. Cautiously I combed my hair upwards, captured it in an elastic band, and pinned my topknot into a neat bun. It looked fine, but the band showed.

I hunted through a drawer for slides or clips — and there it was, an elderly stretch bracelet of green carved beads. Two loops of it round my hair and I had a little coronet. I gave my aching arms a rest. Had I overdone it? The mirror didn't help. I looked all right. . .

Steppy was more decisive. "That's lovely," she said. "You should always wear your hair up."

"I'd need a spare set of arms."

There were some pretty lively noises coming from the Perrys' house. Irene Perry opened the door and we all took turns to kiss her 'Happy anniversary'.

The twins moved in on a table of snacks and were deftly headed into the kitchen by Steppy to eat with the Perry children. Dad joined his cronies bemoaning Kent against Essex, and Irene led me to a small group.

"You know most people, of course," she said, "but here's our new doctor."

At her touch on his arm he turned. I should have known him before that, because of the suit.

"Hello," he said, and there was that smile in those blue-grey eyes I'd been living on since Saturday. "Hoped I'd see you again. How's the wheel?" At least I think that's what he said. There was this blur of sight and sound, and in the centre even he was scarcely in focus. Irene's slightly disappointed "Met

Continued overleaf

before?'' sounded as though it was coming down a badly distorted telephone line.

It was a strange thing, but all the time we stood there chatting—what a nice village it was, such a hot summer, lovely walks in this part of the country—I knew he understood how I felt and was giving me time to sort myself out. And I needed to sort myself out. Prince Charming! Here he was, at a dance, and I was quite ready to go whirling away that minute, never mind the glass slipper.

CHRIS TURNER-HAMILTON he was called. He told me he'd been at a London hospital before. He was wonderful to dance with, considerately guiding me round less careful couples. It was like being driven in an expensive car with smooth cornering and superb road holding, as they say in the ads.

When I drifted away to sleep on my pillow that night, his goodnight kiss still tingled on my lips. "I have to start work tomorrow," he'd said. "But I'd like to take you out soon. May I ring you?"

I didn't know when he would phone. After a weekend when I suspected the phone was out of order, I spent the longest Monday of my existence. He rang on Tuesday morning.

"He said he hadn't realised you went to work," smiled Steppy, all sympathy. "He hopes you'd like to have dinner with him this evening, and he'll collect you from here at 8 o'clock."

We sat a long time over our coffee at the old pub restaurant he'd been recommended to try. Evening crept in on us slowly through the open windows, bringing with it sounds from the river beyond the garden. Ducks and water creatures splashed quietly about their evening activities.

The sympathetic waitress had left the light switches alone, so we sat with the candles burning shorter in their tall glasses, and no one to see how we held hands across the table.

He could listen as well as talk, which I appreciated, and his ideas and ideals were remarkably in tune with my own hopes for the future.

It was time to leave. His face, as he searched for his car keys in the pub doorway, held a curious expression. Half-smiling mouth and those amused eyes again.

"What's the joke?" I asked stiffly.

"No joke." He was immediately serious. "Tell you in the car." He took my hand.

THE NEWS of our engagement spread fast in the village. Mrs. Pringle buttonholed me as I tried vaguely to do helpful things with coffee cups at the church social.

"Prince Charming," she said mistily, her face all soft and comfortable.

"Prince Charming?"

"I'm so pleased for you. You've had such a hard life up to now."

I stared. "A hard life?"

"Of course. I heard about your own dear mother. So sad. I'm sure Stephanie never intends any unkindness to you, but she's so totally capable herself — " 'You haven't seen her driving,' I thought—"so *robust.*" It was as though I were fading fast from some awful disease. "I know how loyal you are to your dear father, but I have been at your house and I have seen," she ended, significantly.

It was all as clear as mud to me. What had she seen?

"Cindy," she murmured. "Cinderella."

Understanding filtered slowly into my mind, like sunlight through stained glass. "You can't imagine," I said slowly, scarcely knowing what to emphasise, "that Steppy and the twins. . . Now look — "

I didn't dare laugh. She really did care, was genuinely concerned. She had convinced herself that I was Cinderella for real—badly treated, living a life of untold misery—and that she, Mrs. Pringle, had witnessed Cinderella meeting her handsome Prince Charming. Well, that bit *was* true.

"Steppy," I said, trying to sound severe, "is the kindest, most adorable stepmother any girl could hope for. The twins are fun and I love them dearly. Button — " I'd spotted another clue — "is only a dog, and if my dress did come from Fay's, I promise you I paid for it. Not a magic wand in sight."

"But the day I came to tea, you had such a heavy tray," Mrs. P. struggled on desperately. "And the family does shout at you, I've heard them."

"The tray was my own fault," I said unrelentingly. "And the family does indeed shout at me, usually when I'm about to flood the house or blow the mains."

I convinced her at last, as far as she wanted to be convinced, but I was sad for her as well. She'd so believed in fairy stories.

THE END

© Rosemary Suttill, 1983

BUILD A BUGGY

Our streamlined version of the traditional child's buggy will keep an active youngster happy for hours in the safety of the garden. See the colour picture on page 78

PREPARATION

From prepared softwood, cut the centre board, steering bar and back wheel bar to length (for measurements, see diagram on page 65). Mark pencil lines on both sides of the centre board to denote the centre of the width along the length. Then mark the curve at the front end of the board (see diagram) using a pair of compasses. Cut the curve to shape with a coping saw and finish off with a file followed by glasspaper. Now drill an 8mm ($^5/_{16}$ in.) dia. hole centrally through the centre board, 152mm (6 in.) away from the front end.

Mark and cut to shape the tapers along the front edge of the steering bar, then drill an 8mm ($^5/_{16}$ in.) dia. hole centrally through the bar. Also drill a 6mm ($^1/_4$ in.) dia. hole, 64mm (2$^1/_2$ in.) away from each end of the bar, for the steering cord.

Using the steering bar and back wheel bars as a guide, cut the four wheel blocks to length (see diagram). Drill a 6mm ($^1/_4$ in.) dia. screw thread hole, 38mm (1$^1/_2$ in.) deep centrally in one long edge of each block (see diagram). Then glue and screw the blocks in place on the bars, using four 32mm (1$^1/_4$ in.) screws for each block.

Continued overleaf

Materials Required

L = Length (mm)
W = Width (mm)
T = Thickness (mm)

Approximate Imperial equivalents in inches are shown in brackets.

Prepared Softwood

	L	W	T
Centre board—1 piece	915(36)	146(5$^3/_4$)	22($^7/_8$)
Steering bar—1 piece	534(21)	96(3$^3/_4$)	22($^7/_8$)
Back wheel bar—1 piece	432(17)	96(3$^3/_4$)	22($^7/_8$)
Seat sides—2 pieces	350(13$^3/_4$)	146(5$^3/_4$)	22($^7/_8$)
Seat bearers—2 pieces	305(12)	22($^7/_8$)	22($^7/_8$)

Prepared Hardwood

	L	W	T
Front wheel blocks—			
2 pieces	74(2$^7/_8$)	45(1$^3/_4$)	22($^7/_8$)
Back wheel blocks—			
2 pieces	96(3$^3/_4$)	45(1$^3/_4$)	22($^7/_8$)

Plywood

	L	W	T
Seat base—1 piece	305(12)	368(14$^1/_2$)	12($^1/_2$)
Spacing disc—1 piece	90(3$^1/_2$)	90(3$^1/_2$)	3($^1/_8$)
Wheel stop—1 piece	76(3)	76(3)	12($^1/_2$)

Note: All nominal measurements shown above are nett, and small allowances should be made for cutting pieces to length.

Other Items

Four 152mm (6 in.) plastic spoked wheels with 9mm ($^3/_8$ in.) dia. hub.
Four 64mm (2$^1/_2$ in.) by 9mm ($^3/_8$ in.) dia. coach screws and eight washers.
One 64mm (2$^1/_2$ in.) by 8mm ($^5/_{16}$ in.) dia. carriage bolt, two nuts and one washer.
Four 45mm (1$^3/_4$ in.) by 6mm ($^1/_4$ in.) dia carriage bolts, four nuts and four washers.
Twenty six 32mm (1$^1/_4$ in.) and ten 25mm (1 in.) no. 8 countersunk screws.
Two metres of thick nylon cord.
Wood glue, medium grade glasspaper and paint.

Note: For the No. 8 screws used to assemble the buggy, first drill 4.5mm ($^3/_{16}$ in.) dia. clearance holes and countersink them so that the screw heads are well below the wood surface.

From 12mm ($^1/_2$ in.) thick plywood, prepare the seat base to size (for measurements see diagram). Then round over the front edge, using a file and glasspaper. From 22mm ($^7/_8$ in.) square softwood, cut two pieces 305mm (12 in.) long for the seat bearers. Bevel the ends of each bearer (see diagram) then glue and screw them to the underside of the base, flush with the side edges. Use three 25mm (1 in.) screws (inserted through the base) to secure each bearer.

Mark the shape of one seat side on a length of 146 by 22mm ($5^3/_4$ by $^7/_8$ in.) prepared softwood (for details of shaping see squared diagram). Cut to shape using a coping saw, then smooth sawn edges with glasspaper. Use this as a template and mark out and cut the second seat side to size. Drill and countersink three screw holes through each piece (see diagram).

From 12mm ($^1/_2$ in.) plywood, cut one piece 76mm (3 in.) square for the wheel stop. Glue and screw this to the underside of the centre board using four 25mm (1 in.) screws. Place the stop with two opposing corners against the centre line drawn on the board, and 229mm (9 in.) away from the rounded end of the board.

For the spacing disc, first mark a 90mm ($3^1/_2$ in.) dia. circle on a piece of 3mm ($^1/_8$ in.) thick plywood. Cut to shape with a fretsaw then drill an 8mm ($^5/_{16}$ in.) dia. hole through the centre.

Smooth all the surfaces, and round over sharp corners and edges, using medium grade glasspaper.

As a final check, run your fingers along all the edges to make sure that any splinters have been removed.

ASSEMBLING THE BUGGY

First glue and screw the centre board centrally across the back wheel bar with the back edge overhanging the bar by 50mm (2 in.). Use four 32mm ($1^1/_4$ in.) screws for this.

Glue and screw the seat sides to the seat base with the bottom edges of the base bearers and the sides flush. Use three 32mm ($1^1/_4$ in.) screws, inserted through the holes drilled in the seat sides, for each join. Now attach the seat centrally to the centre board with the back edges of both pieces flush, using four 45mm ($1^3/_4$ in.) by 6mm ($^1/_4$ in.) dia. carriage bolts (see diagram). Position the bolts in the seat base so that they enter the centre board, avoiding the back wheel bar. **Note:** Drill a 16mm ($^5/_8$ in.) dia. starting hole 4.5mm ($^3/_{16}$ in.) deep in the seat base before

drilling the necessary 6mm (¼ in.) dia. hole for the shank of each bolt, so that each bolt head is recessed below the surface.

To attach the steering bar to the centre board, first knock a 64mm (2½ in.) carriage bolt through the hole drilled near the front of the centre board. Thread the plywood disc on to the bolt then knock the bolt through the hole drilled centrally through the steering bar. Place a washer followed by two nuts on the end of the bolt. Tighten the first nut up to the washer; hold this nut firmly with a spanner, then tighten the second nut against the first to lock both firmly together.

Before attaching the wheels, first remove any sharp corners from the heads of the coach screws, using a file. Also check that the wheels spin freely on the screws and scrape paint from the shanks of the screws if necessary. Slip a washer on to a coach screw and insert the screw through the hole in a wheel hub. Place a second washer on the screw then insert the point in a screw thread hole drilled in a wheel block. Tighten the screw with a spanner until the wheel

spins freely without wobbling. Attach the remaining wheels in the same way.

FINISHING

Painting the buggy is much easier if the wheels, seat and steering bar are removed and painted separately. Apply wood primer or emulsion paint thinned with water as advised on the tin, to act as a sealer. Then apply undercoat followed by a top gloss paint.

When paint is completely dry, reassemble the buggy and attach the steering cord by passing an end through each of the holes in the steering bar and knotting them on the reverse side. A flame passed over the ends of nylon cord prevents fraying.

CAUTIONARY NOTE:
This toy is intended entirely for use in the garden, and it must not be taken out on the public highway.

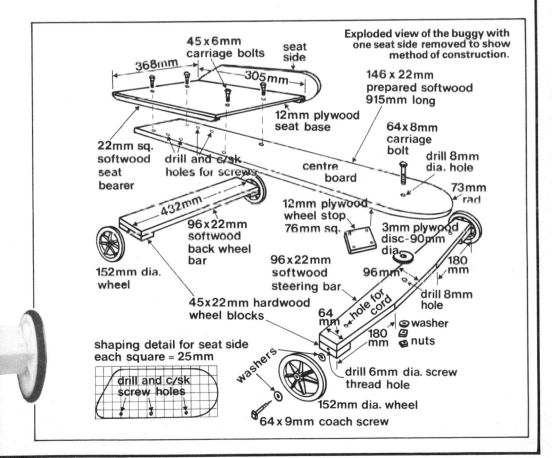

Exploded view of the buggy with one seat side removed to show method of construction.

45 x 6mm carriage bolts
seat side
368mm
305mm
146 x 22mm prepared softwood 915mm long
12mm plywood seat base
64 x 8mm carriage bolt
drill 8mm dia. hole
22mm sq. softwood seat bearer
drill and c/sk holes for screws
centre board
73mm rad
432mm
12mm plywood wheel stop 76mm sq.
3mm plywood disc-90mm dia.
96x22mm softwood back wheel bar
96x22mm softwood steering bar
96mm
180 mm
drill 8mm hole
152mm dia. wheel
45x22mm hardwood wheel blocks
64 mm
hole for cord
180 mm
washer
nuts
shaping detail for seat side each square = 25mm
washers
drill 6mm dia. screw thread hole
drill and c/sk screw holes
152mm dia. wheel
64 x 9mm coach screw

SOFT AND SUBTLE

A delicate cable and lacy stitch
ensures that this charming sweater in silky-look
yarn is glamorous as well as warm

Instructions in 4 sizes

Colour photo on page 76

MATERIALS: *Allow the following quantities in 20 g balls of Jaeger Wool Silk: 18 for 81 cm size; 19 for 86 cm size; 20 for 91 cm size; 21 for 97 cm size. For any one size: A pair each of No. 10 (3¼ mm) and No. 12 (2¾ mm) knitting needles; a cable needle.*

TENSION: *Work at a tension of 35 stitches and 40 rows to measure 10 x 10 cm, over the pattern, using No. 10 (3¼ mm) needles, to obtain measurements given below.*

ABBREVIATIONS: To be read before working: *K., knit plain; p., purl; st., stitch; tog., together; dec., decrease (by working 2 sts. tog.); up 1, pick up loop lying between needles and k. or p. into back of it; y.fwd., yarn forward to make a st.; p. or k.2 tog.b., p. or k.2 tog. through back of sts.; c. 5b., cable 5 back (slip next 3 sts. on to cable needle and leave at back of work, k.2, then k.3 from cable needle); single rib is k.1 and p.1 alternately.*

NOTE: *Instructions are given for the 81 cm (32 inch) size. Where they vary, work figures within first brackets for 86 cm (34 inch) size; work figures within second brackets for 91 cm (36 inch) size, and so on.*

THE BACK: With No. 12 (2¾ mm) needles cast on 118 (128) (138) (148) sts. and work 21 rows in single rib.

Increase row: Rib 7 (8) (9) (10), up 1, * rib 4, up 1; repeat from * 25 (27) (29) (31) times, rib 7 (8) (9) (10) — 145 (157) (169) (181) sts.

Change to No. 10 (3¼ mm) needles and work the 24-row pattern as follows:

1st row: P.1, k.9, * c. 5b., k.7; repeat from * until 15 sts. remain, c. 5b., k.9, p.1.

2nd row: K.1, * p.2, k.7, p.2, k.1; repeat from * to end.

3rd row: P.1, * k.2, p.7, k.2, p.1; repeat from * to end.

4th to 7th rows: Repeat 2nd and 3rd rows, twice.

8th and 9th rows: As 2nd, then 1st rows.

10th row: All p.

11th row: K.1, * y.fwd., k.11, y.fwd., k.1; repeat from * to end.

12th row: P.6, * p.3 tog., p.11; repeat from * until 9 sts. remain, p.3 tog., p.6.

13th row: K.2, * y.fwd., k.9, y.fwd., k.3; repeat from * until 11 sts. remain, y.fwd., k.9, y.fwd., k.2.

14th row: As 12th row.

15th row: K.3, * y.fwd., k.7, y.fwd., k.5; repeat from * until 10 sts. remain, y.fwd., k.7, y.fwd., k.3.

16th row: As 12th row.

17th row: K.4, * c. 5b., k.7; repeat from * until 9 sts. remain, c. 5b., k.4.

18th row: K.4, * p.5, k.7; repeat from * until 9 sts. remain, p.5, k.4.

19th row: P.4, * k.2, y.fwd., k.1, y.fwd., k.2, p.7; repeat from * until 9 sts. remain, k.2, y.fwd., k.1, y.fwd., k.2, p.4.

20th row: K.1, k.2 tog., k.1, * p.7, k.3 tog., k.2; repeat from * until 11 sts. remain, p.7, k.1, k.2 tog., k.1.

21st row: P.3, * k.2, y.fwd., k.3, y.fwd., k.2, p.5; repeat from * until 10 sts. remain, k.2, y.fwd., k.3, y.fwd., k.2, p.3.

MEASUREMENTS *in centimetres (and inches, in brackets)*								
To fit bust sizes	81	(32)	86	(34)	91	(36)	97	(38)
All round underarms	83	(32¾)	89.5	(35¼)	97	(38)	103.5	(40¾)
Side seam	33.5	(13¼)	33.5	(13¼)	33.5	(13¼)	33.5	(13¼)
Length	50	(19¾)	50	(19¾)	51.5	(20¼)	51.5	(20¼)
Sleeve seam	44	(17¼)	44	(17¼)	44	(17¼)	44	(17¼)

22nd row: K.2 tog., k.1, * p.9, k.1, k.3 tog., k.1; repeat from * until 12 sts. remain, p.9, k.1, k.2 tog.

23rd row: P.2, * k.2, y.fwd., k.5, y.fwd., k.2, p.3; repeat from * until 11 sts. remain, k.2, y.fwd., k.5, y.fwd., k.2, p.2.

24th row: K.2 tog., * p.11, k.3 tog.; repeat from * until 13 sts. remain, p.11, k.2 tog.

Pattern a further 90 rows.

Mark each end of last row to denote end of side seams. **

Pattern 64 (64) (70) (70) rows.

To slope the shoulders: Cast off 47 (51) (55) (59) sts. at beginning of next 2 rows — 51 (55) (59) (63) sts.

Leave sts. on a spare needle.

THE FRONT: Work as given for back until ** is reached.

Pattern 1 row.

To divide for neck: Next row: Pattern 72 (78) (84) (90) and leave these sts. on a spare needle for right half neck, pattern 1 and leave this st. on a safety pin, pattern to end and work on these 72 (78) (84) (90) sts. for left half neck.

The left half neck: Keeping continuity of the pattern where possible, dec. 1 st. at neck edge on next row, then on the 20 (24) (24) (28) following alternate rows — 51 (53) (59) (61) sts.

Work 3 rows, then dec. 1 st. at neck edge on next row, then on the 3 (1) (3) (1) following 4th row(s) — 47 (51) (55) (59) sts.

Pattern 5 (5) (3) (3) rows — pattern 6 (6) (4) (4) rows here when working right half neck.

Cast off.

The right half neck: With right side of work facing, rejoin yarn to sts. on spare needle and work as left half neck, noting variation where indicated.

THE SLEEVES (both alike): With No. 12 (2¾ mm) needles cast on 68 (68) (74) (74) sts. and work 29 rows in single rib.

Increase row: Rib 2, up 1, * rib 1, up 1; repeat from * 63 (63) (69) (69) times, rib 2 — 133 (133) (145) (145) sts.

Change to No. 10 (3¼ mm) needles and repeat the 24 pattern rows of back, 6 times.

Cast off.

This lovely yarn comes in a choice of delectable colours such as willow, pearl, biscuit, helio, azure and gold.

THE NECK RIBBING: First join right shoulder seam.

With the right side of the work facing and using No. 12 (2¾ mm) needles, rejoin yarn and pick up and k.48 (48) (52) (52) sts. down left half neck, k. st. from safety pin, pick up and k.48 (48) (52) (52) sts. up right half neck, then decreasing 1st., in centre, k.51 (55) (59) (63) sts. from spare needle across back neck — 147 (151) (163) (167) sts.

1st rib row: * K.1, p.1; repeat from * to within 2 sts. of centre front st., k.2 tog.b., k.1, k.2 tog., * p.1, k.1; repeat from this * to end.

2nd rib row: Rib to within 2 sts. of centre front st., p.2 tog., p.1, p.2 tog.b., rib to end.

Repeat the last 2 rows, 4 times more.

Cast off in rib, decreasing either side of centre front st. as before.

TO MAKE UP THE SWEATER: Do not press. Join left shoulder seam, continuing seam across neck ribbing. Sew cast off group at top of sleeves between markers on back and front, then join sleeve and side seams.

*H*AVE YOU *noticed how* complicated *the whole business of suntanning seems to have become? There you stand at the counter retailing suntan products, confronted by this overwhelming array of branded creams, lotions, gels, oils, mousses, and milks — some, to add to the confusion, labelled with 'sun filtering factors' — how on earth do you sort out exactly what's best for you? Let's take the points raised one by one:*

What do the 'factors' marked on some of the suntan products mean?

The 'sun filtering factors' indicate the degree of protection afforded by that particular product against the sun's burning rays: the higher the number (within a range of 1-6, 7 or 8, depending on the brand), the higher the degree of protection. (The different suntan products don't all have exactly the same range of factors, by the way — and some don't use factors at all — this is because it's simply a convenient way of indicating the level of protection: it's not a matter of objective, scientific fact.)

The factor you choose depends on three things: (1) how sensitive your skin is; (2) how much of a tan you have already; (3) where you plan to do your sunbathing — under moderate, strong or intense sun.

If you have a very sensitive skin, or not a trace of a tan, or are buying for a small child, or are planning to holiday in, say, the Mediterranean countries (intense sun conditions), choose the highest factor.

If, say, your skin is normal, or you have a bit of a tan already or your holiday is in this country (moderate sun conditions), choose a lower strength factor. Some counters have helpful charts, by the way, to show you just which products are best for which conditions.

Where suntan products that don't go in for 'factors' are concerned, obviously, you should choose the product that's specifically stated to be for your type of skin, whether normal or sensitive, and for the type of sun conditions in the place where you'll be holidaying. Always check to make sure that the product you buy includes a sun-screen.

Once I've decided which strength of protection I need, how do I know whether to choose an oil or lotion, or what?

Choose whichever formulation appeals to you most: it's simply a matter of personal preference.

How many suntan products do I need?

The minimum is: a sun-screen product for use while you're sunbathing and an after-sun preparation (important) to slather on afterwards to counter the drying effects of the sun and cool down your skin. You could add to these, if you have sensitive lips, a lip protection stick to prevent blisters — you can use it on your nose, too, as extra protection.

What actually happens to your skin to make it tan?

Your skin's main defence against the effects of the ultra-violet rays of the sun comes from melanin, or pigmentation, which is produced by special cells in the epidermis called melanocytes.

These melanocytes are responsible for the pigmentation of the body — hair and skin colouring. The amount of melanin produced by the melanocytes determines the colour of your skin (little melanin: very fair colouring; a lot: very dark skin).

When the skin is exposed to ultra-violet light (as it is when you sunbathe), more melanin is produced to protect the genetic material of the skin. Your skin thus becomes more heavily pigmented, or tanned.

I never seem to go darker than a honey colour, no matter how hard I try! Is there actually a maximum tan of which I'm capable?

Yes; this is determined by genetic factors. Everyone has the same number of melanocytes, but the amount of melanin produced varies, and once your body has produced all the melanin of which it's capable, you're not going to get browner.

Does your skin type — dry, normal or greasy, that is — affect the degree of tan you're likely to get?

No, this has no effect on your ability to tan. The only difference your skin type makes is that your skin, if it's dry, is likely to be more sensitive to the effect of the sun, and will also need more moisturising.

Does the wind affect the rate at which you tan?

No; the trouble is, that as you're likely to feel cooler when there's a wind, you imagine you don't need protection against the sun — and you do!

How long is it safe to soak up the sun on your very first day on the beach?

Limit sunbathing to 15 minutes your first day, and gradually step up sunning time by about 20 minutes a day.

Are there any real benefits from tanning?

The best known benefit is the body's production of Vitamin D — essential for the absorption of calcium. Another becomes apparent if you have any greasy skin condition, particularly acne — the ultra-violet rays can help rid you of blemishes, and, also, 'peeling' helps slough off dead and infected skin cells, leaving you with the fresh new layer of skin underneath.

THE SUNTAN EXPERIENCE

How to choose the best protective product for your own skin and how to tan safely

Colour photo on page 77

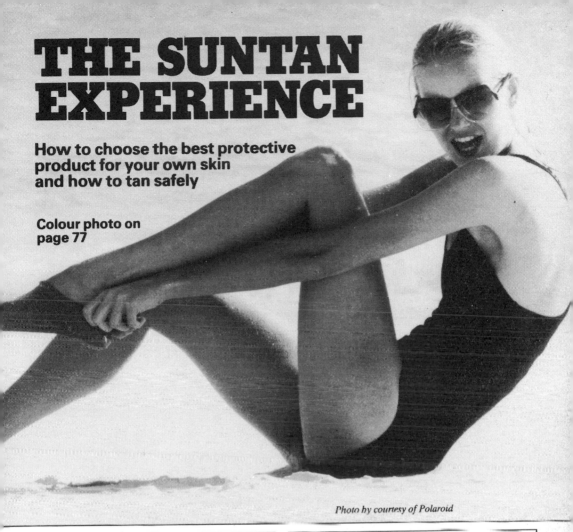

Photo by courtesy of Polaroid

I'm fairly dark-skinned, and I always get a tan very easily— surely I don't need any protective sun-screens?

Yes, you do. It's important to protect your skin against the harmful rays of the sun when you sunbathe, to avoid possible cell damage—you can damage your skin's collagen, which will result, in the long term, in premature ageing and wrinkling. This applies to everyone, whatever their colouring.

How often should you re-apply suntan lotion?

About every two to three hours, and after swimming —unless you're using a water-resistant sun-screen (useful if you enjoy water sports like sailing, waterskiing and so on) in which case, two or three times a day is all you need.

How about all the fake tans—do they give your skin any protection?

No; unless they clearly state on the packaging that they also contain a sun-screen, these fake tans don't give any protection at all.

Are there any parts of your body that need more protection than others against sunburn?

Yes—always be especially careful to protect your nose, shoulders, backs of legs, tops of feet and knees. Men whose hair is thinning, or who are bald, should be very careful, too, to protect the top of the head— either with a sun-screen product or a hat. And always protect small children with a hat, as well as liberal applications of a good sun-screen, re-applied scrupulously every couple of hours or so, and after they've been in the water.

1. To line a hanging basket with moss or polythene, hold it steady on a pot or bucket.

2. Part fill with compost, then place plants in position and pack round compost.

3. Hang the filled basket from a strong bracket and water it at least once a day in hot weather.

Rich red Fuchsia Marinka.

YOUR GARDEN IN SUMMER

Enjoy the rewards of your labours in this, the most productive season, says JOY SIMMONS

FLOWER GARDEN

Finish sowing hardy annuals to flower this summer, applying an animal repellent to deter cats from scratching in the fine soil.

Lift Polyanthus after flowering, planting them in an odd corner of the garden until the autumn. Before replanting the bed with summer bedding plants, fork in a general fertiliser. Suggested flowers for massed bedding are Petunias, Dahlias, Geraniums, French Marigolds, Asters, Antirrhinums and Fuchsias. Any of this selection should give you colour for most of the summer. Leave 6 in. between low-growing plants, 12 in. between medium height plants, and 18 in. between tall plants.

Check Roses for mildew and black spot, spraying with a systemic fungicide.

Support Sweet Peas with tall, bushy pea sticks or a wigwam of canes. Tall perennials should also be supported with brushwood or stout stakes.

Sow perennials and biennials in rows 6 in. apart, to bloom next year. Wallflowers, Forget-me nots, Pinks, Canterbury Bells, Sweet William, Iceland Poppies, Campanula, Lupins and Honesty all come readily from seed.

Flowered shoots of Aubrieta should be cut back to encourage "cushion" growth. Cuttings of Arabis, yellow Alyssum and Aubrieta can be rooted in damp sand and peat, in a semi-shady position.

Feed Roses with a proprietary fertiliser.

Clip formal hedging — Yew, Holly, Cupressus and Lonicera nitida.

Lawns should be mown twice a week during the summer months.

In August and September, several of the hardiest annuals may be sown for early bloom next summer: Godetia, Calendula, Larkspur, Echium, Cornflower, Candytuft, Double Shirley Poppies and Clarkia.

KITCHEN GARDEN

Thin Onions to 9 in. apart, Lettuces 6-9 in. apart, Beetroots 6-8 in., Parsnips 8-9 in. and Spinach 6 in.

Continue sowing Dwarf Beans, Turnips and Dwarf Peas for succession. Sow Runner Beans.

Peas and Beans need frequent watering in dry weather.

Marrows, Tomatoes and Ridge Cucumbers can be planted in the open. Where space is short, grow Tomatoes in pots or tubs, placed where they will get plenty of sun.

Carrots can first be thinned 2-3 in. apart, finally to 5-6 in. apart.

Lift early Potatoes; dig them on a fine day, using a broad-tined fork.

Brassica seedlings — Cabbage, Brussels Sprouts, Broccoli, etc. — should be planted in firm, well-limed ground enriched with rotted manure or vegetable fertiliser, spacing them 2-2½ ft. apart (Cabbages 1½-2 ft.).

Sow Winter Radishes in rows 9 in. apart, thinning the seedlings to 6 in. apart. These make large roots which can be eaten chopped or grated in a winter salad.

Spray Runner Beans overhead with water when in bloom to aid setting.

Early-planted Shallots should be ready for harvesting.

Finish cutting Asparagus.

Protect tub-grown Strawberries from birds by throwing a net over the tub.

Thin out Gooseberries in late May.

Protect Raspberries against Raspberry beetle by dusting with Derris when the first pink fruits appear in June.

Control Apple sawfly and capsid by spraying fruit trees with Malathion immediately after petal fall in May.

Complete thinning of Apples in July.

GREENHOUSE

Pinch out Tomato side-shoots (but not on bush Tomatoes), securing the plants to canes. Start feeding with a Tomato fertiliser when the first truss of fruit forms.

Sow Cineraria, Exacum and Primula kewensis and P. malacoides, for blooming under glass during late autumn and winter.

Prick off seedlings into small pots.

Pot on Chrysanthemums when the pots are full of roots.

Shade greenhouse in hot sun, ventilating freely. Water staging and floor daily.

Root Geranium and Hydrangea cuttings.

Grapes can be thinned when the size of a pea, feeding with liquid manure.

BEFORE GOING ON HOLIDAY

Provide support for flowering plants, using twiggy sticks between fragile annuals and strong stakes for tall perennials.

If the flower borders are weedy, hoe between the plants in dry weather.

Spray Rose bushes with *ICI Rose Plus, Gesal Rose Mildew Treatment* or *Murphy's Systemic Fungicide,* as a precaution against black spot, mildew and rust. Feed with a Rose fertiliser.

Feed Chrysanthemums and Dahlias with a foliar feed such as *Phostrogen.*

Where necessary, apply a total weedkiller to paths.

Weedy lawns can be treated with a selective weedkiller plus fertiliser. If you tidy the edges with a half-moon edge cutter, you'll find it lasts longer than a shear cut. Leave mowing until the day before leaving home, if possible.

Hanging baskets should be lifted down and placed in a shady corner. Water well and protect surface with black polythene.

Hardier house plants can be treated in much the same way, sinking the pots in the ground. Place the not-so-hardy house plants in polythene bags and seal the top with adhesive tape. Or stand them in the sink (out of the sun) on capillary matting under a dripping tap.

In the vegetable garden, hand pollinate Marrows where necessary.

Most pests can be controlled by spraying with *ICI Pestkiller for Fruit and Veg.* Weeds can be destroyed with *Weedol* applied between the rows. Side shoots should be removed from Tomato plants (but not bush Tomatoes) the evening before leaving home. Then water the plants well and mulch with peat, straw or black polythene.

Family days out

A diversity of places to visit — with souvenirs to bring home

Norfolk Lavender Fields, Caley Mill, Heacham: Almost 100 acres of lavender stretching as far as the eye can see — a gorgeous sight, best seen in July and August harvest-time. Visitors can also inspect the distillery where the lavender oil is made, admire the display of garden lavenders and the herb garden, enjoy a cream tea in the old miller's cottage and buy lavender, loose or in sachets, and lavender-scented bath products. Opening times: Late May-mid-September, 10.30am - 6.00pm.

Cheddar Gorge, Somerset: Famous gorge in the Mendip Hills with sheer, dramatic cliffsides, caves containing fantastic coloured stalactites and stalagmites, Jacob's Ladder and Waterfall Grotto. Open all year, 10.00am - 6.00pm in summer, 10.00am - 5.00pm in winter. Cheddar village dates from Saxon times and is the original home of Cheddar cheese-making. Whole cheeses of various sizes are on sale.

Prinknash Abbey, Pottery and Bird Park, near Painswick, Glos.: The Benedictine monks of Prinknash run a thriving pottery in the abbey grounds. You can watch them at work and buy the finished products. The bird park, also in the grounds, is home for snow geese, peacocks, countless birds of exotic hue, plus pygmy goats, Jacob sheep — and a Haunted Monk's fish pond. Pottery open all day Mondays to Fridays, Saturday mornings and Sunday afternoons.

Trefriw Woollen Mills, Llanwrst, Gwnedd: The tradition of Welsh wool weaving goes back nearly 2,000 years. Water from the River Crafnant is still used to drive the looms at Trefriw and visitors can watch the processes of carding, spinning, dyeing and weaving. A wide range of traditional and modern designs is produced, from their own fleeces. Mill and shop open all year, Monday to Friday.

Springfields Flower Park, Spalding, Lincs.: Unique 25-acre spring flower park where over a million bulbs flourish in springtime beauty amid lawns and lakes and under glasshouses. Open daily April to mid-May. Summer rose gardens open daily June to September.

Craster Kippers: The unspoilt fishing village of Craster, Cumbria, has long been famous for its kippers. If you'd like to see exactly how the herrings are kippered, visit Robson & Sons on Haven Hill. Open weekdays June to mid-September (Saturdays until noon). The walk along the shore from Craster to Dunstanburgh Castle is one of the finest coastal walks in Britain.

Royal Worcester Porcelain Works, Worcester: Visit the factory that has produced superb china and porcelain for over two centuries now. Excellent guided tours are arranged daily, Monday to Friday, but prior bookings must be made with: Dyson Perrins Museum, Severn Street, Worcester. The museum, adjacent to the factory, houses the finest collection of Worcester china in the world. The factory's 'seconds' shops are marvellous hunting-grounds for bargains.

Bibury Trout Farm, Glos.: See trout at all stages of development in some 20 different ponds at this modern fish farm. They're bred to stock fishing waters and for the table. Visitors may feed the fish — and/or buy them to take home for supper. Open daily mid-March to end-October, 2.00-6.00pm.

The Mustard Shop, Bridewell Alley, Norwich: Owned by Colmans, the mustard people, this unique shop, prettily decorated in 19th century style, together with a mustard museum, is the place to go if you're a mustard-lover. Thirteen different varieties, including some which are only available from the shop, are on sale, plus specially designed mustard pots, cruet sets, mugs and plates. Open all day, Monday to Saturday, except Thursdays.

Balnakell Craft Village, Durness, Sutherland: Fascinating place to visit on Sango Bay in the far north of Scotland, near Cape Wrath. You can wander round, watching potters, woodcarvers, weavers, silkscreen printers and other craftsmen at work — and buy some of their wares. Open daily, Easter to September.

Loseley Park Farm, Guildford, Surrey: Tours of the farm, famous for its unadulterated dairy products made from Jersey milk, can be made on foot or by trailer. Dairy produce is on sale. Open Wednesday and Saturday afternoons, May to end-September.

Compton House, Sherborne, Dorset: Lovely 16th century manor house and gardens with butterfly jungle and breeding house. You can see all stages of development of the butterfly from egg to full-grown beauty. The long-famous **Lullingstone Silk Farm** is now housed here also — see live silk worms and demonstrations of silk-making. Lullingstone silk has been used on many royal occasions — the Queen's wedding dress was made from it. The silk shop is very tempting. Open daily 10.00am - 5.00pm, April to October.

Epping Bury Fruit Farm, Upland Road, Epping, Essex: A Pick Your Own farm which can provide a fun day out for the family. You will be shown the crops in the fields and can then pick what you like of the fresh produce to bring home. Open daily end-June to mid-September, 9.30am - 6.00pm.

Bruisyard Wines, Bruisyard, Saxmundham, Suffolk: 10-acre vineyard and winery producing Bruisyard St. Peter pleasant white wine. The friendly owners will show you round and explain how the grapes are made into wine — and give you a free tasting. There is a picnic area and children's playground. If the wine goes down well, bottles are on sale in the shop. Open daily May to mid-October, 10.30am - 5.00pm.

*B*road ribbons of brilliant mauve, running into infinity, make an unforgettable, breathcatching sight for summer visitors to the Norfolk Lavender Fields at Caley Mill, Heacham. Lavender was introduced to England by the Romans, who liked lavender-scented baths.

*C*ool, refreshing drinks to laze in the sun with, and various ice creams plus some toppings to make them extra special. Recipes begin on page 51. *Left:* Smart waistcoat, a natural choice with your separates, is knitted in fluffy yarn with set-in pockets and cable panels. (See page 88 for instructions.)

Enjoy your suntanning experience in safety, using the right protection in the right way—see page 68. *Left:* Delicate cable and lacy stitch pattern makes this V-neck sweater knitted in a beautiful luxury yarn something really special. (Instructions on page 66.)

*I*n this delightful view, coloured paving sets off the white wheelbarrow from which cascade Geraniums, Lobelia and Alyssum. ("Your Garden in Summer", see page 70.) *Left:* Build a buggy. This one's designed by our Handyman—it's a streamlined version of the old applebox-on-wheels. For directions see page 63.

*T*he temptation of an outing in the sunshine, the fun of buying something useless but beautiful, turning aside sometimes from routine — these are impulses which can add a necessary zest to life, says The-Man-Who-Sees.

APPETITE FOR LIVING

AT THE LESS impressive end of the main shopping street in a nearby town there is an antique shop where the owner rightly assumes that beauty and value are in the eye of the beholder. You might find anything in the window – a wooden idol, a beaded purse or a devil mask, the remainders of once-treasured tea or dinner services, a brass Buddha badly in need of a rub up, some doll's house furniture which would delight a collector.

On this particular day there was also an oriental print which had beguiled one of the two women who had stopped to stand and stare, as I had. "I like that," one said. "That little picture near the vegetable dish."

The other said the frame was broken, and to "come on", that it was getting late.

But her companion had gone walking into a dream. Into the picture: gazing into the Tea House, passing over the curved, jade bridge, lingering under the cherry blossom trees, then ascending through immeasurable distance to the white mountain.

"I rather fancy that. I think I'll buy it. It's cheap enough."

I, too, thought to myself that eighty pence was a low price for a dream world to walk in, but the other woman did not agree with us. It was probably rubbish, she said, and nothing was cheap if you didn't need it.

"It's your money, of course," she went on, then, "Do come on. We'll never get home at this rate."

Her friend glanced at her wrist-watch and said, "Good Heavens, yes!" She had all that ironing to do. Then, with the faintest of sighs, she turned away and the two hurried off, to disappear down a side street of semi-detached houses, where no cherry blossom grew, and no Bridge of Jade will ever lead one to a white mountain.

LIGHTEN THE SPIRIT

I was sorry. I think that if she had been left to herself to follow her fancy, her spirit would have been lighter for an hour or two while she went about her ironing and prepared tea for the family.

I believe there is a great deal to be said for yielding to these impulses. That voice which suggests you suddenly drop everything and go for a walk, or laze out in the sun with a book, or drop into a sale room instead of going straight home, or go off to visit a friend, might come from your guardian angel.

"A little of what you fancy," just when you fancy it, really *does* do you good. It can sharpen one's appetite for living, which may grow dulled by feeding on the routine day's dish.

The beauty of giving way to a suddenly born desire is that we feel a full pitch of enthusiasm. Zest has not time to diminish, is not whittled away by why's and wherefores and planning which sometimes leaves us with only half-hearted enjoyment. Because of this whole engagement of mind and feeling, we can forget vexations and problems for a while. Irritations are soothed and we return, refreshed, to the known and ordered track, ready again for routine.

Of course we must have order, and most of our living must be done according to plans. Also, unplanned, spur-of-the-moment enjoyments may turn out to be a chapter of accidents and very far from enjoyable! But I don't see why the word "caprice" has such an unfavourable connotation in so many people's minds. They will try to stop you if you have a sudden impulse to turn pram, toddler and dog down that side lane you have always wanted to explore.

DIFFERENT TEMPERAMENTS

"There's nothing down there, and it will make you late home with the children," they say. Or, "At this hour? Remember you have to be up early," if you want to look at the river under a midnight moon instead of going to bed.

After all, even the most duty-bound of us can indulge in small caprices a good many times in the course of a week without seriously neglecting our duties. Even if you do run away on one of those days when you think desperately, "I'd like to shut the door on it all and just go off and enjoy myself today," the good done to you will probably far outweigh the harm done to anyone else. It can be done without worrying or seriously inconveniencing anyone.

I have friends who hate surprises, are suspicious of the unexpected, and like to know at all times what they are about and why and when, and that they can easily afford it. If you are one of these, do try not to impose your sensible view on those who do have joyous impulses.

We are all too often sadly caught in our own common sense, too apt to sigh and forgo and say, "Well, it's probably a mad idea," without your standing at our elbow to say, like the lady at the shop window, "Come on. It's getting late. You don't want that picture."

Miss Truelove's Bequest

By Louise Cooper

The chance encounter left Vivian oddly shaken
and confused. This man with the smiling blue eyes was
unfamiliar to her — and yet he was no stranger . . .

"I'M SORRY, Miss — ah . . ." The elderly estate agent peered at the name he'd just noted down, then glanced appreciatively at the young woman on the other side of his desk. ". . . Miss Howard. The auction was held at two-thirty sharp — you were just half-an-hour too late."

Vivian rose slowly, aware of a huge weight of disappointment settling on her. "That's what I was afraid of. I just thought that — well — maybe if the house didn't reach its reserve price . . ."

"Oh, it did. Not a high figure for these inflationary times, but satisfactory."

"And I suppose you couldn't tell me who . . .?" She let the sentence hang unfinished as she saw the look of mild shock on Mr. Truscott's face. "No, of course you couldn't," she finished lamely. "Thank you for your trouble, Mr. Truscott. I'm sorry to have taken up your time."

He ushered her out. "Not at all. I'm only sorry that your long journey was wasted."

'Wasted?' Vivian wondered as she made her way out into the spring sunlight and crossed the road to the church beside which her Mini was parked. It must be all of five years since her hectic career in London had allowed her to take a weekend off and visit the haunts of her childhood here in the Devonshire countryside. Or, at least, that was the excuse she had always made to herself.

She didn't climb into the car straight away, but instead stood and let the day's warmth bathe her face. The air here smelt so incredibly fresh after the fumes and grime of the city. Someone had recently cut the grass in the churchyard and the scent of new-mown hay drifted lazily on a faint breeze, bringing back memories that for a moment upset her careful equilibrium.

She had steeled herself for disappointment today, and yet when it came it still had the power to hurt. But when all was said and done, she had only herself to blame. If she hadn't made that last-minute decision to go into the office this morning before setting off on her journey, then she would have been in time for the auction, and by now the house could have been hers.

But habit had taken the upper hand, and from the moment she walked through the door there had been people to see, phone calls to take. As Personnel Manager of a large computer company in the West End, Vivian's time and attention were constantly in demand. She enjoyed her job, was to all intents and purposes dedicated to it — but at this moment she found herself regretting the constant calls upon her that it entailed.

If it hadn't been for that decision to go into the office . . . But no amount of 'ifs' would turn back the clock. Since leaving Holmslade five years ago, after her mother died, Vivian had lost touch with the village and with the people she used to know, so that now she was little better than a stranger here. But her roots still remained, along with the childhood memories, despite the fact that being away for so long had blunted her sense of belonging. Somehow London could never quite match up to the village, whatever opportunities it had given her.

And there was one person, one special person, whom she could never forget: Miss Truelove.

TO AN impressionable girl of seven, Miss Truelove was every bit as grand and awesome as Queen Victoria. She lived alone in a beautiful Georgian house which she couldn't really afford to
Continued overleaf

maintain properly, but in which she conducted a determinedly genteel and refined lifestyle. Everything about her had fascinated Vivian, from her frail looks and quaint mannerisms to the clutter of faded bric-a-brac and mementoes of her past with which she surrounded herself. The friendship that developed between them had continued throughout Vivian's adolescence and into adulthood. Only when she left for London did their contact lapse, although they still continued to send each other birthday and Christmas cards every year.

And then Miss Truelove died. Vivian had had the news from the old lady's solicitor. She had cried on reading the letter, unable to help herself, and had had to fight back an impulse to jump into her car and drive straight to Devon. Silly of her — she could do nothing, help no one; it was simply an emotional response.

But when she heard about Miss Truelove's house, matters took on a different perspective. The old lady had left no Will, having no close relatives, so her executors were putting the house up for auction in a month's time.

At first Vivian's idea seemed wild, crazy; but the more she thought about it, the more *right* it seemed. She had always loved that house, holding as it did so many fond memories for her, and the thought of its being knocked down for a song to someone who would neither know nor care one whit about its past associations was unbearable to her. Was it possible that *she* could afford it? She earned a high salary, paid a low rent for her unfurnished flat, had been able to save a good deal over the last few years.

'But whatever would you do with the house?' a small inner voice had said. 'It's two hundred miles from London — you could hardly ever find the time to visit!' And yet, to Vivian, that wasn't important. It was the house that mattered; the house and all it had once meant to her. She had to try for it — *had* to!

And now all her eager plans and dreams were in ashes because she had arrived just half-an-hour too late.

WITH a sigh that only expressed a fraction of what she was feeling, Vivian bent to unlock her car, then paused. She had mentally resigned herself to the fact that there was little point in staying for the whole of her planned long weekend, and she had paperwork to do back in London. But she couldn't leave Holmslade without at the very least making her final farewell to Miss Truelove.

The old lych-gate at the churchyard entrance was as rickety as she remembered it — the wood crumbling, moss rioting over the porch. There was a lump in Vivian's throat, and for a moment she couldn't bring herself to look up and ahead at the church, and the neatly-tended graves.

"Oh! Excuse me, I didn't even see you."

The unexpected male voice startled her, and she jumped as she realised there was someone else there, facing her not two feet away. It seemed they had both tried to push the gate open at the same moment from opposite sides, and now they faced each other across the barrier, each as surprised as the other.

Vivian collected her wits. "I'm so sorry, it was my fault. I wasn't looking where I was going."

He smiled and stood back, opening the lych-gate for her to step through. Under the deep shade of the porch it had been hard to see him clearly, but now they were in full daylight once more and their faces almost on a level, he an inch or two the taller. And Vivian found herself gazing at a pair of eyes of the deepest blue she had ever seen; so blue they were almost violet. Framing them was a strong, square-jawed face, wind-tanned skin, black Celtic hair . . .

"Is anything wrong?" The face broke into a sudden smile and Vivian felt her cheeks reddening with embarrassment as she realised that she had been unashamedly staring at the young man. He was a stranger to her she now saw, not one of the half-familiar Holmslade faces. Swiftly she tried to cover her lapse, and floundered on, "I'm sorry, I didn't mean to be rude. I just wondered —" Seeing those steady eyes still regarding her she laughed self-consciously. "I used to live here, and I wondered if we might know each other."

"'Fraid not." His voice held a faint, pleasant West Country inflection. "I'm a bit of a new boy. A foreigner, all the way from Tiverton!" The smile became a grin at the implied joke.

"Oh. Yes, I see. I'm sorry." Good grief, couldn't she stop saying that? Feeling an utter fool, Vivian edged past him on to the gravel path.

"My pleasure." For a moment he stood still, and she had the distinct impression that he was assessing her. Then he was gone, the lych-gate clicking behind him as he strolled away along the village street.

Vivian stared after him, the colour only just beginning to fade from her cheeks. He was powerfully built, she noticed, an outdoor man; and his clothes marked him out as well-to-do. A stranger, then. Yet wasn't she a stranger too, after all this time?

She began to walk towards the squat Norman church, aware of a discomforting, unsettled feeling inside herself. She was tempted to look back, to see if the man with the vivid blue eyes was still in sight, but she quashed the impulse. Disappointed? No, of course she didn't feel disappointed that he'd gone, that their meeting had been so brief and commonplace. The very idea was nonsensical, wasn't it?

HALF-AN-HOUR later, Vivian's Mini was scudding along the winding lane that led westwards out of Holmslade. Sunlight dappled down through the trees that formed a canopy like a bridal arch overhead, and in the high hedgerows foxgloves and cow-parsley ran amok, splashes of cerise and white among the green.

She had wondered if she might have forgotten the way, but it was as familiar to her as if she had travelled it yesterday. And, just as she remembered, the house came into view so suddenly that she had to hit the brakes abruptly to stop in time.

And there it was, nestled in a fold of farmland hills and surrounded by tall hedges and overgrown garden. A wooden board that read *To Be Auctioned* was now partially obscured by a *Sold* poster — someone had acted very fast — and she turned quickly away from that, concentrating her attention on the house itself.

It looked lonely and forlorn, showing every sign of the years of neglect when Miss Truelove hadn't had the money to keep it in good repair. Gazing over the gate to the front door with its peeling paintwork, Vivian could picture the old lady there, standing on the threshold with her welcoming smile. Miss Truelove was forever baking, and the tantalising aroma could be detected — especially by a hungry child — from here. But there was no such aroma now; only the scents of hay and greenery, and the faint drone of an overburdened bee lurching through the grass that choked the gateway.

The gate still squeaked — no one had oiled it for as long as Vivian could remember — and her footsteps sounded clearly on the paved path as she approached the front door. It wasn't trespassing, not in the real sense. She would just peep in through the downstairs window, and then be on her way after this last glimpse.

Love and the gentle heart are one, as the sage has taught us; neither can exist alone, no more than the head can live without reasoning.
Dante Alighieri

The windows were begrimed and dusty but it was just possible to make out the dim outlines of the rooms beyond. Stripped of most of their furnishings they were bare and cold and unwelcoming, and as she drew back Vivian felt tears prick her eyes and tremble unshed on her long lashes. Poor Miss Truelove. All those beautiful things, and where were they now? Sold, gone, lost . . .

She was turning, determined to say a silent goodbye and go, when the garden gate squeaked again. Through the tears her vision was momentarily blurred; then she blinked, the vista cleared, and she saw the solitary figure of a little girl standing by the gate.

Vivian hesitated. She wasn't at ease with children, having had little experience of their company, but this child was grinning openly at her, a gap-toothed smile that made it impossible not to respond.

"Hello," said Vivian. "Who are you?"

The child didn't answer at first; only leaned against the gate and started to swing it to and fro. She was a funny little thing, with mousy hair cut in an unattractive pudding-basin bob, and a shapeless dress that was too long for her. Her eyes were grey and enormous, her mouth over-generous. She continued to grin at Vivian, then at last said, "I'm Lizzie."

"Well, hello, Lizzie." Vivian began to advance slowly towards her, intrigued, despite herself, by this little imp. "My name's Vivian."

"I know."

"Do you?" She was amused by the child's absurdity, the sheer self-importance that wouldn't let her admit there was anything she didn't know.

"You don't live here, do you?" Lizzie demanded.

"No, I don't." The words brought a pang. "Is this your house?"

Lizzie hesitated for a moment, as if considering, then shook her head emphatically. "No. But I know who's got it now."

IRRATIONALLY, a flicker of hope stirred in Vivian's heart. If she could find out the name of the new owner, it was just possible . . . Hastily, before common sense got the better of her, she asked, "Who has bought it, Lizzie? Will you tell me their name?"

Continued overleaf

Again the child considered, then shook her head in childish caprice. "Don't want to."

"Please, Lizzie. For me? Special favour?"

"No, don't want to." Without another word Lizzie turned, and, so quickly that Vivian had no time to react, skipped away, vanishing into the lane.

"Lizzie!" Vivian was running along the path before she knew it. It was a purely instinctive reaction, with no rhyme or reason behind it. Even if she caught up with the child, she couldn't *make* her give the information, but nonetheless she hastened out of the gate.

She didn't see the Land-Rover parked behind her own car, and didn't see the man who had just climbed out of it until she cannoned straight into him.

"Oh!" And then the apology died on her lips and her heart skipped a beat as she gazed at the twinkling, deep blue eyes.

"Well, it's the lady in a hurry again!" He smiled, catching hold of her arm when she seemed about to lose her balance. "We seem to spend all our time apologising to each other, don't we?"

"Oh, no. I mean, yes. There was a little girl — Lizzie. I was trying to catch up with her."

He looked nonplussed. "Then heaven alone knows where she's gone, because she certainly didn't come past me." His dark eyebrows knitted together in confusion. "Is she your daughter?"

"Oh, no! In fact I'd never even seen her before just now." Vivian took a deep breath, realising she was getting in a terrible tangle, and added, "It's a long story."

"In that case, why don't you tell it to me over a cup of tea?"

It took a few moments before she realised that he was indicating the house behind them. "Miss Truelove's house is *yours*?"

"As of this afternoon," he told her proudly. "In fact, I'd just sneaked an hour off to come and have a look at it, and bring a few bits and pieces over. Otherwise, I'd have pinched myself all day to make sure I wasn't dreaming!"

Dazed, Vivian allowed him to lead her back to the front door. He unlocked it, and ushered her through the hall and into the familiar sitting-room, empty now but for two chairs, a battered sofa and a few faded pictures on the walls.

"Now," he said, placing both hands firmly on her shoulders, "you sit down right there and get your breath back, and I'll go and get my kettle set up!"

"SO, YOU see, I wondered if there might be any chance at all that if I could find out the new owner's name, he might be willing to sell the house to me." Vivian sipped her tea and looked apologetically at her companion over the rim of the cup. "But I see now that I was too late, in more ways than one."

Books haven't been made obsolete by the computer or television or movies, or any other competitive medium. They offer active rather than passive experience, an opportunity for imagination to enter an alliance with that of the writer.
Robert Kirsch

Stuart Ryder smiled sadly at her. "I only wish I'd met you earlier, Vivian. If I'd realised there was another of Miss Truelove's friends wanting the house —"

"You'd have done exactly what you did do, and bought it!"

"Now you're not even giving me the chance to pretend I'm chivalrous!" he protested, and they both laughed. "But, seriously, you must be the same Vivian that Miss Truelove used to talk about. She was very, very fond of you — said you were like the granddaughter she never had."

"Oh, Stuart." Vivian was deeply touched, and hastily wiped her eyes with the back of one hand. "I'm glad she found another good friend," she said after a moment. "I kept promising myself that I'd come down and see her, but what with my job and everything, there just never seemed to be the time." She paused. "That sounds like a pretty lame excuse, doesn't it?"

"Not at all." He leaned back in his chair, stretching out one long leg. "Believe me, as a farmer I know exactly how demanding work can be. Since Dad and I moved into Gatehouse Farm three years ago, I hardly seem to have had a minute to myself."

"But you found time for Miss Truelove, which is more than I did."

Stuart's eyebrows lifted faintly, and this time his smile was wry. "I used to deliver her milk and eggs, and sometimes pick up shopping for her in the village. That's hardly unstinting dedication!"

"But still better than I could manage," Vivian persisted.

He shook his head. "There's a world of a difference between two miles and two hundred."

She gave in gracefully, not wanting to argue the point any further. At least she had the consolation of knowing that Miss Truelove's house was in safe hands, hands that would love and value it as it deserved. He had bought it, Stuart said, because he *had* to; he simply couldn't bear the thought of its being owned by a stranger. Vivian had warmed to him as he said that, sensing a kindred spark between them and almost wishing . . . what? She didn't quite know. But now London called to her. Her moment of nostalgia was over and the spell had to be broken.

Her tea finished, she reluctantly set the cup back on the tray. The cool peace of the room, empty as it was, tried to restrain her, but she had no valid reason for staying.

"I must go," she said, and rose.

Stuart looked up at her. "Do you have to get back to London so soon? I thought you'd planned a weekend here."

"I had, but . . ." She couldn't tell him bluntly that there seemed no point in staying; it would sound churlish. Already her mind was moving ahead; a quick meal on the road, then back to London in time for a passably early night. Paperwork tomorrow, and on Monday back to the office.

Suddenly, the prospect didn't hold the appeal that it should have done. Irrationally, she thought of Lizzie, the little girl at the gate. And suddenly she wanted nothing more than to stay on here in Devon and, just for a while, forget that she was Vivian Howard, Personnel Manager, and become Vivian Howard, country girl, again.

BUT ALREADY she was on her feet, gathering handbag and jacket and fumbling for her car keys. And then she saw the photograph.

It was an old picture, one of the few that had been left because no one wanted it. A family portrait, that must have been taken in the early part of the century, of a stiff, bearded man, an hourglass-waisted woman in a huge picture hat, and two children. With a shock, Vivian realised where she had seen one of those children before.

"Look —" Stuart's voice startled her and she turned. He had risen, was facing her. "Do you really have to go?" he asked gently.

In every thing you do, consider the matters which come first and those which follow after, and only then approach the thing itself.

Epictetus

She looked at the picture again, and suddenly had to know the answer to the question that burned in her mind. "That picture —" she said.

He was taken aback by her abrupt change of topic, but rallied. "Do you remember that one? I wanted to keep it specially. It's Miss Truelove's parents and her sister. And that —" he pointed a finger at the small, mousy-haired girl with the pudding-basin bob and the gap toothed smile "is Miss Elizabeth Truelove herself!"

Miss Elizabeth Truelove. Very slowly, Vivian turned to face Stuart, knowing that she had solved a small and apparently insignificant mystery. Little Lizzie, the girl at the gate.

"*My name's Vivian . . .*"

"*I know . . .*"

Lizzie had, in a strange way, thrown Vivian and Stuart together a second time; almost deliberately, it might seem. And if Miss Truelove, in her wisdom, had caused their paths to cross, then who was Vivian to argue?

She took a breath. "I'm sorry," she murmured, smiling shyly at the man in front of her. "I'm being very chaotic today. But I think you were asking me something?"

Those deep blue eyes kindled. "Well, a little restaurant has just opened in the village. I know it won't be up to London standards, but I thought perhaps you and I might have dinner there. It would be my pleasure, Vivian, my very great pleasure to take you there — if you could stay for a while?"

Not to go back to London tonight, not to return to an empty flat and endless hours of paperwork. A few days' grace — and who knew what could happen in their span? Not that she would dare to predict . . . but then, neither would she dare to argue with Miss Truelove.

Slowly she reached out and took Stuart's hand, feeling his strong, warm fingers close on hers.

"Yes," she said. "I can stay."

THE END

© *Louise Cooper, 1983*

87

NATURAL WINNER

Cable pattern panels up the front turn a
classic button-up waistcoat into something rather special

Instructions in 5 sizes

Colour photo on page 74

MATERIALS: *Allow the following quantities in 40 g balls of Lister-Lee Kaftan: 8 for the 81 cm size; 9 for 86 cm and 91 cm sizes; 10 for 97 cm and 102 cm sizes. For any one size: A pair each of No. 7 (4½ mm) and No. 9 (3¾ mm) knitting needles; 5 buttons; a cable needle.*

TENSION: *Work at a tension of 17 stitches and 23 rows to measure 10 x 10 cm, over the stocking st., using No. 7 (4½ mm) needles, to obtain the measurements given opposite.*

ABBREVIATIONS: To be read before working: *K., knit plain; p., purl; st., stitch; dec., decrease (by working 2 sts. together); s.s., stocking st. (k. on the right side and p. on the wrong side); c.6, cable 6 (slip next 3 sts. onto cable needle and leave at back of work, k.3, then k.3 from cable needle); single rib is k.1 and p.1 alternately.*

NOTE: *The instructions are given for the 81 cm (32 inch) bust size. Where they vary, work figures within first brackets for the 86 cm (34 inch) bust size; work figures within second brackets for 91 cm (36 inch) bust size, and so on.*

THE BACK: With No. 9 (3¾ mm) needles cast on 76 (80) (84) (88) (92) sts. and work 18 rows in single rib.

Change to No. 7 (4½ mm) needles, and beginning with a k. row, s.s. 66 rows.

To shape armholes: Cast off 2 (3) (3) (3) (3) sts. at beginning of next 2 rows, and 2 (2) (2) (3) (3) sts. on the following 2 rows, then dec. 1 st. each end of the next 3 rows—62 (64) (68) (70) (74) sts.

S.s. 41 (43) (45) (47) (49) rows.

To slope shoulders: Cast off 5 (5) (6) (6) (7) sts. at beginning of next 2 rows, then 5 sts. on the following 6 rows.

Cast off remaining 22 (24) (26) (28) (30) sts.

THE POCKET LININGS (2 alike): With No. 7 (4½ mm) needles cast on 24 sts. and s.s. 29 rows.

Break yarn and leave sts.

THE LEFT FRONT: With No. 9 (3¾ mm) needles cast on 49 (51) (53) (55) (57) sts. and, beginning odd-numbered rows with k.1 and even-numbered rows with p.1, work 17 rows in single rib.

Next row: Rib 11 and leave these sts. on a safety pin for button band, rib to end and work on these last 38 (40) (42) (44) (46) sts.

** Change to No. 7 (4½ mm) needles and, beginning with a k. row, s.s. 29 rows.

Pocket row: P. 7 (8) (9) (10) (11), slip next 24 sts. onto a st. holder and in their place, p. across 24 sts. of one pocket lining, then p. remaining 7 (8) (9) (10) (11) sts. of row.

Work in s.s. with cable panel as follows:

1st row: K. 11 (12) (13) (14) (15), p.2, k.1, p.2, k.6, p.2, k.1, p.2, k.11 (12) (13) (14) (15).

2nd row: P.11 (12) (13) (14) (15), k.2, p.1, k.2, p.6, k.2, p.1, k.2, p.11 (12) (13) (14) (15).

3rd and 4th rows: Repeat 1st and 2nd rows, once again.

5th row: K. 11 (12) (13) (14) (15), p.2, k.1, p.2, c.6, p.2, k.1, p.2, k. to end.

6th row: As 2nd row.

These 6 rows form the pattern; pattern a further 16 rows.

To shape front edge: Dec. 1 st. at *end* — read *beginning* here when working right front — of next row and the 3 following 4th rows.

Work 1 row — work 2 rows here when working right front.

To shape armhole and continue shaping front edge: Cast off 2 (3) (3) (3) (3) sts. at beginning of next row and 2 (2) (2) (3) (3) sts. on the following alternate row, *at the same time,* dec. 1 st. at front edge on the 4th row from previous front dec.

Work 1 row — omit this row when working right front — then dec. 1 st. at armhole edge on each of the next 3 rows, decreasing 1 st. at front edge on the last of these rows — 25 (26) (28) (29) (31) sts.

Dec. 1 st. at front only on the next 1 (2) (4) (4) (4) following 4th row(s), then at same edge on the 4 (4) (3) (4) (5) following 6th rows — 20 (20) (21) (21) (22) sts.

Pattern 13 (11) (11) (7) (3) rows — pattern 14 (12) (12) (8) (4) rows here when working right front.

To slope shoulder: Cast off 5 (5) (6) (6) (7) sts. at beginning of next row, then 5 sts. on the 2 following alternate rows.

Work 1 row.

Cast off remaining 5 sts.

THE RIGHT FRONT: With No. 9 (3¾ mm) needles cast on 49 (51) (53) (55) (57) sts. and work 2 rows in rib as given on left front.

1st buttonhole row: Rib 4, cast off 3, rib to end.

2nd buttonhole row: Rib to end, casting on 3 sts. over those cast off on previous row.

Rib 13 rows.

Next row: Rib 38 (40) (42) (44) (46), turn, leaving remaining 11 sts. on a safety pin.

Change to No. 7 (4½ mm) needles and work as given for left front from ** to end, noting variations.

THE BUTTONHOLE BAND: First join shoulder seams.

With wrong side facing, rejoin yarn to inner end of sts. on safety pin of right front, and using No. 9 (3¾ mm) needles, work 5 rows in single rib as set.

Repeat the 2 buttonhole rows given at beginning of right front, then rib 18 rows.

Repeat last 20 rows, twice, then the 2 buttonhole rows again.

Continue in rib until band fits up right front and round to centre back neck.

Cast off in rib.

THE BUTTON BAND: With right side facing, rejoin yarn to inner end of sts. on safety pin of left front, and using No. 9 (3¾ mm) needles, work in rib until band fits up left front and round to centre back neck.

Cast off in rib.

THE ARMHOLE BANDS (2 alike): With right side facing, rejoin yarn and using No. 9 (3¾ mm) needles, pick up and k.70 (72) (74) (76) (78) sts. round armhole edges and work 8 rows in single rib.

Cast off in rib.

THE POCKET TOPS (2 alike): With wrong side facing, rejoin yarn and using No. 9 (3¾ mm) needles, work 8 rows in single rib.

Cast off in rib.

TO MAKE UP THE WAISTCOAT: Do not press. Join side seams, continuing across armhole bands. Sew front bands into position, setting top buttonhole level with first front shaping. Join cast off edges at centre back neck. Sew down pocket linings to wrong side and row ends of pocket tops to right side. Add buttons.

MEASUREMENTS *in centimetres (and inches, in brackets)*										
To fit loosely, bust sizes	81	(32)	86	(34)	91	(36)	97	(38)	102	(40)
All round at underarms, fastened	88.5	(34¾)	93	(36½)	98	(38½)	102.5	(40¼)	107.5	(42¼)
Side seam, including armhole band	37.5	(14¾)	37.5	(14¾)	37.5	(14¾)	37.5	(14¾)	37.5	(14¾)
Length	59	(23¼)	60	(23½)	60.5	(23¾)	61.5	(24¼)	62.5	(24½)

PACKAGE DEAL

GOING on holiday is always an exciting time, but do get yourself well organised beforehand with your packing. The golden rule is DON'T PACK MORE THAN YOU NEED! It's a common mistake; not only do you increase the weight of your suitcase but you lumber yourself with a lot of unnecessary clothes. So make an effort a week or so before your departure to put out everything you want to take and then go through it saying, "Will I really need that?" or "Do I need two of those?" If you look at professional travellers like models, you will find that they take the bare minimum of luggage, mostly of interchangeable separates.

Find out about the type of place you are going to, what the temperatures are likely to be. If you are going on a beach holiday where it will be pretty hot, then you can feel fairly safe in packing lightweight clothes plus bathing items, but it you are going on a sightseeing tour of, say, Switzerland, be prepared to take jackets or cardigans for the times when you go up to the top of a mountain by cable car, because even in summer it can be chilly!

Choose clothes in crease-resistant fabrics like Terylene, viscose, Courtelle, Acrilan, Trevira and Terylene and cotton mixtures. Pack your clothes between layers of tissue paper or in polythene bags to avoid creasing, and pack heavy garments as flat as possible; this applies to woollens too. Pleated skirts travel best rolled lengthways and pushed into a nylon stocking or tights that have the foot cut off, and then placed down the side of your suitcase. Always pack heavy items such as shoes, brushes, bottles (carefully wrapped in polythene bags to prevent leakage) at the bottom of your case. Conserve space by wrapping your jewellery and other small items in tissue paper and stuffing them in the toes of your shoes.

Plan your wardrobe round a few basic items and colours and take things that will mix and match — i.e. skirts and trousers should all interchange with tee shirts, tops and blouses, and if you are staying in an hotel take a couple of dresses or skirts and tops for the evening. If you plan to spend a lot of time on the beach, pack an extra swim-suit, a beach towel and a large plastic or waterproof bag to take all your swimming

things down to the beach. Be sure to include your suntan cream and sunglasses. Don't take too many pairs of shoes as they are heavy: a pair of beach shoes, a comfortable flat-soled pair for walking and sightseeing and a dressy pair for evening, should be sufficient. A large bag for your souvenirs and presents is handy, and it's as well to pop in a stole or cardigan just in case the evenings are chilly, plus a light mac, because downpours in tropical climes will soak you through very quickly, and last but not least, a headscarf for windy days or to protect you against the sun, and of course, it's handy to keep by you if you are visiting a church or cathedral and are obliged to wear something on your head.

If a coach trip or a sightseeing holiday is on the agenda, do make sure you take comfortable clothes, as you will be sitting down for long periods and won't want anything that is tight round the waist or sleeves. If possible, include items in cotton or cotton mixes as it can get hot on a coach, and take easy fitting shoes that are comfortable enough to wear all day and to walk round ruins and cobbled streets! If you're going to be doing a lot of walking, be sure you take long sleeved shirts, so that if your arms do get a bit sunburnt you can keep them covered.

And a happy holiday to you all!

AUTUMN

Autumn, the fairest season of the year
Ovid

BRIGHT BEAUTY

A wild and stormy summer!
But, at last,
The clouds dispersed,
And golden sunlight cast a spell of gold
Over the fallen leaves,
Turning them into sheaves of beauty,
On this September day.
Although the winds had hastened the flowers away,
The sturdiest ones remained,
And grass grew tall;
A blackbird sang on an old garden wall;
The light seemed sharper,
All things fresh and new,
For, oh, it's true
That when storms pass,
All beauty seems more bright;
The smallest sunbeam gives us new delight,
And we are quite enchanted
By all the lovely things we took for granted!

Aileen E. Passmore

The White Birds

by Rosamunde Pilcher

Jane had been an only child, doubly cherished
and protected by her parents. But now she was prepared to
risk her life to bring a child into the world, and Eve
was powerless to help her. Surely — and soon now — the
white birds would appear with their message of hope . . .

FROM THE garden, where she was engaged in cutting the last of the roses before the frost set in, Eve Douglas heard the telephone ringing inside the house. She did not instantly rush indoors because it was a Monday and Mrs. Abney was there, pushing the vacuum cleaner around like a mad thing and filling the house with the smell of furniture polish. Mrs. Abney loved to answer the telephone, and, sure enough, a moment later the sitting-room window was flung open to reveal her, waving a yellow duster to attract Eve's attention.

"Mrs. Douglas! Telephone."

"Coming."

"I think it's your son-in-law, from Scotland."

Eve's heart gave a faint lurch. She put the flowers and the secateurs down on the hall chest and went into the sitting-room. The furniture was all over the place; the curtains draped over chairs to facilitate floor-polishing. The telephone stood on her desk. She picked up the receiver. "David?"

"Eve . . . look . . .it's Jane."

"What's happened?"

"Nothing's happened. It's just that we thought last night that the baby was coming — and then the pains sort of stopped. But this morning the doctor came, and her blood pressure was a bit high, so he's taken her into hospital."

He stopped. After a little Eve said, "But the baby isn't due for another month."

"I know. That's it."

"Do you want me to come?"

"Could you?"

"Yes." Her mind flew ahead; checking the contents of the deep freeze, cancelling small appointments, trying to work out how she could abandon Walter. "Yes, of course. I'll catch the five-thirty train. I should be with you at about a quarter to eight."

"I'll meet you at the station. You're an angel."

"Is Jamie all right?"

"He's OK. Nessie Cooper's keeping an eye on him. She'll look after him till you get here."

"I'll see you, then."

SLOWLY, CAREFULLY, she replaced the receiver. She looked up at Mrs. Abney, who stood in the open doorway. Mrs. Abney's cheerful expression had gone, to be replaced by one of anxious concern which Eve knew was mirrored by her own.

Continued overleaf

There was no need for spoken word or explanation. They were old friends. Mrs. Abney had watched Jane grow up, had come to Jane's wedding. When Jamie was born, Mrs. Abney had knitted him a blue blanket for his pram. She was, in every sort of way, one of the family.

She said, "Nothing's gone wrong?"

"It's just that they think the baby's on the way. It's a month early."

"You'll have to go."

"Yes," said Eve faintly.

Mrs. Abney said, "Don't you worry about Mr. Douglas. I'll keep an eye on him."

"But Mrs. Abney, you've got enough to do with your own family."

"If I can't make it in the mornings, I'll nip up in the afternoons."

"He can make his own breakfast." But somehow that only worsened the situation, as though poor Walter was capable of nothing more than boiling an egg. But it wasn't that, and Mrs. Abney knew it. Walter had the farm to run; he was out working from six o'clock in the morning until sunset, or later. He needed, and got, and consumed, meals of enormous proportions because he was a big man, and a hard-working one. He took, in fact, a good deal of looking after.

"I don't know how long I'll be away."

"All that matters," said Mrs. Abney, "is that Jane's all right—and the baby, too. That's your place. That's where you've got to be."

"Oh, Mrs. Abney, what would I do without you?"

"Lot of things, I expect," said Mrs. Abney, who was a true Northumbrian and didn't believe in showing emotion. "And now, why don't I make us a nice hot cup of tea?"

T HE TEA was a good idea. While she drank it, Eve made lists. When she had finished drinking it, she got out the car and drove the short distance to the local town where she went into the supermarket and stocked up on all the sorts of food that Walter could, if necessary, cope with by himself: tins of soup; quiches; frozen pies; frozen vegetables. She stocked up on bread, butter, and pounds of cheese. Eggs and milk came from the farm, but the butcher wrapped chops and steaks and sausages, found scraps and bones for the dogs, agreed to send a van out to the farm should the need arise.

"Going away?" he asked, slicing a marrow bone in two with his cleaver.

"Yes. Just up to Scotland to stay with my daughter."

"That'll be a nice change."

"Yes," said Eve faintly. "Yes, it will be very nice."

She got home and found Walter, who had come in early, sitting at the kitchen table and eating his way through the stew, boiled potatoes and cauliflower cheese which Mrs. Abney had left for him. He wore his old working clothes and looked like a ploughman.

Once, and it seemed a long time ago now, he had been in the Army. Eve had married him as a tall and dashing Captain. They had had a traditional wedding with herself in flowing white, and an archway of swords waiting for them as they emerged from the church doorway. There had followed postings in Germany and Hong Kong and Warminster, always living in married quarters, never having a home of their own.

And then Jane arrived, and soon after that Walter's father, who had spent his life farming in Northumberland, announced that he had no intention of dying in harness, and what was Walter going to do about it? Eve and Walter made the great decision together. Walter said goodbye to the Army, spent two years at an agricultural college, then took over the farm.

H E LOOKED up as she appeared, borne down with laden baskets. "Hello, darling."

She sat down at the other end of the table, without even taking off her coat. "Did you see Mrs. Abney?"

"No, she'd gone before I came in."

"I have to go to Scotland."

Across the table, their eyes met. "Jane?" said Walter.

"Yes."

The sudden shock of anxiety seemed, visibly, to drain him, to diminish him in some horrible way. Her every instinct was to comfort him. She said quickly, "You mustn't worry. It's just that the baby's going to arrive a little early."

"Is she all right?"

Matter-of-factly, Eve explained what David had told her.

Walter said what Eve had been trying not to tell herself ever since David's telephone call. "She was so ill when Jamie was born."

"Oh, Walter, *don't*."

"In the old days she'd have been told never to have another child."

"It's different now. Things are so different. The doctors are so clever . . ." She went on vaguely, trying to reassure not only her husband but herself. "Mrs. Abney will take care of you," she ended up.

"I should be coming with you," he said.

"Darling, you can't. David knows that, he's a farmer himself. Jane knows it. Don't think about it."

"I hate your having to go alone."

"I shan't be alone. I'm never alone as long as I know that you're around somewhere, even if it's a hundred miles away."

"Would she be so special," Walter asked, "if she hadn't been an only child?"

"Just as special. No person could ever be as special as Jane."

WHEN WALTER had taken himself off, Eve busied herself: putting the shopping away; making a list for Mrs. Abney; stacking up the deep freeze; washing the dishes. She went upstairs to pack a suitcase, but when all this was accomplished it was still only half-past two. She went downstairs and pulled on her coat and boots, whistled up the dogs then set off across the fields towards the cold North Sea, and the little sickle of beach which they thought of as their own.

She thought of Jane. Not now, lying in some anonymous hospital bed waiting for Heaven-knew-what to happen, but as a little girl. Jane growing up. Jane grown-up. Jane with her tangle of brown hair and her blue eyes and her laughter. The small, industrious Jane, sewing doll's clothes on her mother's old machine; mucking out her little pony; making rock buns in the kitchen on wet winter afternoons.

She remembered Jane as a leggy teenager; the house filled with her friends, the telephone endlessly ringing. Jane had done all the maddening, harum-scarum things that all teenagers do, and yet had never herself become maddening. She had never been plain, never sulky, and her natural friendliness and vitality ensured that there had never been a time when she had not had some adoring male in attendance.

"You'll be getting married next," Mrs. Abney used to tease her, but Jane had ideas on that score.

"I'm not getting married until I'm at least thirty. I'm not getting married until I'm too old to do anything else."

But when she was twenty-one she had gone to spend the weekend in Scotland where she had met David Murchison and fallen instantly in love. The next thing, Eve was in the thick of wedding plans, trying to work out how the marquee was going to fit on to the front lawn, and searching the shops of Newcastle for a suitable wedding dress.

JANE HAD never been ill in her life, but she was very ill when Jamie was born four years ago, and the baby had been kept in intensive care for two months before he was allowed home. Eve had gone to Scotland that time too, to take care of the little household, and Jane had taken so long to recover and get back her strength that privately Eve prayed that she would never have another child. But Jane thought differently.

"I don't want Jamie to be an only child. It isn't that I didn't adore being one, but it must be more fun to be one of a family. Besides, David wants another."

"But, darling . . ."

"Oh, it'll be all right. Don't fuss, Mumma. I'm as strong as a horse. It's just that my insides don't seem to be very co-operative. It only goes on for a few months, anyway, and then you've got something marvellous for the rest of your life."

The rest of your life. The rest of Jane's life. All at once Eve was gripped in a freezing panic. She shivered, chilled to the bone, overwhelmed by every sort of cold. She was out in the middle of the beach, where an outcrop of rock, invisible at flood tide, was now revealed, like a wrecked hulk abandoned by the sea. It was crusted with limpets, fringed with green weed, and on it sat a pair of herring gulls, beady-eyed, screaming defiance at the wind.

She stood and watched them. White birds. For some reason white birds had always been an important, even symbolic, part of her life. She had loved the gulls of childhood, sailing against the blue skies of seaside summer holidays, and their cry never failed to evoke those endless, sunlit days.

And then there were the wild geese which, in winter, flew over David and Jane's farm in Scotland. Morning and evening the great formations crossed the skies, skimming down to settle on the reedy mudflats by the shores of the great tidal estuary which bordered David's land.

And fantail pigeons. She and Walter had spent their honeymoon in a small hotel in Provence. Their

Continued overleaf

bedroom window had faced out over a cobbled courtyard with a dovecote in the centre of it, and the fantails had woken them each morning with their cooing and fluttering and sudden idyllic bursts of flight.

White birds. She remembered being a child during the war, with an older brother reported missing. Fear and anxiety, like a sort of canker, had filled the house, destroying security. Until that morning when she had looked from her bedroom window and seen the gull poised on the roof of the house opposite.

It was winter, and the early sun, a scarlet fireball, had just crept up into the sky. As the gull suddenly launched itself into flight, she saw the underside of its wings stained with rosy pink. The delighted shock of such marvellous and surprising beauty filled her with comfort. She knew then that her brother was alive, and when, a week later, her parents heard officially that he was safe and well and a prisoner-of-war, they could not understand why Eve took the news so calmly. But she never told them about the gull.

And these gulls? But they were giving nothing away, no reassurance for Eve. They turned their heads, searching the empty sands, spied some distant piece of edible rubbish, screamed, stood on tiptoe, spread their massive, snowy wings and were away, wheeling and floating on the wind.

She sighed, looking at her watch. It was time to return. She whistled for the dogs.

IT WAS nearly dark when the train drew into the station, but she saw her tall son-in-law waiting for her on the platform, standing beneath one of the lights, huddled into his old working jacket with the collar turned up against the wind. Eve got herself out of the warm interior of the train and felt that wind, which on this particular station always seemed to blow with piercing chill, even in the summer.

He came towards her. "Eve." They kissed. His cheek felt icy beneath her lips, and she thought he looked terrible, thinner than ever, and with no colour to his face. He stooped and picked up her suitcase. "Is this all you've got?"

"That's all."

Not speaking, they walked together down the platform, up the steps, out into the yard where his car waited. He opened the boot and slung her case in, and then went around to unlock her door. It was not until they were away from the station and on the road that led out into the country that she steeled herself to ask, "How is Jane?"

"I don't know. Nobody will say for certain, one way or the other. Her blood pressure soared. That's what really started it all."

"Can I see her?"

"I asked, but not this evening, Sister said. Maybe tomorrow morning."

There was nothing much else to be said except, "And how's Jamie?"

"He's fine. I told you, Nessie Cooper's been marvellously kind. She's been looking after him, along with her own brood." Nessie was married to Tom Cooper, David's foreman. "He's excited at the thought of your coming to look after him."

When they arrived at last, Jamie and Mrs. Cooper were watching television together in the sitting-room. Jamie was in his dressing-gown, drinking a mug of cocoa, but when he heard his father's voice he set it down and came to meet them in the hall, partly because he was fond of Eve and looking forward to seeing her again, and partly because he had a very good idea that she might have brought him a present.

"Hello, Jamie." She stooped and they kissed. He smelled of soap.

"Granny, I had lunch today with Charlie Cooper. He's six and he's got a pair of football boots."

"Heavens above! With proper studs?"

"Yes, just like real ones, and he's got a football and he lets me play with him."

She pulled off her hat, and began to unbutton her coat. As she did so, Mrs. Cooper emerged through the open sitting-room door and took her own coat off the hall chair.

"Nice to see you again, Mrs. Douglas."

She was a neat, slim woman, and looked far too young to be the mother of four — or was it five? — children. Eve had lost count.

"And you, too, Mrs. Cooper. You've been so kind. Who's looking after your lot?"

"Tom. But the baby's teething, so I must get back."

"I can't thank you enough for all you've done."

"Oh, it's nothing. I just hope everything goes all right."

"I'm sure it will."

"It doesn't seem fair, does it? I have babies with no trouble — one after the other. Easy as a cat, Tom always says. And there's Mrs. Murchison . . . Well, I don't know. It doesn't seem fair." She pulled on her coat and did up the buttons. "I'll come along tomorrow to give you a hand, if you like, if you don't mind me bringing the baby. He can sit in his pram in the kitchen."

"I'd love you to come."

"Makes it easier, the waiting," said Mrs. Cooper, "if you've got a body to talk to."

WHEN SHE had gone, Eve and Jamie went up to her bedroom. She opened her suitcase and found his present, a model tractor which he insisted politely was exactly what he had been wanting, and how had she known? With the tractor safely in his possession, he was happy to go to bed. He kissed her good night and went with his father to be tucked into bed.

Eve unpacked and washed her hands, then changed her shoes and did her hair. She went downstairs where she and David had a drink together, and then she went into the kitchen and assembled a little supper for them both, which they ate off a tray by the fire. After supper David got into the car and went back to the hospital, and Eve washed up. When this was done she telephoned

---

If pleasures are greatest in anticipation, just remember that this is also true of trouble.

Elbert Hubbard

Walter and they talked for a little, but somehow there didn't seem to be very much to say. She waited up until David returned, but still he had no news.

"They said they'd ring if anything started," he told her. "I want to be with her. I was with her when Jamie was born."

"I know." Eve smiled. "She always said she'd never have had Jamie without you. And I told her that she'd probably have managed. Now, you look exhausted. Go to bed and try to get some sleep."

His face was haggard with strain. "If . . ." The words seemed to be torn from him. "If anything happens to Jane . . ."

"It won't," she said quickly. She laid a hand on his arm. "You mustn't even think about it."

"What *can* I think?"

"You must just have faith. And if there's a call in the middle of the night, you will come and tell me, won't you?"

"Of course."

"Good night then, my dear."

SHE HAD told David to sleep, but she could not sleep herself. She lay in the downy bed, in the darkness, watching the patch of paler darkness that was the night sky beyond the drawn curtains and the open window. She listened to the hours chime by on the grandfather clock which stood at the foot of the stairs. The telephone did not ring. Dawn was breaking before she dozed off at last, and then, almost instantly, was awake again. It was half-past seven. She got up, pulled on her dressing-gown and went to find Jamie who was awake too, sitting up in bed playing with his tractor.

"Good morning."

He said, "Do you think I can play with Charlie Cooper today? I want to show him my tractor."

"Won't he be at school this morning?"

"This afternoon, then?"

"Perhaps."

"What shall we do this morning?"

"What would you like to do?"

"We could go down to the foreshore and look at the geese. Do you know, Granny — do you know this? — there are men who come and shoot them? Daddy hates it, but he says he can't do anything to stop them, because the foreshore belongs to everybody."

"Wildfowlers."

"Yes, that's right."

"I must say it seems hard on the poor geese to fly all the way from Canada and then get shot."

"Daddy says they *do* make an awful mess of the fields."

"They have to feed. And talking of feeding, what do you want for breakfast?"

"Boiled eggs?"

"Up you get, then."

In the kitchen, they found a note from David on the kitchen table.

"*7 a.m. Have fed the cattle. Am just going up to the hospital again. No call during the night. I'll ring you if anything happens.*"

As they finished their breakfast, Mrs. Cooper arrived, with her large rosy-cheeked baby in a

Continued overleaf

perambulator which she manoeuvred into a corner of the kitchen.

She gave the baby a rusk to chew. "Any news, Mrs. Douglas?"

"No, not yet. But David's at the hospital now. He'll ring us if there's any news."

S HE WENT upstairs and made her bed, and then Jamie's, and then, after a moment's hesitation, went into Jane and David's room in order to make that bed as well.

It was impossible not to feel that she was trespassing. There was the smell of Lily of the Valley, which was the only perfume Jane ever used. She saw the dressing-table, with all Jane's small, personal possessions: her grandmother's silver hairbrushes; the snaps of David and Jamie; the strings of pretty, junky beads that she had hung from the mirror.

Clothes lay about: the dungarees that she had been wearing before she was taken off in the ambulance; a pair of shoes; a scarlet sweater. She saw the childish collection of china animals ranged along the mantelpiece; the big photograph of herself and Walter.

She turned to the bed, and saw that David had spent the night on Jane's side, with his head buried in her huge, white, lace-frilled pillow. For some reason this was the last straw.

'I want her back,' she said furiously, to nobody in particular. 'I want her back. I want her home, safely, with her family. I can't bear this any more. I want to know *now* that she's going to be all right.'

The telephone rang.

She sat on the edge of the bed, reached out and picked up the receiver.

"Yes?"

"Eve, it's David."

"What's happening?"

"Nothing yet, but there seems to be a bit of a panic on and they don't want to wait any longer. She's being wheeled along to the labour room now. I'm going with her. I'll call you when there's any news."

"Yes." *There seems to be a bit of a panic on.* "I thought I'd take Jamie out for a walk. But we won't be long, and Mrs. Cooper is here."

"Good idea. Get him out of the house. Give him my love."

T HE FORESHORE lay beyond an old apple orchard, and then a field of stubble. They came to the hawthorn hedge, and the stile, and then the grass sloped down to the rushes and the water's edge. The tide was out, and great mud-flats spread to the further shore. She saw the shallow hills and the huge sky; patches of palest blue, hung with slow-moving grey clouds.

Jamie, climbing over the stile, said, "There are the wildfowlers."

Eve looked and saw them, down by the edge of the water. There were two men, and they had built a hide of the brushwood that had been washed up by the high tides. They stood in this, silhouetted against the shining mud-flats, their guns at the ready. A pair of brown and white springer spaniels sat nearby, waiting. It was very quiet, very still. From far out in the middle of the estuary, Eve could hear the chatter and gobble of the wild geese.

She helped Jamie off the stile, and, hand-in-hand, they made their way down the slope. Where this levelled off they came to a group of plaster birds which the wildfowlers had arranged to resemble a flock of feeding geese.

"They're toy ones," said Jamie.

"They're decoys. The wildfowlers hope that any geese that fly over will see them and think it's safe to come down and feed."

"I think that's horrid. I think that's cheating. If any come, Granny, if any come, let's wave our arms and chase them away."

"I don't think we'll be very popular if we do."

"Let's tell the wildfowlers to go away."

"We can't do that. They're not breaking any law."

"They're shooting our geese."

"The wild geese belong to everybody."

The wildfowlers had seen them. The dogs had their ears pricked and were whining. One of the men swore at his dog. Nonplussed, not knowing now quite which way to go, Eve and Jamie stood by the ring of decoys, hesitating. As they did so, a movement in the sky caught Eve's eye and she looked up, and saw, coming from the direction of the sea, a line of birds.

"Look, Jamie."

T HE WILDFOWLERS had seen them, too. There was a stir of activity as they turned to face the incoming flight.

"Don't let them come!" Jamie sounded panic-stricken. He pulled his hand free from Eve's and began to run, stumbling on his short, gum-booted legs, waving his arms, trying to divert the distant birds and turn them away from the guns. "Go away, go away! Don't come!"

Eve knew that she should try to stop him, but there seemed little point. Nothing on earth could halt that relentless flight. And there was something unusual about these birds. The wild geese flew from north to south on regular flight lines, but this flock approached from the east, from the sea, and with every second they grew larger. For an instant Eve's natural sense of distance was both dazzled and baffled, and then it all clicked into true focus, and she saw that the birds were not geese at all, but twelve white swans.

"They're swans, Jamie. They're swans!"

He heard her and stopped dead, standing silently, head bent back to watch them fly over. They came, and the air was filled with the drumming and beating of their immense wings. She saw the long white necks stretched forward, the legs tucked up and streaming behind. And then they were over and gone, flying upriver, and the sound of their wings died into silence. Finally they disappeared, swallowed into the greyness of the morning, the distance of the hills.

"Granny." Jamie caught her sleeve and shook it. "Granny, you're not listening." She looked down at him. It felt like looking down at a child she had never seen before. "Granny, the wildfowlers didn't shoot them."

Twelve white swans. "They're not allowed to shoot swans. Swans belong to the Queen."

"I'm glad. I thought they were *beautiful*. Where do you think they're going?"

"I don't know. Up the river. Up to the hills. Perhaps there's a hidden loch where they feed and nest." But she spoke absently, because she was not thinking about the swans. She was thinking about Jane, and all at once it was intensely urgent that they lose no time at all in getting home.

"Come along, Jamie." She took his hand, and began to scramble back up the grassy slope towards the stile, dragging him behind her. "Let's go back."

"But we haven't had our walk yet."

"We've walked far enough. Let's hurry. Hurry! Let's see how quick we can be."

THEY CLIMBED the stile, and ran across the stubble, Jamie's short legs doing their valiant best to keep up with his grandmother's. They went through the orchard, not stopping to look for windfalls or to climb the wizened old trees.

Now they reached the track which led to the farmhouse, and Jamie was exhausted. He could run no further and stopped dead in protest at such extraordinary behaviour. But Eve could not bear to linger. She swung him up into her arms and hurried on, not minding his weight, scarcely noticing it.

They came to the house at last, and went in through the back door, not even stopping to take off their muddy boots. Through the back porch, into the warm kitchen, where the baby still sat placidly in its perambulator and Mrs. Cooper peeled potatoes at the kitchen sink. She turned as they appeared and, as she did so, the telephone began to ring. Eve set Jamie down on his feet and darted to answer it. It had only time to ring once before she had picked up the receiver.

"Yes?"

"Eve, it's David. It's all over! Everything's all right. We've got another little boy. He had a pretty rough ride, but he's strong and healthy, and Jane's fine. A bit tired, but they've got her back into bed, and you can come and see her this afternoon."

"Oh, *David . . .*"

"Can I speak to Jamie?"

"Of course."

She handed the little boy the receiver. "It's Daddy. You've got a brother." She turned to Mrs. Cooper who was still standing with a knife in one hand and a potato in the other. "She's all right, Mrs. Cooper. She's all right." She wanted to hug Mrs. Cooper, to press kisses on her rosy cheeks. "It's a little boy, and nothing went wrong. She's all right . . . and . . ."

It wasn't any good. She couldn't say any more. And she could no longer see Mrs. Cooper because her eyes had filled with tears. She never cried, and she did not want Jamie to see her crying now, so she turned and left Mrs. Cooper standing there. She simply went out of the kitchen, the way they had come in, into the garden and the cold, fresh morning air.

TWELVE WHITE swans. She was glad Jamie had been with her, otherwise, for the rest of her life, she might have suspected that that astonishing sight had been simply a figment of her own overwrought imagination. Twelve white swans. She had watched them come and watched them go. Gone forever. She knew that she would never witness such a miraculous sight again.

She looked up into the empty sky. It had clouded over, and soon it would probably start to rain. As the thought occurred to her, Eve felt the first cold, wet drops upon her face. Twelve white swans. She buried her hands deep in the pockets of her coat, turned, and went indoors to telephone her husband.

THE END

© Rosamunde Pilcher, 1983

SWEETNESS AND LIGHT

Mouthwatering shades of pink, blue and white,
and an enchanting all-over textured stitch with bubbly effect –
put them together and you have a gorgeous
jacket, with bloused sleeves and cosy turn-back collar

Instructions in 4 sizes

Colour photo on page 119

MATERIALS: *Allow the following quantities in 25 g balls of Wendy Mohair: 11 blue, 7 white and 5 pink for 86 cm and 91 cm sizes; 12 blue, 8 white and 6 pink for 97 cm and 102 cm sizes. For any one size: A pair each of No. 6 (5 mm) and No. 8 (4 mm) knitting needles; 8 buttons.*

TENSION: *Work at a tension of 17 stitches and 34 rows to measure 10 x 10 cm, over the pattern, using No. 6 (5 mm) needles, to obtain the measurements given opposite.*

ABBREVIATIONS: To be read before working: *K., knit plain; p., purl; st., stitch; tog., together; dec., decrease (by working 2 sts. tog.); up 1, pick up loop lying between needles and k. or p. into back of it; k.1d., k.1 down (drop next st. off needle and unravel 4 rows down, insert right hand needle into this st. and under 4 loose strands, catching the 4 loose strands k. this st. in the usual way); w., white; b., blue; pk., pink; single rib is k.1 and p.1 alternately; nil, meaning nothing is worked here for this size.*

NOTE: *Instructions are given for the 86 cm (34 inch) size. Where they vary, work figures within first brackets for 91 cm (36 inch) size, and so on.*

THE BACK: With No. 8 (4 mm) needles and b. cast on 65 (69) (73) (77) sts. and, beginning odd-numbered rows with k.1 and even-numbered rows with p.1, work 17 rows in single rib.
   Increase row: Rib 5 (7) (4) (9), up 1, * rib 5 (5) (6) (4), up 1; repeat from * 10 (10) (10) (14) times, rib 5 (7) (3) (8) — 77 (81) (85) (93) sts.
   Change to No. 6 (5 mm) needles, join in w. and pk. and work the 12-row pattern as follows:
   1st row: With w., all k.
   2nd row: With w., all p.
   3rd and 4th rows: As 1st and 2nd rows.
   5th row: With b., k.2, * k.1d., k.3; repeat from * ending last repeat with k.2.

6th row: With b., all p.
   7th to 10th rows: As 1st to 4th rows, but using pk. instead of w.
   11th row: With b., k.4, * k.1d., k.3; repeat from * ending last repeat with k.4.
   12th row: With b., all p.
   Pattern a further 112 rows.
   To shape the armholes: Keeping continuity of the pattern, cast off 4 sts. at beginning of next 2 rows, then dec. 1 st. each end of next row, then on the 5 (6) (7) (10) following alternate rows — 57 (59) (61) (63) sts.
   Pattern a further 51 (53) (53) (51) rows.
   To slope the shoulders: Cast off 5 sts. at beginning of next 4 rows, then 6 sts. on the following 2 rows — 25 (27) (29) (31) sts.
   Leave sts. on a spare needle.

THE LEFT FRONT: With No. 8 (4 mm) needles and b. cast on 33 (35) (37) (39) sts. and work 17 rows in rib as given for back.
   Increase row: Rib 4 (4) (5) (5), up 1, * rib 6 (7) (7) (5), up 1; repeat from * 3 (3) (3) (5) times, rib 5 (3) (4) (4) — 38 (40) (42) (46) sts.
   Change to No. 6 (5 mm) needles, join in w. and pk. and work the 12-row pattern as follows:
   1st row: With w., all k.
   2nd row: With w., all p.
   3rd and 4th rows: As 1st and 2nd rows. **
   5th row: With b., k.2, * k.1d., k.3; repeat from * ending last repeat with k.3 (1) (3) (3).
   6th row: With b., all p.
   7th to 10th rows: As 1st to 4th rows, but using pk. instead of w.
   11th row: With b., k.4, * k.1d., k.3; repeat from * ending last repeat with k.1 (3) (1) (1).
   12th row: With b., all p.
   *** Pattern a further 112 rows — pattern 113 rows here when working right front.
   To shape the armhole: Cast off 4 sts. at beginning of next row, work 1 row — omit this row when working right front — then dec. 1 st.

Fluffy mohair mixture yarn comes in some delicious colours. Try gossamer lilac, swansdown, orchid silk; pink tu-tu, silver cobweb, honeycombe; or blue angel, heather mist, pink tu-tu.

at armhole edge on next row, then on the 5 (6) (7) (10) following alternate rows — 28 (29) (30) (31) sts.

Pattern 26 (28) (28) (26) rows — pattern 25 (27) (27) (25) rows here when working right front.

To shape the neck: Cast off 5 (5) (6) (6) sts. at beginning of next row, — work 1 row here when working right front — then dec. 1 st. at neck edge on next row, then on the 6 (7) (7) (8) following alternate rows — 16 sts.

Pattern 11 (9) (9) (7) rows — pattern 12 (10) (10) (8) rows here when working right front.

To slope the shoulder: Cast off 5 sts. at beginning of next row and following alternate row — 6 sts.

Work 1 row, then cast off.

THE RIGHT FRONT: Work as left front to ******.

5th row: With b., k.3 (1) (3) (3), * k.1d., k.3; repeat from * ending last repeat with k.2.

6th to 10th rows: As 6th to 10th rows of left front.

11th row: With b., k.1 (3) (1) (1), * k.1d., k.3; repeat from * ending last repeat with k.4.

12th row: With b., all p.

Work as left front from *******, noting variations.

THE SLEEVES (both alike): With No. 8 (4 mm) needles and b., cast on 32 (34) (36) (38) sts. and work 13 rows in single rib.

Increase row: Rib 6 (6) (8) (8), up 1, * rib 1, up 1; repeat from * 19 (21) (19) (21) times, rib 6 (6) (8) (8) — 53 (57) (57) (61) sts.

Change to No. 6 (5 mm) needles, join in w. and pk. and work 112 rows in pattern as given for back.

To shape the sleeve top: Cast off 4 sts. at beginning of next 2 rows, then dec. 1 st. each end of next row, then on the 9 (9) (10) (10) following 4th rows — 25 (29) (27) (31) sts.

Work 1 row, then dec. 1 st. each end of next row, then on the 3 (5) (4) (6) following alternate rows — 17 sts.

Work 1 row, then cast off.

THE BUTTONHOLE BAND: With No. 8 (4 mm) needles and b. cast on 11 sts.

1st rib row: K.2, * p.1, k.1; repeat from * ending last repeat with k.2.

2nd row: K.1, * p.1, k.1; repeat from * to end.

Rib a further nil (2) (4) (6) rows.

1st buttonhole row: Rib 5, cast off 2, rib to end.

2nd buttonhole row: Rib to end, casting on 2 sts. over those cast off on previous row.

Rib 18 rows.

Repeat the last 20 rows 6 times, then the 2 buttonhole rows again.

Rib 2 (4) (4) (6) rows.

Leave sts. on a safety-pin.

THE BUTTON BAND: Work as buttonhole band, omitting buttonholes.

THE COLLAR: First join shoulder seams. With right side of work facing and using No. 8 (4 mm) needles, rejoin b. and rib across 11 sts. of buttonhole band, pick up and k.15 sts. up right front neck, k.25 (27) (29) (31) sts. across back neck, pick up and k.15 sts. down left front neck, then rib across 11 sts. of button band — 77 (79) (81) (83) sts.

Work 20 rows in single rib.

Change to No. 6 (5 mm) needles and rib a further 22 rows.

Cast off fairly loosely in rib.

TO MAKE UP THE JACKET: Do not press. Set in sleeves, then join sleeve and side seams. Sew front bands into position. Add buttons.

MEASUREMENTS *in centimetres (and inches, in brackets)*

To fit loosely bust sizes	86	(34)	91	(36)	97	(38)	102	(40)
All round at underarms, fastened	94	(37)	98.5	(38¾)	103.5	(40¾)	113	(44½)
Side seam	42.5	(16¾)	42.5	(16¾)	42.5	(16¾)	42.5	(16¾)
Length	63	(24¾)	64	(25¼)	65	(25½)	66	(26)
Sleeve seam	37.5	(14¾)	37.5	(14¾)	37.5	(14¾)	37.5	(14¾)

BUTTON HOLES

PIPED:

Check button size first and tack mark buttonhole position. For each buttonhole cut 2 strips of fabric 2.5cm (1") wide and 2.5cm longer than buttonhole.

Fold strip in half and tack close to edges. Place raw edges to centre of buttonhole position and stitch to right side of garment to within 1.2cm (½") of each end.

Clip carefully between strips and diagonally into corners.

Push strips through opening and tack the folded edges together. Press in place.

Stitch across triangles and ends of strips.

Cut through facing along centre of buttonhole and diagonally into corners. Turn in raw edges and slipstitch to back of buttonhole.

HANDWORKED:

Cut a slit in the fabric the required length of buttonhole. Oversew raw edges of slit.

Working from right to left, work buttonhole stitch along one side, take 5-7 stitches around the end, turning the fabric as you work and continue along other side.

Work a bar tack at straight end of buttonhole. Work blanket stitch over bar tack as shown. Fasten off on the wrong side.

Vertical buttonholes are worked in the same way but with both ends finished with a bar tack.

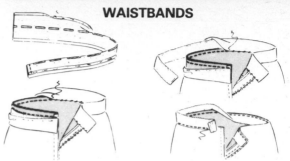

SEW SUCCESSFUL!

An invaluable collection of dressmaking hints that will give your sewing a really professional finish

WAISTBANDS

Iron Fold-a-band to wrong side of waistband. Turn in and tack one long edge over Fold-a-band. Fold waistband along line of slots and stitch across ends. Turn right side out. With right sides together, pin and stitch waistband to skirt with one end to left hand side of zip and underlap on right hand side. Slipstitch tacked edge to previous stitching line.

Turn in and tack one long edge of waistband. Fold lengthways, right sides together and stitch across ends. With right sides together, stitch waistband to skirt. Cut Petersham to fit waistband and tack to turnings above seam line. Slipstitch tacked edge of waistband to previous stitching line.

Either buy shaped Petersham or shrink, press and shape your own using a very hot iron. Pin and stitch inner curved edge of shaped Petersham to right side of waistline, leaving 1.5cm ($^5/_8$") extra at each side of zip opening. Turn to inside of garment, turn in ends of Petersham and slipstitch to zip tape keeping clear of teeth.

ZIPS

CENTRED: This is the simplest way to insert a zip.

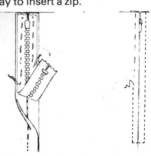

Tack turnings together and press seam open. Place the closed zip face downwards over the seam turnings and tack along centre of zip tape. From the right side, using a zipper foot on your machine, stitch 6mm (¼") either side of tacked seam line and across lower end of teeth.

FACINGS

This understitching keeps the facing in place inside the garment.

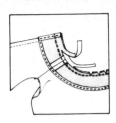

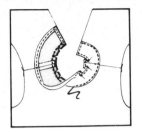

Neaten outer edges of facing. With right sides together, stitch facing to garment. Trim and clip turnings and press towards facing. Stitch through facing and seam allowances on the right side, close to the seam line as shown.

PLEATS

When stitching a seam in a pleated garment, turn up and tack hem first and then stitch seam through all layers. Diagonally trim or turn in and neaten corners of seam allowances.

Finishing your hem this way gives a sharp edge to the inner pleat so it stays in place.

HEMS

HERRINGBONE STITCHED HEM: Used for trousers – so that you don't catch your foot in the hem.

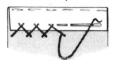

Turn up and tack hem allowance and press. Working from left to right with the needle pointing left, take a small stitch in the garment. Then another to the right but in the hem allowance – continue spacing stitches evenly.

MACHINE STITCHED HEM: (for jersey fabrics) Use synthetic thread for synthetic fabrics, also use a ball point or perfect stitch needle. This avoids a "home-made" look on jersey.

Turn up and tack hem. Work 2 rows of stitching and trim away excess fabric.

SLIPSTITCHED HEM: This is the most useful method and the most invisible.

Turn up and tack hem allowance and press. Fold back raw edge 6mm (¼") and work a small stitch in the garment and then another through the hem allowance. Do not pull threads too tightly.

OPEN ENDED: Also use this method to replace a zip in an anorak or sleeping bag.

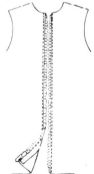

Press seam turnings to wrong side. With zip closed, tack in place with teeth extending past edge.
NOTE: It is important for tape ends to be level at lower edge of garment. Open zip. Using a zipper foot on your machine, stitch in place close to edge. Turn up hem and catch to zip tape, keeping clear of teeth.

CONCEALED: You will need a special plastic zipper foot to apply this type of zip – available from haberdashers. It is inserted before seam is stitched. Used for side and centre back openings in dresses and skirts, especially when the colour is difficult to match exactly

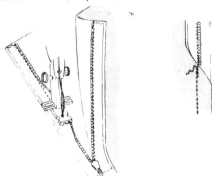

With zip open, place face down along seam line. Pin and stitch with teeth running through the appropriate groove on special machine foot. Stitch as far down as is possible. Pin and stitch remaining side of zip to other garment piece. Close zip and tack lower part of seam. Using a conventional zipper foot, stitch lower part of seam taking stitching as close to previous stitching line as is possible.

Shown in colour on page 116

THE handsome cast-iron fireplace is known as a hob grate, the hobs being the flat places on each side on which a kettle would be slowly heating and the water instantly replenished as used — making a constant supply of hot water. The fireplace is a charming setting for antiques, particularly those of brass.

One would think that the looking-glass overmantel had been made to measure, it fits so superbly. It is mid-Victorian, made of wood, and still retains its original burnished water gilding. The pair of brass candlesticks are 18th century, octagonal and baluster in shape, following the design of silver ones at that period. A handsome carriage clock has pride of place on the mantel-shelf and is mid-19th century. These clocks were not, as the name seems to imply, especially designed for carriages – they were the original travelling clocks, whether by carriage, coach, train or ship.

No folk-art captures so vividly the Victorian scene as Staffordshire figures. There are models of the monarch, statesmen, clergymen, soldiers, sailors, actors, highwaymen and even murderers! The two colourful figures shown depict the Little Red Riding-Hood fairy tale.

It took the owner of this Regency cottage years to find the two brass fenders as they just had to be the right size. They would be dated about 1870. Copper for domestic use was known to exist as far back as the 15th century, but the majority of kitchen pieces date from the early Victorian to the Edwardian era. The small globular kettle shown sitting on the smaller fender is dated about 1880 and the bellows in elm are about the same age.

We are inclined to think of brass and copper warming pans that one sees in beamed cottages and tea-rooms as essentially English, but they were used on the Continent nearly a hundred years before Britain. Early ones were mostly in brass with iron handles; later the handles were made in oak or elm. The use of warming pans declined round about 1825 when brass and copper hot-water bottles, soon to be followed by the well-known stone ones, were introduced. The brass warming-pan has small perforations in the lid and is mid-18th century.

In the past, large country houses had rows of buckets in brass, copper and even leather, hanging behind the baize door leading to the kitchen quarters, containing water or sand to be used in the event of fire. One such bucket is used here to contain coal or wood for burning. The charming mahogany chair covered in old needlework is a Regency harpist's chair of about 1825, and the miniature on the right is on ivory and alleged to be Lady Hamilton; it is dated roughly 1800.

RENÉ CAIRON

104

The Charmer

by Gabrielle Shaw

Just one glance into his gorgeous
grey eyes and Alison was lost. She knew it was hopeless . . .
and yet it was such a temptation — such a
solace — to take him at face value . . .

WHEN SEBASTIAN King first walked into her office at the employment agency, Alison — who liked people — gave her usual quick, welcoming smile. And then, unaccountably, she was on her guard, moving the roses she had brought from her garden that day a fraction of an inch on her desk, smoothing a quite imaginary strand of her long dark hair into place.

It was not that she actively disliked the vitality that exuded from Sebastian as he took the chair she offered. And she had to admit that he wore the universal uniform of blue jeans and leather jacket as if they had been custom-made for him, although perhaps the mud-caked farm boots were slightly unusual in someone looking for a job.

What really shook her was that she found herself instantly enchanted by his gentle grey eyes and slightly crooked smile, and it was the first time she had reacted to a man in such a way in the two years since Stuart, her husband, had died.

She studied Sebastian's completed application form intently, fully aware that the grey eyes were on her and she would eventually have no choice but to look up and meet their gaze. Stifling her quite unbusinesslike reaction to the personal details before her, she made mental notes: 'male' — very much so; 'single' — of course; 'age' — twenty-three. He looked older, but as he was still two years younger than Alison herself that was totally irrelevant anyway. Address: a large Georgian farmhouse in its own grounds which she had often admired from a distance on her drive to and from her cottage five miles out of town.

But when she came to Sebastian's qualifications, her commercial instincts took over. Alison was good at her job, and liked it. She had a high success rate at placing young engineers in local industry, even in these hard times. She knew at once from Sebastian's recently acquired Diploma that she would soon find him work.

"May I ask what you have been doing since you left college this summer?" She pretended to search for a notebook, playing for time, her ringless hands once again restless. Since she had come back to work she had taken to leaving her wedding ring at home, reluctant to embarrass people with the subject of Stuart's death.

When he spoke his voice was not at all the seductive drawl she might have expected from the handsome exterior. It was a good voice, down-to-earth and direct. He told her that he had spent a few months working his passage on a Mediterranean cruise to blow away the cobwebs after studying for his final exams, and since then had been helping with the harvest on the farm at home.

"They're short-handed, and in a hurry now that we have a day or two without rain."

Sadness hit her when he mentioned the sea. Stuart had been a helicopter pilot and had been killed in an air-sea rescue. In recent months she had emerged from the numbness of her grief, but every now and then she took a step backwards. It was her mother — a widow herself — who jolted her out of the past and into the present, on the eve of her daughter Jeannette's third birthday.

"She's old enough to enjoy a party this year. Why should she miss such things? And parties cost money."

A month later she moved in to take care of Jeannette, while Alison went back to work.

"May we have a telephone number where we can reach you?" Alison asked Sebastian.

"You can leave a message in the daytime, if that's all right. This week I'm mostly on the combine. But it's our Harvest Supper eight days from now, and after that I must get down to my own work."

Continued overleaf

She nodded, remembering the wide golden fields each side of the road which must be the King family's land, and the line of graceful poplars she had glimpsed behind the house. "There are several people I'd like you to see, Mr. King. If you'd care to leave it with me, I'll make some appointments for you."

"Fantastic," he said, with a huge grin which she found herself returning. "But why don't I call you? Do you work on Saturdays?"

"Oh, yes, it's one of our busiest days. Mornings only, though. We see people who can't get in during the rest of the week."

He got to his feet and she walked to the door with him, absurdly pleased to find that her head just reached his shoulder.

ON SATURDAY morning she ran down the cottage garden path to the car, dragging on her raincoat, late for work. Jeannette had crept into her bed at dawn, claiming that the rain on the roof had woken her, and they had curled back to sleep together, lulled by the steady downpour and the sound of the wind in the trees that touched the bedroom window.

Her first thought when she woke again was that it was far too wet for Sebastian to work in the fields that day. During her coffee break, which she took at her desk to make up for lost time, she wondered where the King family's Harvest Supper would be held. Between interviews she made several excursions to the cabinet that housed Sebastian's file. When she left the office at midday she was not in the least surprised to find him waiting for her, under the largest, shabbiest black umbrella she had ever seen.

They stood looking at each other for a long moment as the Saturday morning crowds pushed by.

"You don't have to if it's too difficult, but I'd like to buy you a drink before you go home," Sebastian said.

"I do have to get home, but —" He looked so forlorn that she thought she would probably have gone to the ends of the earth with him had he insisted.

"You're not married, are you?" He glanced down at her ungloved hand. "I have to guess, and you know all about me. It's not a very fair system, is it?" He waited.

"No, I'm not married. I'm a widow. And I have to go home fairly soon because I spend all the time I can with my little girl at weekends."

She got through it all in one breath, bracing herself for the way his face would become a polite mask.

Sebastian held out the umbrella in wordless invitation. As she stepped under its shelter a raindrop fell on her small, straight nose. He took her arm. "She's a very lucky little girl," he said.

Five minutes later she settled into a deep leather armchair in the town's most comfortable pub, watching Sebastian's broad shoulders as he ordered their drinks at the bar, becoming slowly aware of a growing sense of well-being. In the long mirror over the counter she could see his face amongst the crowd of lunch-time customers — farmers, young couples, the occasional naval uniform from the nearby port. She had been to the pub several times with Stuart, and now a little rush of pleasure at past happiness remembered caught her unawares.

"Well, if you can't come to a film this afternoon, perhaps you'll let me drive you home instead," said Sebastian, putting her tomato juice on the table.

"My car's in the car park. But if you're at a loose end, you could have lunch with us."

SHE KNEW it was a mistake as soon as the words were out. She had a sudden vivid mental picture of Jeannette's fish fingers in cold disarray on her Peter Rabbit plate; of the haphazard family lunch. And yet Sebastian had such a disarming effect on her that she could see him, too — sitting at the kitchen table, completely at his ease. Which was perhaps the real reason why she regretted her hasty invitation.

Thirty minutes later they trudged up the cottage path together, under the dripping umbrella, and Jeannette ran towards them, squealing a welcome in the rain.

"Mr. King is a client," Alison told her mother, who took one look into his grey eyes and said brightly that if he was looking for work then he would need all the feeding up he could get.

"I put Sunday's joint in the oven an hour ago," she told Alison, as if she had her sixth sense in operation every day of the week. "So if it's fine tomorrow we can have a picnic instead."

Alison watched her in affectionate disbelief as she produced the newly ironed red check tablecloth, home-made mint sauce, and a bottle of red wine which they had been keeping for some unspecified special occasion.

Sebastian found the corkscrew while Alison started to lay the table. It was Jeannette who solved the

106

problem of how they were to spend the time before lunch by her sudden appearance in the kitchen doorway, staggering under the burden of a cardboard box full of assorted Meccano.

"Will the man do something about all this?" she asked the world in general.

There was a moment's silence while the child watched Sebastian's face, daring him to refuse. Then, with a burst of laughter, he scooped her up in his arms, box and all. "It's just my kind of work, Jeannette," he said. "And if we're quick we can build a whole town before lunch."

Escorting them into the living-room across the hall which served as a playroom in the daytime, Alison realised that the Sebastian King charm had taken over the household in five minutes flat. But the thin warning fingers that touched her heart 'He's too young — It's too soon —' were quite ignored during the long, cheerful lunch in the kitchen. And by the time she saw Sebastian again, she was on firmer ground.

As she had anticipated, there were several local firms interested to know of Sebastian's existence, and by the middle of the following week she telephoned the farm to inform him of three appointments.

A young girl's voice answered. Breathless, self-assured, it somehow spoke of money and privilege.

"My sister took the message." Sebastian phoned back within an hour. Alison rapped herself over the knuckles for being so relieved. He had not mentioned a sister. "When can I come to see you?"

"I can give you the appointments over the phone," she said. "It will be better to meet when you've seen everyone and I can find out how you got on first. We usually do things that way."

She dictated the names of two personnel officers at local factories, and the manager of a company that was moving into the district soon, specialising in electronic installations, which was Sebastian's own field. The appointments were all for the last two days of the week.

Continued overleaf

107

"That means you could come to Harvest Supper, and tell me the results then."

"Oh." Alison hesitated. Somehow she had grown used to a routine that did not include going out in the evenings. "I'd like that very much," she said.

I'LL CALL for you at the cottage. Saturday at seven." He put the phone down before she could change her mind, and she was by then in any case making a mental list of things she must do: check that her mother was free, budget for a new dress, get her hair done. She made an appointment at the hairdresser's for Saturday at midday, and was about to pick up the phone again and check with her mother when it rang.

"About the engineering candidate I'm to see later this week." It was the manager of the company that was coming to the town. "Is he married? Only something's developed since I last talked to you. We've just won a contract for the installation of a new scanner in a hospital in Cairo. Our senior man is not too well, but would go out initially with an assistant. They have to train the local people after the installation; all that'll take six months or so. Could your Mr. King be prepared to stay on afterwards? A year in all, I should say."

My Mr. King. Alison's business sense had to battle for existence as she worded her reply.

"No, he's not married. And I think he likes travel. He's already toured the Mediterranean — worked his passage, I think."

"I like the sound of that. Will you put this to him, then, before I see him?"

The new salary figure he mentioned before he rang off should have demolished Alison's strange reluctance about the whole thing. It was more than half again what she could hope to get for Sebastian locally.

She dialled the Kings' farm again, her voice trembling imperceptibly as she asked for Sebastian.

"My word he *is* popular!" It was his sister, and as she went to find him Alison pictured endless phone calls from the fresh-faced beauties of the young farmers' set, to whom Sebastian would be a great catch.

"Sebastian, there's something you have to think about very carefully before one of your interviews."

"I'm listening. What's the matter?"

"Nothing's the matter. What makes you think that?"

"Your voice. It's trembling, Alison. Has someone upset you?"

SHE MADE a supreme effort to control her feelings, and spoke almost sharply down the phone. "There's nothing at all the matter, Sebastian. We're just very busy, and something's happened. Something important. Tell me, how do you feel about going to Cairo? For a year."

Before he could reply she filled in the details of the new job rapidly, stressing the opportunity, and ending with the new salary figure involved.

"And you'll have to be good with people. Which of course you are."

"Thank you for the compliment." For the first time since she had known him, Sebastian's voice was cold and remote.

"Well, are you interested, or aren't you?" She matched his response with a harsh note in her own tone.

"I suppose I'd be mad not to be interested," he said. "Thanks for letting me know."

"See you on Saturday?" He had already rung off, and she put the phone down, hating it for its inadequacy as a means of communication when there was so much they had left unsaid.

On the Saturday morning before the Harvest Supper a letter confirming Sebastian's appointment in Cairo was waiting for her on her office desk. She knew exactly what it was before she even opened it. Her eyes blurred with tears as she read the impressive line in which the salary figure was confirmed. She really was far too good at her job.

And twelve long months from now — twelve months without seeing Sebastian — she would still be here, a permanent fixture, sending other people to the far ends of the earth. When he got back from charming the hide off everyone in the teeming, sophisticated city where she had sent him, Sebastian would find her a whole year older. But perhaps that was a good thing. He had to have his chance.

AT THE hairdresser's she changed her mind about the blow-dry and instead asked for a chignon, sweeping her long dark hair high to off-set the low cut of the lemon silk dress she had bought for the party. It would make her look her true self: a mother, a widow, a career woman. Yet afterwards, she saw reflected in the salon mirror a young girl's face, with shining eyes.

THE ROBIN FAMILY

STOCKING THE LARDER

As their mothers want to make jam for the winter, the little Robins go berry picking

NUTS and berries were ripening all over the Woodlands and the little furry and feathery folk were very busy laying in stores for their winter larders.

"I must make some blackberry jam now that the fruit is ripe," said Mrs. Robin to her family.

"And some berry squash for Christmas," chirped Roley.

"You and Rosemary can help by going blackberrying on Saturday," said Mrs. Robin. "And there are plenty of haws on the hedges too."

So on Saturday afternoon Roley and Rosemary set off for the hedgerows with two large baskets. They were joined by their young cousins, Richard and Rowena, for *their* mother wanted to make jam too!

The blackberries were large and luscious and two of the baskets were very quickly filled.

As Rowena was beginning to look tired, Rosemary suggested she should sit down and watch over the blackberries while they looked for some red haws. So Rowena sat happily between the two baskets.

"Rowena is very quiet," said Rosemary after some little while. "I wonder if she is all right."

"I'll run over and see," offered Roley.

But the tiny Robin was not *looking* all right. She was looking very miserable and one of the baskets was quite empty. Rowena had been feeling hungry as well as tired!

She dressed slowly, after a late tea with Jeannette, and was only just ready when she heard Sebastian's car in the lane. Calling to her mother to give him a sherry, she went in to kiss Jeannette good night.

But at a slight sound on the landing outside Jeannette's room, she looked up to find Sebastian standing there, the crooked grin nowhere at all in evidence.

"Will the man read me a story?" Jeannette's timing was as bad as ever.

"Not this time," Sebastian said gently. "Mummy and I are going to a party."

To Alison's relief, Jeannette accepted the refusal meekly. Such was Sebastian's way with women. With another goodnight kiss she tucked the little girl in and went to get her coat.

In the car she smoothed her dress carefully while Sebastian negotiated the lane. It was getting dark, and as they gathered speed on the main road she watched his reflection in the passenger window, more aware than ever of the physical effect this man had on her. Her mouth went dry.

"The supper's always held in the tithe barn," Sebastian said as the car turned into the drive of the house she had passed so often, not knowing anything of the family who lived there. Now it was to become her reality, for one night.

"I thought we'd have a first drink at the house. The family's already at the barn. Just you and me, Alison." His voice was still very serious.

THERE WAS a log fire of well-dried applewood burning in the small study where they had their drinks. Alison sat comfortably in a beautiful, high-backed chair, savouring an intimacy they had not shared before.

"Now, I think you have some news for me?" Sebastian sat on the far side of the fireplace, staring into the flames.

"You know already, then?" she said. "Why didn't you telephone? Our letter of confirmation came this morning."

"I wanted to see you. The phone gets things wrong. And now — with you looking like this — it's so much harder, after all."

Continued overleaf

It was the first time she had known him to be lost for words.

"You don't need to worry about hurting my feelings, Sebastian. We can keep in touch. Stay friends." She tried to keep her voice lightly unconcerned, and failed.

"You don't understand. I'm taking the job in Cairo because I feel much more than that for you. And when I get back I'll be that much older, with something much more to offer." He looked round the warm, comfortable room. "My elder brother's always wanted to take on the farm and all this. I want other things. Things I've done myself."

She put down her glass. "Sebastian, I know you have to go to Cairo. But when you come back I'll be older, too, and there's Jeannette's schooling, and my mother living with me —"

"Is she against me?" His head went up and he looked at her for the first time. And she saw then that his charm was something of which he was quite unaware. The man who could so effortlessly draw other people to him, was himself terrified of rejection.

"Is that why you've sent me on this Cairo job, Alison? To get me out of your lives?"

She was not conscious of moving from where she sat, but somehow found herself by the fire, clinging to him as if for dear life. "Oh, Sebastian, how can you think that?"

She began to talk. She told him about Stuart's death, the pattern her life had taken as an antidote to grief — a grief which Sebastian himself had finally dispelled, showing her that she had not, after all, lost her capacity to feel.

"But if I did love someone —" she held his hands tight — "I think I'd want something permanent again. Real commitment, not an affair. Especially not with someone younger, and quite so . . ."

She did not use the word 'charming'. because at that moment he kissed her. Afterwards she crept into his arms. "Quite so special," she said.

"Well —" Sebastian sighed — "I don't remember ever mentioning an affair. But if we're not going to have one, then there's only one thing for it. When I get back from Cairo I think you'll be old enough to know what you really want, and you'll have to propose."

She laughed, and they kissed again until Alison said they ought to be on their way to the party.

"There's one other thing," Sebastian said with the crooked grin she thought had gone for good. She waited, smiling. "You'll have to keep your hair like that till I do get back. You see, it makes you look so much younger . . ."

THE END

©Gabrielle Shaw, 1983

Exercise...

In most of our lives there is a great big gap when school games and gym are followed by comparative physical laziness. If only we had known at the time what exercise does for our shape, skin, eyes, hair and general appearance we would never have dropped it.

Make a resolution, right now, to include exercise in your daily schedule. If you have any health or muscular problems do, of course, get your doctor's permission before embarking on anything at all strenuous. It's a mistake, anyway, to try suddenly to perform a set of vigorous exercises after a long spell of inactivity.

Here is a set of gentle exercises which cannot do anything but good. They should not take up more than twenty minutes. Do them once daily (not after a meal!) for a trimmer, firmer and more supple body.

Starting from the top:

Neck: Make a circle with your head, moving it first in a clockwise then in an anti-clockwise direction. Repeat five times in each direction.

Breasts: Raise your elbows sideways so that they are at shoulder level, with fingertips meeting and palms down. Fling your arms sideways simultaneously, keeping elbows level, then bring fingertips together again. Repeat five times. Then place left fist in front of left shoulder and right fist in front of right shoulder and, without moving the position of the fists, make circles outwards with your elbows. Do this three times. Finally, stretch upwards with your left arm as far as you can, then with your right arm.

Midriff: With feet slightly apart, raise arms above your head with fingers clasped. Twist your body as far to the left as you can without moving your feet, then to the right. Repeat three times.

Waist: Stand with feet apart and, without bending trunk forward, slide your right hand as far down the outside of your right leg as possible. Straighten up, then repeat with left hand and left leg. Repeat three times.

Thighs: Try a "knees bend" for firming them. Stand on tiptoe with feet together, knees straight and arms outstretched. Keeping your back straight, slowly bend your knees until you are in a sitting position. Stand up. Repeat three times.

Thighs and tummy muscles: Lie flat on back with legs straight and arms by your sides. Slowly raise one leg to a vertical position, keeping both knees straight. Hold for five seconds. Then repeat with other leg. Do this three times.

Calves: Dancing is a superb exercise for calves. So is raising yourself on tiptoe very slowly, with arms outstretched and lowering your heels slowly to the floor. Also, try stair-climbing on tiptoe, with back straight and head erect.

Ankles: Sit with legs crossed right over left and circle right ankle in a clockwise then anti-clockwise direction, five times each way. Repeat with left leg over right and circling left ankle.

Do your legs *and* feet good by varying your heel height frequently. If you wear low-heeled shoes round the house most of the day, put on higher-heeled shoes in the evening.

Finally, never underestimate the benefits of a good, brisk walk every day.

Take a rest

This is as important as exercise. But a better word for it is relaxation. It's a fact that most of us are far too tense. Take a look at people in a bus or train, in shops or in the office. Frowns, hunched shoulders, screwed-up faces, legs wound round chairs and sitting on the edge of a chair instead of firmly ensconced in it, are all signs of tension.

Always sit comfortably, with your thighs supported by the seat of your chair and your back supported by the chair back. Sounds logical, but few of us do it. And just to sit with your hands loosely in your lap with palms uppermost helps to dispel tension.

If you've been on your feet all day, lie down for ten minutes when you get home, with your feet raised on pillows, so that they are higher than your head.

When you're feeling fraught, give yourself a brief relaxation session. Lie down with a small cushion under your knees, arms slightly away from body with palms uppermost, and consciously let yourself go, starting with your jaw, then shoulders, wrists, fingers, knees, calves, ankles, toes, until you feel as floppy as a rag doll.

Sleep is vital for looks, as well as health. Skin has more radiance, eyes more sparkle and little lines can disappear when you get adequate, restful sleep. Most of us need eight hours, some can do with less. Find what's right for you, and make up for the odd late night with two extra early ones.

TAKING EXERCISE

Try some gentle exercises to get you into beautiful trim

Colour photo on page 118

Photo by courtesy of Danskin

London for everyone

Vast, sprawling, cosmopolitan, ever-changing, London is surely the most fascinating city in the world

LONDON'S PLEASURES are richly diverse. Pageantry and historic splendour, palaces and parks and little streets that still retain their original village atmosphere; fine shops and colourful markets, superb restaurants, theatres, night-spots and entertainment of every kind—few places offer more delight. These are some favourite London pleasures:

Watch the **Ceremony of the Keys**, the ritual locking-up of the Tower for the night, at the Tower of London—a centuries-old tradition still faithfully performed by the colourfully-dressed Chief Yeoman Warder and his guard each evening at 21.35 hrs. For tickets, apply in writing to the *Resident Governor, Tower of London, Tower Hill, London EC3*, enclosing an s.a.e. and stating preferred date and alternative, plus the number of people in your party.

Visit the **Royal Mews**, in Buckingham Palace Road at the back of the Palace itself, to admire the Queen's horses and the State coaches used on ceremonial occasions. Open Wednesday and Thursday afternoons between 14.00 and 16.00 hrs. (except on State occasions and during Ascot).

Take a **boat-ride down-river** from Westminster or Charing Cross Piers to historic Greenwich, treasure-chest of Britain's sea heritage, where you will find the famous tea clipper *Cutty Sark, Gypsy Moth IV*, the yacht in which Sir Francis Chichester sailed single-handed round the world, the National Maritime Museum, the Royal Naval College, once a royal palace and birthplace of Henry VIII, Mary I and Elizabeth I, and the Old Royal Observatory in Greenwich Park—the red time-ball on its roof falls at 13.00 hrs. each day, marking Greenwich Mean Time all over the world. The Trafalgar Tavern, overlooking the river, is a lovely place to lunch, its whitebait famous since Queen Victoria's day.

London's **parks and open spaces** provide oases of green delight amid the city's clamour—and the autumn colours are superb. The Royal Parks, once Henry VIII's favourite hunting forest, together cover more than 5,500 acres and it is possible to walk some three miles through London's heart by way of Kensington Gardens, Hyde Park and St. James's Park. The Regent's Park squirrels look forward to socialising with any titbit-laden passer-by and, as you stroll beside the pretty lake and through Queen Mary's rose garden, you are quite likely to hear the incongruous-sounding roar of the zoo's lions.

Hampstead Heath, with its green hills and wooded dells, its Whitestone Pond for model boat sailing, its famous inns like The Spaniards and Jack Straw's Castle and its fine views over the city, plus its weekend artists and Sunday morning orators, is always agreeable. And Hampstead Village boasts some fascinating shops, boutiques, restaurants and wine bars, as well as enchanting streets of old houses.

Shopping in London provides endless temptation, whether you choose to make for the main shopping streets like Knightsbridge, home of the incomparable Harrods, Regent Street, Oxford Street, Bond Street and Kensington High Street; or one of the little streets of enormous character—Beauchamp Place, Camden Passage, South Molton Street, St. Christopher's Place, Shepherd Market. Covent Garden has become an enthralling place to shop, stroll through, pause for a leisurely coffee or drink, enjoy a full-scale meal or a snack. St. Katharine's Dock, beside the Tower, is another new delight, full of maritime atmosphere, with shops, restaurants and inns as well as a variety of ships, including Scott's *Discovery*, the *Nore* lightship and some old Thames barges.

The most renowned of London's **shopping arcades** is Burlington Arcade, off Piccadilly, where you may not run, whistle or sing, carry an outsize parcel, open an umbrella or push a pram without running the risk of meeting the uniformed beadle's disapproving eye. The most elegant is the Royal Opera Arcade, running between Pall Mall East and Charles II Street—admire its vaulted ceiling, wrought-iron lamp holders and bow-fronted shops.

London's **street markets** have a long and flamboyant history and can be relied on to provide a fun, if not a fruitful, outing. Try the Portobello Road, Bell Street, Church Street or Greenwich High Road on a Saturday morning, or the New Caledonian on a Friday morning, if you're looking for interesting antiques or bric à brac. The Petticoat Lane market in Middlesex Street swings on Sunday mornings, Camden Lock on Saturdays and Sundays, Leather Lane and The Cut on weekdays.

Theatre buffs way make for the booth in Leicester Square which sells that day's spare tickets at half-price from lunchtime onwards—or they may like to go backstage at the National Theatre (book at the Lyttleton Theatre Information Desk between 10.0 and 11.0 on a Saturday).

If there's a **football fan** in the family, tours of Wembley Stadium are arranged on Saturdays and Sundays, except of course when matches are taking place. Visitors can visit the changing rooms and Royal Box and walk through the Players' Tunnel to the sound (taped) of the spectators' roar—real Walter Mitty stuff, this.

*F*ew ceremonies bring Britain's rich heritage of pageantry more vividly to life than the time-honoured inspection of the Yeoman Warders, dressed in the splendid uniform of bygone days, on Tower Green, within the centuries-old walls of the Tower of London.

*C*hild's choice is a useful button-up cardi with V-neck and all-over three colour bands of patterning. (Instructions on page 123.) *Left:* Stitch a wallhanging that's bright enough to capture the imagination of a child, and useful for storing pencils and pens. Directions start on page 130.

*T*he versatile sponge—once mastered, it has many gorgeous guises. Step by step instructions and variations on page 125. *Above:* Victoria Sponge and Black Forest Gâteau. *Left:* Collectomania . . . Here an obsession for antiques finds a happy home in a country cottage. For more about the items shown in this picture, see page 104.

*I*n a striking three-colour slip-stitch pattern with turn-back collar and bloused
sleeves — just the jacket to keep you warm and snug. (Instructions on page 100.)
Left: Are you lissom and fit, even if not quite to the standard of this lovely dancer on the
sands? On page 110 is a gentle routine of exercises to keep you in shape.

*C*hrysanthemums, best-loved of autumn flowers, originated from China and Japan. They come in a wide range of forms and colours. There are smaller types suitable for edging and tall varieties for the back of the border, while the greenhouse kind make fine cut flowers. They are easy to propagate from cuttings.

YOUR GARDEN IN AUTUMN

It's a time to tidy up, but also to plant for a prospect of flowers, says JOY SIMMONS

FLOWER GARDEN

Madonna Lilies may be planted now.

Shrub cuttings can still be taken, choosing *hardwood* shoots of the current year's growth, with or without a heel of old wood attached.

Feed Sweet Peas with liquid manure, removing faded blooms daily.

Seed bare patches on the lawn, protecting the seed from birds with twiggy sticks until germination takes place.

Earwigs attacking Dahlias and Chrysanthemums can be trapped in inverted flower pots stuffed with hay or balls of newspaper. Treating the surrounding ground and plants with Sevin Dust can also prove effective.

Lavender can be lightly trimmed as soon as the flowers fade.

Remove worn-out stems of Philadelphus, cutting back old flowering shoots to fresh young growth on the main branches.

SUCCESS WITH CYCLAMEN

When my Cyclamen finished flowering earlier this year, I put the pot outdoors under a hedge and forgot about it. Now, in October, I see that the corm is putting out new leaves. Will it flower again?

It should do, if you take the plant indoors and keep the soil moist. The Cyclamen does best in a humid atmosphere around 10-13°C (50-55°F) away from direct sunlight; a north-facing windowsill is ideal. To offset lack of humidity, put the pot in an outer container and pack it round with damp peat.

Divide rock plants where necessary, keeping the new plants well watered in dry weather.

Lift summer bedding plants as soon as the flowers fade.

Most of the spring bedding plants can be set out in their final quarters towards the end of October. These include Wallflowers, Forget-me-nots and the white, pink and red Dwarf Daisies (Bellis).

Plant Daffodil bulbs, Dutch and English Irises, Crocuses, Scillas, species Tulips and the dwarf Iris histrioides. The species Tulipa tarda, which bears three to five blooms to a bulb, and Iris histrioides look lovely in a rockery.

Dig up Dahlia tubers after the tops are frosted, and label with the name of the variety. Spread the tubers in an airy place under cover to dry off, then clean away the soil and store them for winter in a frost-free place.

Paeonies can be lifted and divided in October, replanting with the crown no more than 2 in. below surface.

**Dahlias come in many delightful forms.
(Photo: Bulb Information Desk).**

Continued overleaf

KITCHEN GARDEN

Sow Lettuces, Stump-rooted Carrots, Turnips and Cabbages (variety *April* or *Flowers of Spring*) by the end of August for cutting next spring.

Finish gathering herbs for winter use.

Sow Broad-leaved Prickly Spinach for winter or spring use.

Lift and store maincrop Carrots to be used later on.

Onions should be ready for harvesting, leaving the bulbs on the ground to finish ripening before storing them in ropes or shallow trays.

Plant winter varieties of Lettuce and Cabbage seedlings.

Continue sowing winter and summer Radishes.

Late-sown French Beans should be protected with a cloche now.

Carrots may be stored in layers in boxes, with sand, soil or peat packed round them.

Feed Tomatoes and stop the plants at four trusses.

Beetroots can be lifted and stored.

Remove the yellowing leaves from Brussels Sprouts.

Continue picking Raspberries, Loganberries, Currants and Strawberries.

After harvesting, spray Gooseberry bushes against mildew with a systemic fungicide where necessary.

Complete the removal of fruited Raspberry canes, tying in the new growth.

Prune Blackcurrants, cutting out a third of the old wood.

Remove surplus Strawberry runners (except on perpetual fruiting varieties).

Top and bush fruits can be planted from October onwards.

GREENHOUSE

Take Geranium and Fuchsia cuttings.

Pot up hardy and half-hardy annuals for flowering under glass. Later, pinch out the tips.

Pot up Roman and Dutch Hyacinths.

Feed Chrysanthemums every week to ten days using a liquid fertiliser.

Brompton Stocks should be potted on for transplanting into the open next spring.

Continue pinching out Tomato side shoots, stopping the plants at five trusses.

In October, begin withholding water from tuberous-rooted Begonias.

Check for whitefly, spraying plants with a suitable insecticide.

Coleus can be sown in a warm greenhouse at any time. *Wizard* is a good branching dwarf variety in many lovely colour combinations.

MAKING A COMPOST HEAP

Garden and kitchen refuse can be valuable if properly composted.

What materials can be used? Lawn clippings (untreated by weedkiller), herbaceous tops, vegetable leaves, soft hedge clippings, fallen leaves (oak or beech are best), potato peelings and pea pods all rot down well. Do not include woody material. Thick stems like cabbage stalks should be crushed first.

You can buy a suitable bin for holding the compost or make your own with wire netting supported at the corners with stakes. A heap roughly 5 ft. by 5 ft. by 5 ft. is about right.

Build the heap in 6 to 12 in. layers, treading or tamping down as you go and dusting each layer with a proprietary compost accelerator. Water any dry patches. When complete, cover with 1 to 2 inches of soil.

MY LITTLE CHICKADEE

She may be young, but she knows what she likes,
and this novelty banded cardigan in three colour patterning
with casual V-neck pleases her greatly!

Instructions in 3 sizes

Colour photo on page 115

MATERIALS: *Allow the following quantities in 50 g ball of Wendy Shetland Double Knitting: 3 beige, 1 green and 1 pink for the 61 cm size; 3 beige, 2 green and 2 pink for the 66 cm size; 4 beige, 2 green and 2 pink for the 71 cm size. For any one size: A pair each of No. 8 (4 mm) and long No. 10 (3¼ mm) knitting needles; 7 buttons.*

TENSION: *Work at a tension of 26 stitches and 26 rows, to measure 10 x 10 cm, over the pattern, using No. 8 (4 mm) needles, to obtain measurements given overleaf.*

ABBREVIATIONS: **To be read before working:** *K., knit plain; p., purl; st., stitch; tog., together; inc., increase (by working twice into same st.); dec., decrease (by taking 2 sts. tog.); k.1b., k.1 through back of st.; twisted single rib is k.1b. and p.1 alternately; s.s., stocking st. (k. on the right side and p. on the wrong side); bg., beige; g., green; pk., pink.*

NOTE: *The instructions are given for the 61 cm (24 inch) size. Where they vary, work the figures within the first brackets for the 66 cm (26 inch) size; work the figures within the second brackets for the 71 cm (28 inch) size.*

BACK AND FRONTS (worked in one piece to armholes): With No. 10 (3¼ mm) needles and bg., cast on 156 (168) (180) sts. and work 16 rows in twisted single rib.

Change to No. 8 (4 mm) needles, then joining in and breaking off colours as required, work the 3-colour pattern which is worked entirely in s.s. beginning with a k. row, so only the colour details are given.

1st and 2nd rows: All bg.

3rd row: * 2 bg., 1 g.; repeat from * to end.

4th row: 2 g., * 3 bg., 3 g.; repeat from * until 4 sts. remain, 3 bg., 1 g.

5th row: * 2 g., 1 bg.; repeat from * to end.

6th row: 2 bg., * 3 g., 3 bg.; repeat from * until 4 sts. remain, 3 g., 1 bg.

7th row: As 3rd row.

8th to 10th rows: All bg.

11th row: * 1 pk., 1 bg.; repeat from * to end.

Continued overleaf

123

12th row: All pk.

13th row: 2 pk., * 2 g., 1 pk., 2 g., 3 pk., 1 g., 3 pk.; repeat from * until 10 sts. remain, 2 g., 1 pk., 2 g., 3 pk., 1 g., 1 pk.

14th row: * 3 g., 2 pk., 5 g., 2 pk.; repeat from * to end.

15th row: * 2 g., 1 pk., 3 g., 1 pk., 2 g., 1 pk., 1 g., 1 pk.; repeat from * to end.

16th row: * 3 pk., 3 g., 1 pk., 1 g., 1 pk., 3 g.; repeat from * to end.

17th row: 1 pk., * 3 g., 1 pk., 3 g., 2 pk., 1 g., 2 pk.; repeat from * ending last repeat with 1 pk.

18th row: * 3 pk., 3 g., 1 pk., 1 g., 1 pk., 3 g.; repeat from * to end.

19th to 26th rows: As 15th row back to 8th row in that reverse order.

27th to 31st rows: As 3rd to 7th rows, but using pk. instead of g.

32nd to 34th rows: All bg.

35th to 47th rows: As 11th to 23rd rows, but using g. instead of pk. and bg. instead of g.

48th to 50th rows: All bg.

51st row: All pk.

52nd row: 3 pk., * 1 bg., 5 pk.; repeat from * ending last repeat with 2 pk. instead of 5 pk.

53rd row: 1 pk., * 3 bg., 3 pk.; repeat from * ending last repeat with 2 pk.

54th row: * 1 pk., 2 bg.; repeat from * to end.

55th row: 1 bg., * 3 pk., 3 bg.; repeat from * ending last repeat with 2 bg.

56th row: * 1 bg., 5 pk.; repeat from * to end.

57th row: All pk.

58th to 60th rows: All bg.

The 3rd to 60th rows form the pattern.

Pattern a further 2 (6) (10) rows.

Divide sts. for back and fronts and shape front edges: Next row: Maintaining continuity of the pattern, dec., pattern 35 (38) (41) and leave these 36 (39) (42) sts. on a spare needle for right front, cast off 2, pattern a further 77 (83) (89) and leave these 78 (84) (90) sts. on a spare needle for back, cast off 2, pattern until 2 sts. remain, dec. and work on these 36 (39) (42) sts. for left front.

** The left front: Pattern 1 row.

Dec. 1 st. at armhole edge on each of the next 3 (4) (5) rows, *at the same time*, dec. 1 st. at front edge on the first of these rows and the 11 (12) (13) following alternate rows — 21 (22) (23) sts.

Pattern 3 rows — pattern 4 rows here when working right front.

To slope the shoulder: Cast off 10 (11) (11) sts. at the beginning to the next row — 11 (11) (12) sts.

Pattern 1 row. Cast off.

The back: With wrong side of work facing, rejoin yarn to the 78 (84) (90) sts. on spare needle.

Pattern 1 row.

Dec. 1 st. at each end of the next 3 (4) (5) rows — 72 (76) (80) sts.

Pattern 23 (24) (25) rows.

To slope the shoulders: Cast off 10 (11) (11) sts. at beginning of each of the next 2 rows, then 11 (11) (12) sts. at the beginning of each of the following 2 rows.

Cast off remaining 30 (32) (34) sts.

The right front: With wrong side of work facing, rejoin yarn to remaining 36 (39) (42) sts. on spare needle and work as given for left front from ** to end, noting variation.

THE SLEEVES (both alike): With No. 10 (3¼ mm) needles and bg. cast on 48 sts. and work 16 rows in twisted single rib.

Change to No. 8 (4 mm) needles and work 8 rows in pattern as given for back and fronts.

Maintaining continuity of the pattern to match back and fronts, and taking extra sts. into the pattern as they occur, inc. 1 st. at each end of the next row and the 3 (6) (9) following 12th (8th) (6th) rows — 56 (62) (68) sts.

Pattern 17 (9) (7) rows.

To shape the sleeve top: Dec. 1 st. at the beginning of each of the next 2 rows, then dec. 1 st. at each end of the following 1 (3) (5) row(s).

Pattern 1 row, then cast off 4 sts. at the beginning of each of the next 8 rows.

Cast off remaining 20 (22) (24) sts.

THE FRONT BORDER: First join shoulder seams. Using No. 10 (3¼ mm) needles rejoin bg. and pick up and k. 248 (260) (272) sts. evenly along row ends of right front, across back neck and along row ends of left front.

Work 3 rows in twisted single rib.

1st buttonhole row: Rib 4, * cast off 2, rib 9 (9) (10); repeat from * 5 times, cast off 2, rib to end.

2nd buttonhole row: Rib to end, casting on 2 sts. over each group cast off on previous row.

Rib 3 rows. Cast off in rib.

TO MAKE UP THE CARDIGAN: Press work lightly on the wrong side, using a warm iron over a damp cloth. Set in sleeves, then join sleeve seams. Add buttons.

Colours she'll approve of in this nice Shetland yarn include: Hebrides with Loch Ness green and Tudor rose; Orkney beige, piper red and pasture green; Aran, tartan blue/scarlet tattoo.

MEASUREMENTS *in centimetres (and inches, in brackets)*						
To fit chest sizes	61	(24)	66	(26)	71	(28)
All round at underarms fastened	62.5	(24½)	67	(26½)	72	(28½)
Side seam	28.5	(11¼)	30	(11¾)	31.5	(12½)
Length	40.5	(16)	43	(17)	45	(17¾)
Sleeve seam	28.5	(11¼)	30	(11¾)	31.5	(12½)

Simple and Special Sponges

How to make the perfect sponge, step by step; then
some splendid and luscious variations—see our colour photos of
Black Forest Gâteau and Victoria Sponge on page 117

Once you know how to make a perfect creamed sponge you'll be able to make an almost infinite variety of cakes. Simply by adding other flavours, baking in small or large cake tins, adding a baked-on topping or by decorating differently you'll have increased your repertoire of cakes from a simple, perfect sponge to a special and popular Black Forest Gâteau.

BASIC SPONGE MIXTURE

6 oz. block margarine
6 oz. caster sugar
3 large eggs, size 2, beaten
6 oz. self-raising flour
2-3 tablespoons water

Cream the margarine until it is soft, then add the sugar and cream them together until soft, pale and fluffy. Add the beaten egg a little at a time, beating well after each addition. Sprinkle half the flour and 1 tablespoon of water over the creamed mixture and fold it in. Fold in the rest of the flour and a further 1 tablespoon of water, then add a further tablespoon of water if needed. Use and bake as liked.

1. LINING THE TIN
Base-lining the tin with greaseproof paper is worth the extra trouble as it protects the cake crust as well as ensuring the cake slips out easily after baking.

Cut out a piece of greaseproof paper the size of the base of the tin. Place in the tin and lightly brush it and the tin sides with oil.

2. CREAMING
All the ingredients should be at room temperature, so take the margarine and the eggs out of the fridge at least 1 hour before using. If the margarine is very hard, put it in a bowl and leave it in a warm place to soften but never let it become oily. One of the secrets of success for a light sponge is very thorough creaming: beat the fat first on its own until soft and creamy and then add the sugar and cream again until soft, pale and fluffy – it will take 5 to 10 minutes creaming hard with a wooden spoon.

When creaming by hand, it is easier if a fairly large mixing bowl is used and the bowl is tilted. Stand the bowl on a damp, folded cloth to prevent it slipping.

Creaming incorporates air as it breaks up the fat globules and some of the sugar dissolves, making a mixture called an 'emulsion', which is capable of holding air. A fine sugar, such as caster, is recommended as it dissolves more easily. Granulated can be used but, being coarser, may cause sugar 'spotting' on the baked crust of the cake.

3. ADDING THE EGGS
Always use the size of eggs recommended in the recipe.

When mixing by hand, beat all the eggs together in a basin then add to the creamed fat and sugar a little at a time – about the equivalent of half an egg – and beat very thoroughly after each addition. If an electric mixer is used or a very strong beating action, the eggs can be beaten in one at a time without the mixture curdling. (Curdling, which is due to separation of the fat and the sugar, causes the mixture to hold less air and gives the sponge a closer texture.)

4. ADDING THE FLOUR
Unless spices are added we find it unnecessary to sift the flour. Instead, sprinkle half the flour over the creamed mixture together with a tablespoon of water and then, using a large metal spoon, fold in the flour using a 'figure-of-eight' cutting action. Repeat with the rest of the flour and water.

The water should be added with the flour as it is important to keep the same consistency throughout the mixing – do not let it become too stiff at any stage during the folding-in process. Do the folding as quickly as possible, taking just long enough to incorporate the dry ingredients – in this way, the maximum amount of air will be retained.

Note: The amount of water required will vary depending on the absorbency of the flour.

Continued overleaf

Perennial favourite Victoria Sponge—
two feather-light sponges sandwiched
with jam, or jam and cream.

SIMPLE AND SPECIAL SPONGES *Continued*

5. BAKING HINTS

Turn the mixture into the tin and level the surface with the back of a spoon. Tap the tin sharply on the working surface to settle the mixture.

To give an even rise, make a small hollow in the centre of the mixture with the back of a spoon.

Always bake the sponge mixture in the centre of a pre-heated oven. Small cakes should be baked just above the centre.

Test with a warm skewer placed at an angle through the cake – it should come out clean. The cake should also feel firm and spring back when pressed lightly with the finger and it should be evenly risen and a rich golden brown in colour when cooked.

Leave the cake to cool in the tin for 5 minutes, so that the mixture firms slightly, then turn it out carefully on to a wire rack to cool completely. Remove the paper lining when cold.

For extra moist cakes, wrap them in foil while still slightly warm.

VICTORIA SPONGE

The basic sponge mixture
¼ pint whipping or double cream
3-4 tablespoons redcurrant jelly or raspberry jam
1-2 tablespoons icing sugar
Two 7½ inch sandwich tins, oiled and base lined

Set the oven to moderate, Gas Mark 4 or 350°F/ 180°C.

Make up the sponge mixture as in the basic method. Divide the mixture between the tins and level the surface with the back of a spoon, making a slight hollow in the centre of each. Place in the oven and bake for 25 minutes or until firm to the touch.

Leave the cake to cool in the tin for 2 to 3 minutes before turning it on to a wire rack to cool completely. When cold, remove the greaseproof paper.

Whisk the cream until thick. Sandwich the cake layers together with the cream and the jelly or jam, and dust the top with a little sifted icing sugar.

LEMON CRUNCH SPONGE

The basic sponge mixture
3 level tablespoons lemon curd
For the topping:
1 lemon
4 oz. granulated sugar
A 2 pint shallow ovenproof dish, greased

Set the oven to moderate, Gas Mark 4 or 350°F/ 180°C.

Make up the sponge mixture as in the basic method. Spread the lemon curd over the base of

Lemon Crunch Sponge.

the dish, spoon over the sponge and level the top. Bake in the centre of the oven for 45 minutes, until the cake is cooked and firm to the touch.

Meanwhile, pare the rind from the lemon, avoiding all the white pith. Cut the rind into needle-sized shreds, put them into a pan and cover with about 1 inch of water. Bring to the boil and simmer for 1 minute, then drain.

Cut the lemon in half and squeeze out the juice. Strain it on to the lemon shreds and sugar in a basin and stir.

When the cake is cooked, remove it from the oven and immediately spoon over the lemon mixture, spreading it evenly over the surface. Serve as a cake or a pudding.

Unusual layered Cornflake Streusal Cake.

CORNFLAKE STREUSAL CAKE

The basic sponge mixture
For the filling and topping:
2 oz. cornflakes
1 oz. glacé cherries, quartered
2 oz. chopped nuts
2 oz. demerara sugar
1 level teaspoon cinnamon
2 oz. margarine, melted
A 7½ inch round cake tin, greased and base lined

Set the oven to moderate, Gas Mark 4 or 350°F/180°C.

Make the filling. Mix the cornflakes, cherries, nuts, sugar and cinnamon together. Melt the margarine and stir it into the cornflake mixture.

Make the sponge as in the basic method and spoon half of it into the tin, levelling the top, then crumble half the cornflake mixture evenly over it. Spoon the rest of the cake mixture over the filling, being careful not to disturb the layer of cornflakes. With the back of a spoon, make a hollow in the centre of the cake, then crumble the rest of the cornflake mixture evenly over the top. Bake in the centre of the oven for 1½ to 1¾ hours.

BLACK FOREST GÂTEAU *(see page 117)*

Serves 8-10

For the cake:
The basic sponge mixture, but using only 4 oz. self-raising flour plus 1 oz. cornflour and 1 oz. cocoa powder
For the cream custard filling:
Canned cherry juice – see below
2 level tablespoons cornflour
Few drops vanilla essence
1 egg, size 3
1 level tablespoon sugar
2 tablespoons whipped cream – see recipe
For the cherry filling:
15 oz. can cherries
8 oz. cherry jam
3 tablespoons Kirsch
For the covering:
½ pint whipping cream
Plain chocolate curls
8 inch round cake tin, base-lined and greased

Set the oven to moderate, Gas Mark 4 or 350°F/180°C.

Sift the flour, cornflour and cocoa together then make the basic sponge mixture.

Spoon the mixture into the prepared tin. Bake in the centre of the oven for 1 to 1¼ hours or until cooked. Leave in the tin to cool.

Make the cream filling: Drain the juice from the can of cherries. In a small pan blend the cornflour to a smooth paste with some of the cherry juice then stir in the rest. Bring to the boil, stirring, and cook for 1 minute or until thick. Remove from the heat and beat in the vanilla essence, then add the egg and beat well. Sprinkle the sugar over the top and leave to cool.

Make the cherry filling: Stone the cherries and reserve some of the fruit for decoration and chop the rest. Add the chopped fruit to the cherry jam together with the Kirsch.

To assemble the cake: Carefully cut the cake into three layers. Whisk the whipping cream until thick. Take out 2 tablespoons of the cream and whisk it into the custard.

Spread half the cherry filling over the bottom cake layer and cover with half the cream custard. Place the middle cake layer on top and add the rest of the cherry and custard fillings. Place the last cake layer on top and transfer the gâteau to a serving plate. Spread the whipped cream all over the cake and place the chocolate curls on the cake as shown in the photograph on page 117. Place the whole cherries in a circle on top.

Delicious eaten the day it is made, but even better if kept in the fridge overnight and eaten the day after.

More recipes overleaf

SIMPLE AND SPECIAL SPONGES *Continued*

BUTTERSCOTCH BRITTLE CAKE

The basic sponge mixture
For the icing:
1 egg, size 2, separated
2 oz. icing sugar
4 oz. margarine
½ teaspoon butterscotch essence
A 3½ oz. bar or bag of peanut brittle
A 13 by 9 inch Swiss roll tin, oiled and base lined

Set the oven to moderate, Gas Mark 4 or 350°F/
180°C.

Make the sponge mixture as in the basic
method, spread it in the tin and bake in the
centre of the oven for 20 to 25 minutes until firm
and springy to the touch. Turn out on to a wire
tray and leave to cool completely. Trim the
edges, then cut the cake crossways into three
3-inch wide strips.

Meanwhile, make the icing. Whisk the egg
white in a medium-sized basin. Add the icing
sugar and stand the basin over a pan of boiling
water, whisking for 3 to 4 minutes until the icing
is stiff and glossy. (If using a rotary whisk, it will
take a few more minutes to achieve the right
consistency.) Remove basin from the pan.

Cream the margarine until soft, then beat in
the egg yolk and essence. Gradually mix in the
icing to give a soft mixture. Cover the basin and
chill in the fridge for 30 minutes.

Put 2 oz. peanut brittle into a plastic bag and
crush with a rolling pin. Break the remainder of
the brittle into large pieces.

Spread half the icing over two of the cake
strips (i.e. a quarter over each), and sprinkle
each with crushed peanut brittle. Place one on
top of the other.

Spread the remaining half of the icing over the
third cake layer and stand it on top of the other
two layers. Make a pattern in the icing with a
palette knife, and decorate the top edges with
large pieces of the peanut brittle.

CHEQUERBOARD CAKE

The basic sponge mixture
4 level teaspoons instant coffee powder
2 teaspoons hot water
1 teaspoon vanilla essence
For the filling:
4 level tablespoons chocolate spread
4 tablespoons cake crumbs made from the trimmings
For the icing:
4 oz. icing sugar
1 teaspoon coffee essence
3-4 teaspoons water
Chocolate curls
An 8 inch square tin

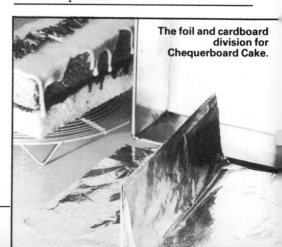

The foil and cardboard
division for
Chequerboard Cake.

Grease the tin and divide it in half: line the base with a pleated piece of foil and support the pleat by inserting a strip of cardboard inside the pleat.

Set the oven to moderate, Gas Mark 4 or 350° F/180°C.

Make up the sponge mixture as in the basic method and spoon half of it into a basin. Add the vanilla essence to one half and carefully mix it in; add the coffee powder which has been dissolved in the hot water to the other half of the sponge and mix it in thoroughly.

Spread the coffee and vanilla mixtures in different halves of the tin. With the back of a spoon, hollow out the centre on each side of the foil, then bake the cakes in the centre of the oven for 40 minutes or until they are cooked.

Leave the cakes to cool in the tin for 5 minutes then turn them out on to a cooling rack and leave to become cold.

Trim the sides and top of the cakes.

Crumble some of the trimmings and add about 4 tablespoons of crumbs to the chocolate spread.

Cut each cake in half lengthways then sandwich the layers together, alternating the colours, with the chocolate spread mixture.

Sift the icing sugar into a basin and stir in the coffee essence and 3 teaspoons of water. Add more water if necessary to give an icing that finds its own level after 5 seconds. Spoon the coffee icing over the top of the Chequerboard Cake and decorate with chocolate curls.

SMALL DECORATED CAKES

Makes 22-24

The basic sponge mixture

For the Chocolate Cup Cakes:

2 oz. plain chocolate

A knob of butter

For the Flower Cakes:

4 oz. icing sugar, sifted

About 4 teaspoons water

1 tube Smarties

A little angelica

For the Feather Cakes:

5 oz. icing sugar, sifted

4-5 teaspoons water

Pink food colouring

5-6 jelly sweets

A greaseproof paper icing bag

For the Mushroom Cakes:

3 oz. soft margarine

6 oz. icing sugar, sifted

A few drops rum essence

A few drops brown colouring

A piping bag with star icing nozzle attached

Sweet little cakes for the tea party.

Set the oven to moderately hot, Gas Mark 5 or 375°F/190°C.

Set out 24 paper cake cases on baking sheets or stand the cases in patty tin trays. Make up the sponge mixture as in the basic method. Fill 6 paper cases two-thirds full of sponge mixture – these are for the Chocolate Cup Cakes – and fill the rest of the cases three-quarters full.

Bake in the oven for 20 to 25 minutes until firm. Cool on a wire tray.

To decorate the Chocolate Cup Cakes: Break the chocolate into pieces, then melt them in a basin over a pan of hot water. Stir in the knob of butter to melt, then remove from the heat. Cover the slightly smaller cakes with a thick layer of chocolate, then leave them to set.

To decorate the Flower Cakes: Add enough water to the icing sugar to give a consistency which holds a 'trail' for 5 seconds, then use it to ice the tops of 5 to 6 small cakes. Cut some Smarties in half and arrange them in a flower shape and leaves on the top of each cake. Make the stalk from a strip of angelica.

To decorate the Feather Cakes: Make up the icing as for the Flower Cakes. Put 2 teaspoonfuls into a cup and add a few drops of pink food colouring to give it a delicate shade. Spoon the pink icing into a greaseproof icing bag and fold over the open end to secure. Spread a layer of white icing over 5 to 6 small cakes. Before the white icing dries, snip the end off the icing bag to make a small hole, then pipe lines of pink icing over each cake. Draw the point of a skewer across and through the lines of piping at ½ inch intervals. Place a small jelly sweet on top of each.

To decorate the Mushroom Cakes: Cream the soft margarine and sifted icing sugar in a bowl until fluffy. Add the flavouring and colouring to taste, then spoon it into an icing bag with star nozzle attached. Using a plain 1 inch round cutter or the point of a sharp knife, cut out a small round plug from the top of each cake, reserving these. Pipe the buttercream in lines radiating out from the centre, then replace the plug of cake.

Rooftops, trees and fields of this enchanting appliqué picture wallhanging are pockets! They'll store away a small child's crayons, rubbers and other treasures. Fun to sew, too, with the zig-zag stitch on your sewing machine

Colour photo on page 114

TO MAKE THE PICTURE

First cut out all the strips of patterned fabric for the frame round the picture, cutting each strip across the fabric width (you can trim it to the correct length later).

For the inner frame, cut four strips of green spotted corduroy 3.5 cm (1⅜ in.) wide. For the middle frame cut four strips of red floral print 4.5 cm (1¾ in.) wide. For the outer frame cut four strips of green floral print 7 cm (2¾ in.) wide. Lay all the frame pieces aside until later.

Lay out the blue denim background and place the tan denim piece over it, with raw edges level round base and sides. Fold the tan denim 1 cm (⅜ in.) to wrong side at the horizon line (see chart on page 133), and pin fold in place.

For your patterns: Join sheets of metric graph paper together as necessary to give you a sheet 61×48 cm (24×19 in.). Over-rule the graph lines into 5 cm squares. Then copy the chart on page 133, square by square, on to the graph paper (each square on the chart equals 5 cm).

From your graph paper pattern trace off all the fields (the shaded areas on the chart); cut

WHAT YOU NEED

Blue demin—a piece 65 x 52 cm (25½×20½ in.), for background of complete picture, plus 30 cm (⅜ yd.) extra for backing pockets.

Tan denim—a 52 cm (20½ in.) square for paths (this piece covers all the lower area of picture, from base up to the topmost fields, and the appliqué pieces are laid over this).

Green towelling—30 cm (⅜ yd.) for fields.

Gold towelling—a scrap for cornfield.

Dark green floral print—30 cm (⅜ yd.), for outer frame and hedges and bushes.

Red floral print—20 cm (¼ yd.), for middle frame and two trees.

Green spotted corduroy—30 cm (⅜ yd.), for inner frame and trees.

Plain fabric—70×84 cm (27½×33 in.), for backing the picture.

Brown felt—scraps for chimney pots.

Brown velvet—scraps for tree trunks, dog and church door.

Mid-brown cotton—scraps for cows, doors, hair and bench.

Blue fabric — scraps for windows.

White fabric—20 cm (¼ yd.), for timbered houses, picket fence, signpost and cows.

Beige linen—20 cm (¼ yd.), for cottage, and details on church.

Stone-coloured linen—20 cm (¼ yd.), for church and tower.

Sand-coloured fabric—20 cm (¼ yd.), for paved paths and walls.

Light and dark red cotton repp—20 cm (¼ yd.) of each, for roofs and chimneys.

Narrow black braid—3.50 m (3⅞ yd.), for timbers.

Heavy duty sew-in Vilene interfacing—50 cm (⅝ yd.).

Soft sew-in Vilene interfacing—40 cm (½ yd.).

Vilene Bondaweb—2 packs.

Sewing threads—to match fabrics.

Three curtain rings—to hang the picture.

Metric graph paper. Tracing paper.

page and use the traced patterns to cut out the various fabric pieces; assemble these on Bondaweb and then on Vilene as before.

Add all architectural details next—use our colour picture (page 114) as a guide to cutting out and positioning these. Cut out fabric doors and windows for houses and church, plus stone shapes and bush for the lowest house, and eaves, window surrounds, lighter stones and gravestones for the church; tack them in place.

For the beams on timbered houses, mark pencilled guidelines then tack and machine stitch braid over them.

When you have positioned all fabric details on

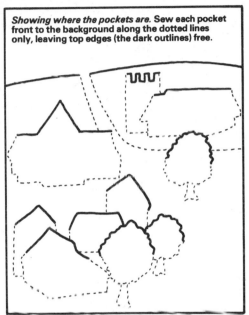

Showing where the pockets are. Sew each pocket front to the background along the dotted lines only, leaving top edges (the dark outlines) free.

these out (adding 2 cm/¾ in. extra all round for turnings) in green towelling, plus one strip of gold towelling for the cornfield above the church. Lay towelling fields aside for the time being.

Then trace off all the houses, church, trees, hedges and bushes, paved paths, walls, and fence with signpost; cut out each pattern in tracing paper.

Cut out each complete traced pattern in Bondaweb, then cut out each pattern (or section of it) in the appropriate fabric, using our "What You Need" list and the colour picture on page 114 as a guide. Assemble the fabric bits that make up each complete pattern (house walls, roof, chimney, each tree and trunk, etc.) and lay them right side up over the matching Bondaweb pattern; iron the Bondaweb in place following the maker's instructions. Now remove the paper backing from the Bondaweb and iron each shaped piece on to soft, sew-in Vilene. Cut out all the Vilene-backed pieces—no turnings are needed as each piece will be satin-stitched round the edges.

Patterns for the people, cows and dog are given full-size on page 132. Trace these off the

each building, pick the appropriate thread colour, set your machine to a close zig-zag (satin stitch) and machine round each door, window, etc. Draw in, then satin stitch stonework effect on church, and paved path and walls; then go round roof and wall outlines.

Satin stitch round the edges of the three largest trees next.

Making the pockets: All the buildings, the three largest trees and the fields on the horizon, actually form the pocket fronts on the picture. The diagram above shows all the pocket positions (the top edge of each pocket is shown in dark outline).

To complete each pocket front, place the building, tree or field over a double layer of heavy, sew-in Vilene, then over blue denim. Tack all layers together and satin stitch round edges. Use sharp scissors to trim round edges
Continued overleaf

through all layers, then satin stitch all round again to build up a crisp outline.

To assemble the picture: Use our colour picture (page 114) as a guide to positioning each piece. Pin, then machine round the edges of the piece to secure it to the background. Use satin stitch for all the smaller pieces, which are being sewn for the first time (hedges, bushes, small trees, topmost building, cows, people, dog, fence). Choose the appropriate thread colour each time, and satin stitch details like faces, hair, legs, shoes, etc.

For the three large trees and all other buildings, use straight stitch to secure the pieces to the background.

Start at the top of the picture and work downwards. First sew on the house, tree and bushes on the horizon, tucking them behind the tan denim; then machine along tan denim edge.

For left-hand field sew cows and the hedge below to green towelling shape, then position towelling on the tan denim with raw edges level at left-hand side; turn in other edges of towelling 2 cm (¾ in.) and machine them in place. Sew on the large timbered house with its adjacent bushes, leaving rooftop edges free.

For top right-hand field sew gold towelling strip to green towelling, turning in gold edges all round. Add the church, then sew field to tan denim and add bushes, gravestones, walls and man on tractor.

Sew on the field below, then add tree (leaving top edge free), children and dog. Sew paved path in front of large timbered house. Then add other houses with bushes, paved path and two trees at lower left (leaving tops of houses and trees free).

Finally add the lower right-hand field with remaining bushes, picket fence and signpost.

Press carefully, then tack round the finished picture area (61×48 cm/24×19 in.) and trim to 1 cm (⅜ in.) outside tacking stitches.

To frame the picture: Start with the inner frame. Pin and machine each strip centrally to one edge of the picture, with right sides facing and raw edges level, taking 1 cm (⅜ in.) turning. Pin and sew a mitred join at each corner, and trim away surplus framing fabric.

Join on the middle and then the outer frame strips in the same way. Press all seams flat.

Place picture and backing fabric together, right sides facing, and pin then machine them together round three sides and four corners, leaving a gap at lower edge. Trim seams at corners, turn right side out, turn in remaining raw edges and slipstitch them together.

Sew three curtain rings close to the top back edge of picture, for hanging.

Trace off these patterns for people, dog and cow. Cut out two cows for the picture.

132

KEY TO CHART

———— BUILDINGS

⌃⌃⌃ TREES AND BUSHES

▫ ▫ ▫ GREEN AND GOLD TOWELLING

——— PAVED PATHS, WALLS AND FENCE

······ ROOF AND WALL POSITIONS

——— TAN FABRIC BACKGROUND

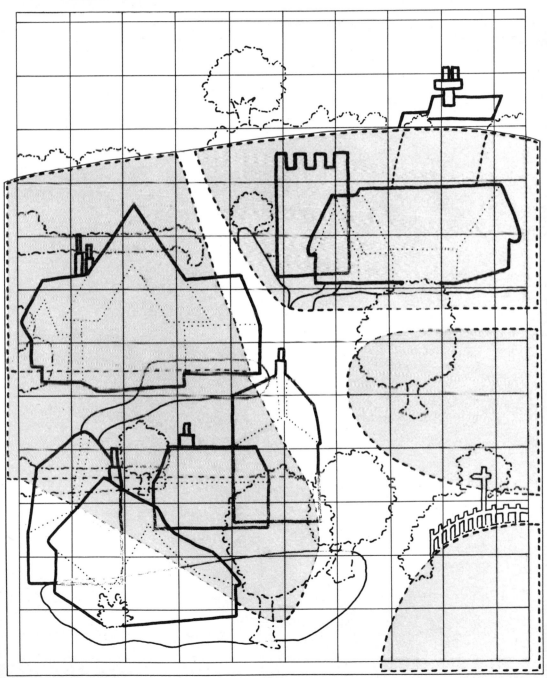

Each square on chart = 5 cm

133

Sweet Rosalind

by Louise Collins

Ben was one of us — the family's
closest friend. For years, we had told each other everything,
and when he fell in love I gave him advice, and
steered him towards sweet, engaging, infuriating Rosalind!

I HAD forgotten just how comfortable it felt, walking with Ben. Ploughing through the thick leaves in Halfacre Wood; coming out by the stile that led down to the farm; chatting about everything under the sun and setting the world's problems to rights. From the year dot, Ben and I had told each other everything.

"Isn't it a pity —" I sighed — "that you can't train men to come to heel?" I watched Wellington come bounding back across the field at Ben's command. Wellington is Ben's Irish setter. "I mean, it would all be so much easier. I could just shout, 'Here, boy!' and Simon Carsdale would come running."

"Who's Simon Carsdale?" Ben asked.

"The Carsdales moved into the Toll House a couple of months ago, just after you went off to university. Simon drives a scarlet sports car, and he's dark and terribly dishy." I let out a hefty sigh. "But he doesn't even know that I exist!"

Ben appeared to be contemplating the distant horizon. "I know how you feel," he ventured at last.

"You do?" That startled me rather. For as long as I can remember, Ben has had a good, sound aversion to anything in the least romantic.

"Yes." Ben cleared his throat. I studied him curiously. With his blue-grey eyes and that old brown chunky sweater, he looked just the same. And yet . . ?

"Yes, I know the feeling," he said again. He was gaining in confidence. He shot me a swift glance. He had decided to go on. "Absolute hell," he said. "But what can you do?"

"Who is she?" I asked.

"Who is she?" He seemed surprised by the question.

"I shouldn't have asked," I said quickly. "Perhaps you don't want to tell me."

"No, it's all right." He sounded resolute and brave. "She's just a girl I know."

"Where did you meet her? What's her name?" I was still flabbergasted.

"Her name? Wellington, stay!" Ben busied himself with the lead for a minute. "There are sheep up here," he explained. Then, with casual nonchalance, "Ros . . . Rosalind. She's called Rosalind."

"Crikey!" I eyed him with new respect. "How distinguished! I suppose she's small and dark and terribly elegant? She'd have to be, with a name like that."

"Couldn't be closer." Ben seemed relieved that he hadn't actually been forced to catalogue the details. He suddenly changed the subject. Enough was enough, for the present, it appeared. "Everything seems to be in hand for the Dog Show. A record number of entries, Dad thinks. I don't suppose you'd like to sell my batch of dance tickets, would you, Kate? You're better at that kind of thing than I am."

H ONESTY COMPELS me to admit that this last request pushed all curiosity about the beautiful Rosalind out of my mind. Ben had given me an idea. As far as I knew, no one had taken dance tickets up to the Toll House. And waiting until the scarlet sports car was parked in the drive was not really a ploy, I told myself. It was just plain initiative.

The same might have been said of the way that I promptly dropped the whole box of dance tickets at Simon Carsdale's feet when he opened the door and smiled at me.

Continued overleaf

"I've heard of issuing invitations," Simon Carsdale said, eyes twinkling, "but isn't this a little excessive?"

I could hear the sudden pounding of my heart. "Oh, dear," I said breathlessly. "Julia always said I was born clumsy."

"Who's Julia?" he asked.

"She's my sister. She went to ballet lessons, and whatever she does is graceful."

"I bet she's not half so pretty, though." He bent to help me retrieve the tickets. He had a way of crinkling his dark eyes at you that seemed both admiring and teasing. "I'm Simon Carsdale," he added. "Who are you?"

"I'm Kate — Kate Mallory. I live at the Rectory. And I wondered if you'd like to buy some tickets for the Dog Show Dance?"

"Well, who could resist that?" he said. Then, "You'll have to tell me all about it first, though, while I decide. It might take quite a time. Do you mind?"

Mind? He must have been joking! The next hour was spent sipping cider shandy in The Partridge while Simon told me all about a Beethoven concert he'd just been to in London. It was by far the most exciting hour I'd ever spent in my life. When, at the end of it all, he bought four tickets and asked me who was judging the Dog Show, I was too deliriously happy to remember.

"I'll have to ask Ben," I said. "He's just come home for his first vacation. His father's the local vet, and he organises the whole thing."

B EN WAS standing by the kitchen window, staring out at the bare beeches, when I found him the next morning. He didn't hear me open the door and I ought to have sailed in on him with some inconsequential remark, but somehow I didn't. It was strange to see him look depressed like that.

"Ben?"

He turned with a start. "Kate! How long have you been there?"

"Not long. Simon wanted to know about the judges. He's got a pedigree boxer and he doesn't know whether to enter her or not." I rambled wildly on about selling Simon the tickets. "He's taking me out to dinner," I ended happily. "Isn't it fantastic?"

"Fantastic." He didn't sound in the least bit thrilled. His expression was distinctly rueful.

"Well, cheer up, then!" I came over to jolly him out of it. "Does it hurt terribly?" I asked sympathetically. "About Rosalind, I mean?"

"Terribly." Ben stood there, just looking down at me. The blue-grey eyes were really wretched. "Ask her to come to the dance with you," I suggested. I hated seeing him like this. It really troubled me. "And wear that new velvet jacket your mother was telling me about. She said you looked amazingly elegant in it. I can't imagine you looking elegant."

"Thanks!"

"That's all right." I grinned. "Where is your mother, by the way?"

"Out shopping."

Casting around for something to say, I tried a little philosophy. "It's never as bad as it seems, you know."

"Isn't it?"

"No, it isn't!" 'Life is very strange,' I thought, 'doing this to poor old down-to-earth Ben.' "Confidence. That's what you need. And a little initiative. It worked for me."

"Ben's in love," I told Julia that night. "With a girl called Rosalind. He's got a sort of soulful look about him, and I still can't get used to the idea."

"Why not? Ben's gorgeous," Julia said.

"Just because he brought you home theatre tickets from town," I said indulgently. My sister is a Shakespeare freak. "I wish he'd stop moping, though. It makes everything so odd, somehow."

I T OCCURRED to me on the night of the dance that, if I wanted things to be normal again, I should have to help Ben in some more practical way instead of just doling out advice. Looking back, I suppose I was in a state of euphoria. Simon had come to pick me up in the scarlet sports car and I was fully aware that his dark good looks were attracting female attention wherever we went. And also, though he undoubtedly registered the fact, that he was steadily ignoring them all and was focussing his considerable charm on me alone.

I suppose I got rather carried away. "I've just spotted Ben over there," I said, extricating myself from Simon's grasp as the music ended. "He's all on his own again. Simon, I must just see if he's all right. Come and be introduced."

Simon said, "Actually, Kate, I think I'll shove my way through to the bar. You run along. Don't worry about me for five minutes. I can take care of myself."

Ben had planted himself next to the door. He had taken my advice and was wearing the velvet cord jacket. If he hadn't been just Ben, I'd have said he looked positively attractive.

"Where is she?" I asked, *sotto voce*, linking my arm through his. Then I spotted a dark, pretty little girl emerging from the cloakroom at the other end. "Now don't tell me . . . that has got to be Rosalind! She's the only girl I don't know, and she looks like a Rosalind. And she's kept you waiting here for ages! I've been watching you." The idea that had been taking shape in my head suddenly surfaced. "Come and dance with me," I demanded, practically dragging him on to the floor. "I've decided to make your Rosalind just a tiny bit jealous. It's time that girl stopped taking you for granted." I wrapped my arms around his neck. "Is she watching?"

"I don't know." Ben's voice was muffled by my hair but it had a distinctly frantic sound to it. It must have been because of my surprise ambush.

"Pretend to be gazing into my eyes — like this." I gave him a demonstration. "And try to look really entranced. Do you know what's the matter with you, Ben Fletcher?"

"No." He was actually getting into the mood of the thing now, I thought. Even overdoing it a little. If he held me any closer he'd have the whole village talking.

"You're much too nice!" Gently I eased myself to a more decorous distance. For no reason at all, I was finding Ben's intense gaze strangely disconcerting. "You've got to be ruthless," I told him. "Let Rosalind do all the chasing. Make yourself unattainable now and then. In fact —" I went on — "it wouldn't do any harm to give her the brush-off for a while."

"You think that would work?" Ben asked solemnly. "I mean, would it make her want me?"

"Of course it would! It's elementary psychology. Don't you trust me at all?"

"**S**O WHAT happened then?" Julia asked when we got home. We were sitting on the floor at two in the morning.

"I'm not sure. When the music ended I steered him back to his Rosalind. Silly name, isn't it? And I made a big thing of thanking him for the dance and I saw him talking to her a little later — coolly, and rather distantly. And then Simon took me off to this little restaurant for supper because he was bored with the dance, and that was that." I put down the poker. "It's a most peculiar thing, I mean, I know that everything's going to change one day. Ben's been away for two whole months now. And there'll come a time, perhaps, when he won't come home for the holidays. He'll get a job and settle down somewhere else and get married to some strange girl like this Rosalind . . . But it felt very odd tonight. I suppose I never thought about it before. Ben's always been — well — one of us. Our closest friend."

"Your closest friend," Julia said. She fixed me with her tawny eyes. "You're jealous," she said.

"I am not! Don't be ridiculous, Julia."

Jealousy? Ben and I had known each other far too long for that, I concluded airily. And hadn't I done everything in my power to help him catch the fair Rosalind? I'd tell Ben all about it when I saw him again. He would think it an enormous joke!

But I didn't see him for three whole days. He didn't turn up for tea on Sunday, which was practically unheard of, "Perhaps he's ill," I said.

"No, he's not ill. I saw him out with Wellington this morning," said Julia "Perhaps he's seeing Rosalind. Perhaps your advice worked."

"He might have rung! Not that it matters!" My feathers were definitely ruffled, though. So when Simon rang I couldn't find much to say except: "Dinner tomorrow night? That would be nice!" I forced gaiety into my voice. "How about the Three Crowns? I love it there."

Simon had already booked a table at some place in Fendale. I stifled my disappointment and accepted prettily. It was only afterwards that I found myself wondering what he would have done about the table if I had refused the invitation, and whether Simon was not just a shade too sure of himself.

I RANG Ben next day. It wasn't that I wanted him to explain his absence. Nor was I in the least bit anxious, I assured myself. But we always teamed up on the morning of the Dog Show and got all the paperwork well under way, and this year, so far, we hadn't even mentioned the subject.

"You didn't come to tea on Sunday," I accused him when he picked up the phone. I hadn't intended to sound reproachful but that was how it sounded.

"Sorry, Kate." He didn't sound very sorry. In fact, he sounded as if he were being agreeably pleasant to a complete stranger. "Didn't have time."

"I suppose Rosalind turned up. I don't mind," I lied nonchalantly. "I mean, don't feel that you've got to come over. How is Rosalind, by the way? How are things coming along?"

"Fine! Everything's absolutely wonderful! I think your advice is working."

It may sound silly, but I could *hear* his smug smile over the telephone. I ought to have been pleased,

Continued overleaf

but I had to fight to sound it. And Ben didn't even mention arrangements for the Dog Show!

"Something wrong, dear?" Mother asked mildly as I marched back into the kitchen.

"Of course not!" I replied. "Why should there be? I do wish people wouldn't ask such stupid questions!"

I'm ashamed to say that that was how I behaved for the rest of the day. I was truculent and irritable and downright surly. And nothing seemed to help. Not even Simon arriving on the doorstep to take me out to dinner. It was a perfectly delicious meal and I ought to have been exhilarated by the assiduous attention he paid me, but I wasn't. I sat there, restlessly wishing that he wouldn't use the word 'basically' quite so often and wondering why his blue silk tie seemed a fraction too tasteful for comfort.

O F COURSE, they were all vaguely surprised that Ben didn't come and pick me up on the morning of the Show. I forestalled their curiosity. I told them Ben had to help his father in the surgery and that I'd told him not to bother. At first I felt relieved that they had swallowed this little white lie. It was only later, as I set out to walk up to The Beeches — the Show was always held in the field at the back of Ben's house — that I noticed the sharp ache in my heart.

There's this old summer house right at the bottom of Ben's garden, where we always start all the organising. I suppose you would call it the nerve centre. It is not at all convenient. On a wet day it leaks and the door creaks on its rusting hinges every time anyone pushes it open, which almost drives us mad by the end of the day. But that's the way things have been done since Ben's grandfather's time and no one would ever dream of trying to change them.

As I tramped across the twig-littered lawn, I already knew how I would greet him. I wouldn't be peevish; I would behave perfectly. That way he would feel the maximum of guilt for neglecting his oldest friend.

The door gave its long, protesting squeak as I pushed it open and assumed my expression of injured pride. At the very last minute I added the sweet, regal smile that would force him into hurried apologies. It didn't, as it happened. He was far too engrossed in clasping the fair Rosalind to his manly chest. It was quite a performance — straight out of one of those old romantic movies — only I didn't particularly want to be in the front row.

In my hurry to get away, I promptly tripped over a pile of rosette boxes and cracked my head on the door. Ben did catch one brief glimpse of my face before I turned tail and ran. For one indignant moment, I thought he was going to grin. He didn't seem in the least bit embarrassed or guilt-stricken. Just utterly and outrageously pleased with himself.

And suddenly I hated him and his sweet Rosalind. I didn't tell them so then and there. I just put all that emotion into one fierce, burning glare and made a positively theatrical exit.

J ULIA WAS bound, at some time or other, to ask why I was avoiding Ben. I didn't think it had been that obvious, but my big sister has very sharp eyes.

"Have you and Ben had a quarrel?" she demanded. She had caught me sneaking through the back door because I thought I had seen Ben's car at the front.

"No." I started to clear the kitchen table of its usual clutter of books and newspapers and church magazines and coffee cups.

"Well, something's wrong. That's obvious. And why are you tidying up? It's not like you at all!"

Sometimes Julia's acute perception is very hard to live with. "It's tea-time, isn't it?" I said testily.

"Not for an hour. It's only cup-of-tea time. Mrs. Fletcher's here. Come for her Tuesday gossip with Mother. She wondered if you were ill. Ben couldn't find you when she sent him down to ask you to supper the other night. What's-her-name went instead, I gather. The little dark girl."

"Rosalind," I corrected scratchily. So it wasn't Ben who was here at all, only his mother. And there was no rational explanation for my reaction; the swift, sharp pang of disappointment.

"Yes, Rosalind." Julia regarded me with her pretty tawny eyes. "Your plan must have worked, then. That's nice for Ben. Mrs. Fletcher says Rosalind's a talented musician. She plays the piano like a dream. After supper they had Chopin for an hour."

"Really?" It's funny how the most trifling things hurt most. Supper at Ben's had always been special, with just the two of us. Spaghetti in the kitchen, and lots of laughter. It wasn't for strangers . . . at least, not until now.

"I suppose it must be serious," Julia was saying. "If Ben has taken her home to supper, I mean. It's strange how things change. It'll be dull without Ben around."

That about summed it up.

I found that I wanted to be terribly busy; not to have time to think. I tried to read and couldn't. I wrote half a letter to my cousin, Dinah, and tore it up again. In the end, I took myself off down to the bottom of the garden and set myself to yanking weeds out of the borders.

IT WAS one of those sharp, clear dusks with birds twittering in a clear autumn sky. Not a good time to be alone. Alone meant lonely. What was extraordinary was that I felt so betrayed. I was absolutely miserable. I felt ignored and redundant and out in the cold.

I was glad Ben had got the girl he wanted. Of course I was glad! I heaved at a tough-rooted dandelion. Only he didn't have to parade it to the world quite so blatantly, did he? For one thing, it was positively embarrassing, all that bluebirdy stuff. 'And what else?' a small voice asked.

The other thing was that I was going to miss him so. That the days yawned ahead, as grey and empty as the sky above. Only knowing what you had lost was not at all the same as being able to do anything about it. I snatched at a bundle of weeds and discovered a rose briar inside.

"Ouch!" It was hard to tell whether the angry tears that followed were of frustration or pain. I flung the offending weeds as far as they would go.

"Kate?" asked a voice behind me. "Are you hurt? Or do I detect a touch of temper?"

I swung round, glared at Ben, and gave him the full force of my fury. "Of course I'm hurt! I've just stuck this six-inch thorn into my thumb! Anyone with the least bit of sensitivity would be showing some sympathy!"

"Poor old Kate!" Ben uttered with hammy fervour. Before I could grasp what was happening, he was enveloping me in a great, over-enthusiastic hug. "Did she she get a nasty old thorn in her thumb, then?"

"I'm not 'poor old Kate'!" I exploded. "So don't you dare come down here pitying me! I suppose your conscience started playing you up! Well, I don't care if you ignore me or not. I don't care if you go around kissing your precious Rosalind in summer houses, or inviting her to supper to play the stupid piano. And I'm not at all jealous, so you needn't think —"

"Oh, Kate, shut up for a minute." And then he kissed me. When he stopped at last, he said, "There isn't any Rosalind. I made her up."

Both optimists and pessimists contribute to society. The optimist invents the aeroplane and the pessimist the parachute.

G.S.

"Made her up? How could you make her up?" My anger seemed to have evaporated. To tell the truth, the world was still whirling from that kiss.

"Kate, don't you know how I felt that first evening? Coming back and seeing you — really seeing you — for the first time in months? And all you could do was ramble on about this idiot called Simon. Where is he, by the way?"

"I don't know and I don't care. What do you mean, you made her up?"

"I thought that if I invented a girl friend, you'd get a little jealous, perhaps. You nearly floored me when you asked her name. But I had Julia's theatre tickets in my pocket — for *As You Like It* — so I called her Rosalind."

"But she *does* exist!" I made an effort and pushed him away. "I saw her. You were kissing her in the summer house."

"That was Theresa," he explained patiently. "You practically planted me at her feet at the dance, if you remember. A nice little thing with a wonderful sense of humour. She's staying down here with friends. She offered to help me carry out your plan and add a little authenticity to it all."

"My plan?"

"Don't say you've forgotten! I had to be absolutely ruthless, you said." The blue-grey eyes were wicked. "Make myself unattainable. The scene in the summer house was Theresa's idea."

"I'll bet it was!" I said with feeling. "You'll be telling me next that you didn't enjoy kissing her at all."

Ben hesitated just long enough for the desired effect. "Now that you mention it . . ." he began. Then: "Kate, come here. You can shout at me if you like — but later. First things first."

I ought to have given him a long lecture. The old Kate would have done. The new one was poised between intoxication and relief. I felt like a sort of Pandora's box, chock-full of new and surprising emotions.

"First things first," I repeated, and kissed my darling Ben with loving fervour.

THE END

© *Louise Collins, 1983*

WINTER

FARM IN THE SNOW

Plump curves, blue shadowed;
Bird tracked, white backed
Humps, and hollows under trees;
Marrow-freeze wind whirling
Fat flakes from big boughs;
Smoke curling,
Sky clearing icily, bluely;
Frost-sparkled washing line,
Fern-fronded window shine;
Birds round the newly
Flung bread crumbs;
Ice-water streaming
Into pail from lagged pump;
Children's breath misting icy air;
White cold, bright cold
Everywhere!

Aileen E. Passmore

IT'S PARTY TIME

The party invitations are coming in thick and fast and you haven't a clue what to wear? Our Fashion Department gives you a variety of simple ideas

A sparkly little jacket can highlight a simple black dress which is perfect for evening wear.

Photograph courtesy of Quorum

If you're not aiming to buy a complete new outfit, with just a little thought and inspiration last year's outfit can happily be used and still manage to look right up-to-the-minute.

The favourite little black dress can be transformed with clever accessories. Try wearing a pretty shawl draped round the shoulders or tied casually at one side. Look for them in high street stores — Littlewoods, British Homes Stores, C & A. Or knit one to tone with your outfit — all the well-known spinners sell leaflet patterns for pretty shawls.

A white lace collar can highlight a basic style; most department stores sell detachable collars. Or hunt round antique shops or markets for an original Victorian or Edwardian one. Alternatively, you may be able to buy a collection of old lace quite cheaply at a local auction.

Another good idea is to buy a piece of brightly coloured fabric and make it into a sash or cummerbund, matching it with a few bangles or a little bag. Or buy a length of suède and make a wide suède belt that ties at the front. If you have difficulty in buying suède write to: Gomshall Tanneries, Gomshall, nr. Guildford, Surrey. They have a marvellous selection of lovely colours. To make your belt, all you need do is to stick down hems all round with Copydex. You could make a simple little envelope evening bag to match in the same way. Offray Ribbons (address on page 13) do quite a few free leaflets on using ribbons, either plaited or woven, to make bags and belts – and they are really very simple to do!

For a casual evening where 'anything goes' you can wear a simple dress or separates. Often a pair of velvet or satin trousers teamed with a pretty blouse — the frilly blouse is still 'in' — or a strappy little top with delicate floaty jacket over it will fill the bill. Most chain stores produce a special collection for Christmas. And don't forget you can always knit yourself a little top. Patons produce a lovely silk yarn, for instance, that would look great made up into a top or two-piece; then there are the soft mohairs in delicious colours and the pretty 4-ply yarns ideal for lacy tops.

Don't forget the little waistcoat/bolero look, which can be so effective. A velvet or quilted bolero looks very glamorous teamed with evening wear.

Dressing for parties should be fun. It's a time when you can experiment with new ideas and different styles. The secret lies in pre-planning; try on everything together beforehand to make sure you've not overdone the effect or that it is dressy enough, and sit down to check for creasing. It's worth getting a second opinion on the finished effect as once you feel happy and confident with what you're wearing, you're bound to have a really enjoyable time!

Twelfth Night Party for Twelve

Plenty of good food and hot spicy drinks for this special festival

Colour photo page 154

Twelfth Night, or the Feast of the Epiphany, is a splendid night for a party; the Christmas festivities are over, the excitement of the New Year has faded and weatherwise it's cold, damp and dreary – so what other excuses are needed for a party! Traditionally there's always a special cake in which a bean is baked. When the cake is cut, the guest who has the slice with the bean in it is rewarded with a small gift and good luck in the coming year. Imaginative choice in food and drink can make it reasonably inexpensive, and what we've done is to give you a choice of main dishes. So, serve either the Paprika Pork or the Oven Baked Kebabs. Serve only one of the hot punches – the Negus is traditional to Twelfth Night.

Christmas decorations are not usually taken down until the next day so that the friendly background of tree, balloons and streamers is still there.

SPICY CHEESE DIP

12 oz. cottage cheese
1 level tablespoon chopped parsley
3 level tablespoons mayonnaise
1 level tablespoon tomato ketchup
½ level teaspoon curry powder
½ level teaspoon turmeric
¼ level teaspoon salt
Pepper

Serve with:
Celery and cucumber sticks,
   potato crisps

A good start – Spicy Cheese Dip and some crispy savouries to go with it.

Mix all the ingredients together then chill for about 1 hour before serving.

Serve in a bowl, surrounded with the cucumber, celery and crisps.

PORT WINE NEGUS

1 lemon
2½ pints water
2 oz. granulated sugar
About ½ pint port or more to taste
½ level teaspoon grated nutmeg

Pare the skin from the lemon in a long strip. Place in a pan with the water and bring to the boil. Remove from the heat and leave to infuse for 10 minutes.

Place the sugar, port and nutmeg in a large heated bowl or jug.

Bring the lemon water back to the boil then slowly pour over the port, stirring to dissolve the sugar. Remove the lemon rind and serve hot.

THE CUP THAT CHEERS

1 bottle red wine
1 litre of medium sweet cider
1 pint fresh orange juice – from a carton
1 pint of water
2 oz. granulated sugar
2 apples, sliced
2 small oranges, sliced
Grated nutmeg

Heat all the liquids and the sugar together in a large pan – do not boil or the alcohol will evaporate. Pour the punch into a heated bowl and decorate with sliced apples and oranges. Serve sprinkled with nutmeg.

TWELFTH NIGHT CAKE

8 oz. margarine
6 oz. caster sugar
2 level tablespoons golden syrup
4 large eggs, size 2
12 oz. self-raising flour
4 oz. walnuts, chopped
1 tablespoon coffee essence
3 tablespoons milk
1 dried haricot bean
For the frosting:
12 oz. soft light brown sugar
3 tablespoons water
½ level teaspoon cream of tartar
1-2 teaspoons coffee essence
Chocolate drops
Two 8 inch sandwich tins, greased and base lined

Set the oven to moderate, Gas Mark 4 or 350°F/180°C.

Cream the margarine with the caster sugar and golden syrup until light and fluffy. Add two eggs, one at a time, beating well after each addition. Separate the yolks from the whites of the other two eggs; beat the yolks into the creamed mixture and reserve the whites in a bowl for the frosting. Fold in the flour and walnuts. Mix the coffee essence into the milk then add to the

Fruity hot punch – the Cup That Cheers, Cookery Editor Liz Burn calls it.

creamed mixture and fold in – the consistency should be soft enough to drop from a spoon. Stir in the bean. Divide the mixture between the tins and level the tops. Bake above the centre of the oven for 50-60 minutes until firm and springy to the touch. Cool for a few minutes in the tins before turning out.

Make the frosting: Place the sugar, egg whites, water, cream of tartar and the coffee essence into a bowl over a pan of hot water. Stir until the sugar has dissolved, then whisk with an electric beater until the mixture stands up in peaks – this takes about 7 minutes. Scrape down the sides occasionally so the frosting does not harden.

Sandwich the cakes together with some of the filling. Spread the rest of the frosting over the top and sides of the cake, using a palette knife to get a fairly smooth finish. Arrange the chocolate drops in the shape of a crown to decorate the cake, adding a piece of tinsel if liked.

The special Twelfth Night Cake has a lucky bean in it.

More recipes overleaf

One main dish – casseroled Paprika Pork.

PAPRIKA PORK

3 lb. boned pork – hand or spring joint
1 oz. lard
1¼ lb. medium onions, peeled and quartered
1 level tablespoon Hungarian or hot paprika
1 level teaspoon caraway seeds
2 level tablespoons plain flour
14 oz. can tomatoes
¾ pint hot water and 1 chicken stock cube
1 tablespoon lemon juice
4 level tablespoons tomato purée
½ level teaspoon salt
3 lb. potatoes, peeled
6 fl. oz. carton natural yogurt
6 pint casserole

Set the oven to moderately hot, Gas Mark 5 or 375°F/190°C. Trim off excess fat from pork then cut into 1½ inch cubes. Melt the lard in a large frying pan and brown the meat on all sides, then transfer to the casserole. Fry the onions until brown then stir in the paprika, caraway seeds and flour and fry for one minute. Stir in the tomatoes, water, stock cube, lemon juice, tomato purée and salt. Bring to the boil, stirring, then pour over the meat and stir well. Cover casserole with lid and cook in the centre of the oven for 2 hours. Cut the potatoes into neat pieces and add to the pork; cook for a further 45 minutes.

Stir in the yogurt just before serving.

RED AND GREEN SALAD

2½ lb. red cabbage, cut in ½ inch cubes
2½ lb. white cabbage, cut in ½ inch cubes
1 large green pepper, deseeded and diced
6 inch piece of cucumber, cut in ½ inch cubes
3 sticks celery, washed and chopped
4 oz. walnuts, coarsely chopped or quartered
4 oz. raisins
For the dressing:
½ pint oil
¼ pint vinegar
2 level teaspoons French made mustard
2 level teaspoons clear honey
Pepper and 1 level teaspoon salt

Place all the salad ingredients in a large mixing bowl and stir together.

Put the salad dressing ingredients into a basin and beat lightly together, using a fork, then pour over the vegetables and turn until they are evenly coated.

Colourful Red and Green winter salad.

GARLIC BREAD BROCHETTES

1 French bread stick
4 oz. butter or margarine
1 large or 2 small cloves garlic, peeled and crushed
1 tablespoon finely chopped parsley
Wooden or metal skewers

Set the oven to moderately hot, Gas Mark 5 or 375°F/190°C. Cut the bread into 1½ inch thick slices then cut each slice into half or quarters, depending on size of loaf stick. Melt the margarine or butter; stir in the garlic and parsley. Dip each cube of bread into the fat and thread them on to the skewers. Place on a baking sheet, cover with foil and bake for about 30 minutes, until crisp and golden. Serve hot.

KEBABS

2-2½ lb. minced beef
1 lb. onions, peeled and very finely chopped
4 level tablespoons tomato purée
8 oz. fresh breadcrumbs
2 eggs, size 2 or 3, beaten
Pepper and 1 level teaspoon salt
1 tablespoon Worcestershire sauce
1 level teaspoon marjoram
12 longish wooden or metal skewers

Set the oven to moderately hot, Gas Mark 5 or 375°F/190°C.

Mix all the ingredients together until well mixed. Divide the mixture into 36 and with floured hands shape each one into a sausage shape. Thread three of these on to each skewer. Place in a greased roasting tin and bake for 30-35 minutes until cooked, turning once during cooking.

Serve with a relish made by mixing the following ingredients together:

6 tablespoons tomato ketchup, 1 small finely chopped onion, ½ chopped red pepper, 2 chopped pickled gherkins, 1 tablespoon Worcestershire sauce, a teaspoon of honey and pepper to taste.

Crisp and golden Garlic Bread Brochettes.

SAVOURY SLICES

1 French stick
4 oz. onion, peeled and finely chopped
2 oz. garlic sausage, or salami, finely diced
3 oz. grated Cheddar cheese
¼ level teaspoon cayenne pepper
½ level teaspoon salt
1 large egg, size 2, beaten
1 clove garlic, peeled and crushed, optional
3 oz. margarine or butter

Alternative main dish: Kebabs, well-flavoured and moulded from minced beef and onion.

Set the oven to moderately hot, Gas Mark 5 or 375°F/190°C. Cut the French stick in half lengthwise. Remove the crumb from the centre of each, leaving about ¼ inch wall. Make the crumb into crumbs, then mix with the onion, garlic sausage or salami, Cheddar cheese, cayenne pepper and salt. Stir in the egg.

If used, cream the garlic with the butter or margarine before spreading over the bread shells. Spoon the stuffing down the centre of each, then sandwich the two halves together. Cut in half crosswise, wrap both halves in foil and bake for 25 minutes. Serve in thick slices.

Savoury Slices from a French stick loaf, hollowed, filled and sliced.

Because of the Tigers

By Thea Ride

Sue didn't want to stop thinking about her
lost love. It was as though her thoughts could reach out
and wind round him, tugging him back to her . . .

MONDAY morning. Sue rolled over and groaned into her pillow. Thank goodness the weekend was over. She didn't think she could bear another weekend without Alan. (Oh, Alan, where are you now?) The pain of it seemed to get worse, not better.

"Sue!" It was Gilly's voice, bright and cheerful. "Are you awake?"

Delicious smells of bacon and coffee, and in swung Gilly, carrying a loaded tray. "I've brought you breakfast in bed, and you're to eat it."

Sue pulled herself up. "Gilly, it's awfully nice of you, but I couldn't."

"Yes you could. You need something warm inside you, it's snowing outside."

Gilly planted the tray on Sue's lap before she could retreat under the duvet, and sat down on the bed, arms folded. "If you don't eat it up like a good girl, I shall be very cross."

Sue almost smiled, but she really couldn't eat. "Gilly, I know you're being kind, but . . ."

She glanced at Gilly's face and took a quick mouthful. Gilly said, "Look, love, it really is time you snapped out of it. It's been three months, now."

"Nine weeks and three days."

"He's not coming back, and you'd better just face it. Forget about him."

"I can't!"

"Yes you can. Think about something else. Take up macramé, learn Chinese. It's pointless making yourself ill just because some stupid, arrogant male ditched you!"

"Gilly, he wasn't—"

"Sue, he wasn't even all that nice to you. I never wanted to say anything at the time, but he was awfully casual sometimes. And always expecting you to run round doing things for him."

"I liked doing things for him. Gilly, you don't understand. I've never loved anyone before, not like that."

"Well, that's great. Now he's buzzed off, you'll find someone like that to love again. Someone who's worth it."

"Like who?"

"Oh, I don't know. There's lots of nice men around if you look. How about your boss? He's very nice, from what I've seen of him. And he likes you."

"Of course Simon likes me, and I like him. You have to get on when there's just two of you working together."

"Well, then! I bet all he needs is a bit of encouragement."

"Oh, don't be silly. He's never been anything other than friendly."

"Does he know about Alan?"

"I haven't talked to him about it."

But he must have guessed. It was nearly a year since she'd decided to give up commuting to London from her parents' Sussex home, and share a flat with Gilly in the nearest town.

It was only a short time after starting work there in Simon's second-hand bookshop that she'd met

Continued overleaf

146

Alan, who lectured at the university ten miles away. When they first met it must have been obvious to the most simple-minded onlooker that she was living on Cloud Nine.

It must have been equally obvious that she had been walking round in a cloud of grief ever since Alan had walked out.

She had stayed in bed for two days, crying, and Gilly told Simon she had 'flu. At the end of that week he'd taken her out for a drink and said, "Sue, you're not your usual perky self. It wasn't just 'flu, was it?"

She shook her head, unable to speak.

"Want to talk about it?"

"No. Thanks."

"It can help to talk," said Simon. "Get things out of your system."

BUT SHE didn't want Alan out of her system. If she couldn't have him, she could have her memories of him. She read and re-read the few letters she had received from him. She re-lived their relationship from beginning to end, wondering where it had gone wrong; sure, finally, that if he came back she could put it right.

Meanwhile Gilly was trying so hard to help that it almost made things worse. Gilly, energetic and optimistic herself, was all for pulling one's socks up, bracing oneself, putting one's best foot forward — and all those other clichés which were the more irritating because they were probably absolutely right.

What Gilly didn't understand was that Sue *couldn't* do any of those things. Alan had been her first love. She had been obsessed by him while he was around, and now that he was gone she was still obsessed. And she couldn't believe that he really was gone. One of these days he would telephone. Or, better still, there he would be at the door. He would scoop her up in his arms, tell her it had all been a mistake. He'd really loved her all along . . .

You will not go far wrong if you garden for pleasure. But you cannot go wrong at all if you garden for love.

C.U.P.

"Sue!" Gilly sounded exasperated. "You've gone into a trance. Listen, it's not good for you. You've got to snap out of it!"

Sue did snap. "Oh, Gilly, stop nagging! I wish you'd leave me alone!"

Gilly stood up. "OK, if that's what you want. I'm going to be late anyway." She was gone before Sue had calmed down enough to apologize.

SUE ARRIVED at work furious with herself, late, and with wet, cold feet. She hadn't thought about the snow when she'd put on her shoes. Simon had already opened up the shop and switched on the kettle.

"It's freezing," he said. "Let's have coffee straight away to warm ourselves up."

It was a quiet morning. Outside the snow fell; inside it was cold. Sue made an effort to concentrate on work, but her mind returned to its usual groove. 'Oh, Alan . . .'

Gilly didn't understand. Sue didn't *want* to stop thinking about Alan. Thinking about him bound him to her, as if her thoughts could reach out and wind round him, tugging him back to her. If she stopped thinking about him, she would lose him altogether.

At lunchtime Simon said, "Let's go and get something warm inside us."

"What, together?" Usually one of them minded the shop while the other went to lunch.

Simon stared out at the street, which had taken on the appearance of a Christmas card. "You know what? I'd like to go up on Windy Hill and get some fresh air. Shut up shop for the afternoon. Want to come?"

Sue hesitated. "I haven't got the right shoes."

"Hang on a bit. I might have some." Simon dived into a cupboard in the back of the shop, and after some scrabbling reappeared with a pair of wellingtons. "Try these for size."

"They're a perfect fit." Sue wriggled her toes about.

"Good. Well, what do you say?"

"OK. Why not?"

He took her to a pub which served lunches. As with so many places in the small town, it was full of memories of Alan. It was here he had said, "I'd better tell you that I don't go in for permanent relationships." And Sue had smiled, thinking, 'Of course you do. This is permanent.'

148

She glanced up as Simon walked over, bearing two plates of steaming steak and kidney pie. Slightly built, rather quiet, with unexpected flashes of humour, he was good-looking in an obvious way. Although he wasn't Sue's type, someone else might easily find him attractive. And he *was* nice. After that one time, he'd never asked her what was wrong, never probed.

She said, surprising herself, "I've been a rotten assistant lately. I can't think why you put up with me."

Simon grinned. "Well, I keep hoping you'll improve. Eat up. You look as if you could do with some nourishment!"

'Everyone seems to want to feed me up,' thought Sue. 'Gosh, I must make it up with Gilly this evening.'

"**W**E SHOULD have brought a tea-tray," said Simon as they stood on top of the hill. "We could have tobogganed."

Only a few people were out and about, the red of a sweater and the emerald green of a scarf making vivid splashes of colour on the expanse of white below them. In the distance there was a faint triangle of steely-grey sea.

"Magical, isn't it?" Simon went on. "I come up here a lot. Helps to blow the cobwebs away."

"Do you have many?" Sue ventured.

"Not too many these days. But coming up to a place like this helps put things in proportion. Look, you can just see the High Street and the roof of the shop, down there. Like a doll's house."

"Oh, yes," said Sue. "And I can see a queue of rich customers beating on the shop door, furious because they can't buy all your most expensive volumes."

They both laughed, and then Sue shivered in a sudden gust of wind. "No wonder they call it Windy Hill!"

"You're cold. Let's go back." Simon started off down the hill.

Sue looked back at their trail of footsteps. "The way we came is shorter."

"There's not much in it. Anyway, I make it a rule never to go back the way I came — because of the tigers." He gave her a serious look.

Sue did a double-take, and then laughed at the idea of tigers padding in their wake over the snow-covered hill. "It would be a pity to get eaten on our afternoon off," she agreed.

They half-ran, half-slid, down the hill, and then walked companionably back through the fields towards the town, not speaking much. 'If it had been Alan,' Sue thought, 'he'd have been talking non-stop. But if it had been Alan, we wouldn't have gone up there at all.'

"Sorry, what did you say?" Simon was beside her, not Alan.

"I said walking obviously does you good. You look all rosy and sparkling. We ought to do this again sometime."

"I've really enjoyed it."

"Good! I like to keep my staff happy. You may be a rotten assistant, but you're the only one I've got."

It wasn't till she was home, with the liver and mushrooms she'd bought on the way — Gilly's favourite supper — that Sue realised she was still wearing the boots Simon had lent her. She wondered whose they were. A former girl friend's? If he had a current girl friend, she'd have known. She suddenly realised how little she did know about Simon. But it seemed too late to start asking personal questions. That would make it look as though she were interested in him, which of course she wasn't.

"**I** TOLD you!" said Gilly triumphantly. "All he needed was a bit of encouragement." Over the last three weeks Simon had taken Sue to the cinema twice; now he'd asked her to dinner.

Sue sighed. "Gilly, it isn't like that. He's having a few friends in on Saturday, that's all."

It was true that ever since their snowy walk their relationship had altered. They had drawn closer together in a pleasant, comfortable way. But Simon had done nothing to show that he was interested in her as more than a friend, and that was fine by Sue.

"We're just friends, really," she added, wishing the phrase wasn't so corny.

"Well, the friendship seems to be doing you good," said Gilly.

"It doesn't mean I've stopped caring about Alan. If he walked in now I'd — " Sue made a helpless gesture.

"Oh, Sue, I thought you were getting over him."

"I suppose I don't feel quite so bad as I did. But Simon isn't going to replace Alan."

"In that case," said Gilly, "I don't think you're being fair on Simon. He's been through enough, I should have thought."

Continued overleaf

"What do you mean?"

"His wife, of course."

"What wife? What are you talking about?"

Gilly stared at her. "I'm sorry. I thought he was bound to have told you. I only heard about it the other day. I was talking to Jack at work, who's a friend of his."

"Heard about *what?* You don't mean he's married?"

"He was. It was awful. His wife was killed in a car crash when they'd only been married about a year. I really thought you knew."

Sue shook her head slowly. "When was this?"

"Not all that long ago. About three years, I think."

Sue felt very strange, rather as if she were heading into a car crash herself. "How terrible. I'm glad you told me."

She could only think, 'Poor Simon. Poor, poor Simon. How could he bear it?'

When she went in to work she found herself looking at him as a person she'd never really known; wondering, 'How do you cope with something like that? How do you go on being busy and cheerful and funny?'

Those boots must have belonged to Simon's wife. "Keep them if you like," he'd said casually when she'd tried to return them. She couldn't imagine handing over anything that had belonged to Alan.

She remembered what Simon had said about tigers. The phrase had sounded even then as if it meant something more to him than a joke. Did he mean you just walk on, turn your back on something totally devastating? But you *can't.* 'Poor Simon,' she thought. 'He's putting on a brave face, but he must be suffering terribly inside.'

When I play with my cat, who knows whether she is not amusing herself with me more than I with her?

Michel de Montaigne

SATURDAY CAME. Sue arrived at Simon's flat above the shop slightly early. "In case I can do anything to help," she explained.

Simon was pink-faced from cooking, cheerful and brisk. "How thoughtful of you. I'm afraid I've got things horribly under control. Why don't you go in the sitting-room and have a drink? Put a record on, if you like."

Sue looked around the small, cosy sitting-room. She picked a record, Mendelssohn's Violin Concerto, and put it on. As she turned away a photograph on the mantelpiece caught her eye. It was of a pretty, happy-looking young woman. Not for the first time that week she felt an almost irresistible desire to rush into the kitchen and put comforting arms round Simon.

Then the doorbell rang and Simon's other friends arrived. There were introductions and jokes and laughter and chat, an amazingly good meal, and more jokes and more laughter. When the other couples had left, Sue offered to help wash up. Simon protested, but she said, "No, I'd like to, really. That was a fantastic meal—I'd no idea you were such a good cook."

"Oh, I hide my light under a bushel," said Simon. "Except for a favoured few." He smiled at her and Sue wondered, as she had been wondering all evening, what was going on behind that smile. But how could she ask him without plunging into what must be private territory?

When everything was washed and dried, they returned to the sitting-room and Simon said, "Let's finish up the wine, then I'll walk you home. I'll get a couple of glasses."

While he was gone, Sue took another look at the girl in the photograph, wondering what she had been like.

"That's Sarah," said Simon, matter-of-factly.

Sue jumped; she hadn't heard him come in. "Your wife?"

"Yes. She was a great girl."

"Simon, I only just heard about . . . I'm terribly sorry. It must have been awful."

"It was," he said simply, sitting down and pouring out the wine. "It seemed like the most awful thing that could ever happen to anyone. But I'm over it now. I keep that particular photo to remind me of the good things we had."

Sue turned her glass in her hands. "Does it just—sort of—get better?"

SIMON GAVE a slightly wry laugh. "I don't know about other people, but no, it didn't just get better for me. People say time is a great healer, but I didn't find it so. By the end of the first year it seemed worse, if anything. Trouble is, when you're a man you're not supposed to cry. You try and keep a stiff upper lip, and people say how marvellously you're taking it . . . But inside I was bottling up all sorts of things. Do you really want to know about it?"

"Yes. If you don't mind talking about it."

"Of course not; I like talking to you. Well, I really thought I was going to crack up so I went to the doctor's, expecting to be given tranquillizers or something. But instead of the usual chap there was a locum — a rather fat, elderly woman. I nearly walked out. But there was something about her . . . I didn't walk out; I broke down and cried.

"She was marvellous; she told me to come back after surgery, and then she let me talk and talk. She listened mainly, but the few things she said helped me see that I had to let go of Sarah. You know, when you've had something good you hang on to it, even after it's gone . . ."

"I know," said Sue, with feeling. "But how *do* you let go?"

"Deciding to was the hardest part. I didn't want to. Until then, I think I'd never really accepted that Sarah was dead. It felt as though if I did, I would somehow be betraying her. But as we talked I began to see that a lot of what I was hanging on to wasn't Sarah at all. It was all tied up with other things . . . anger that I'd lost her, and guilt that it was her and not me, and a great load of self-pity! None of it helped me, and it wasn't going to bring Sarah back. She made me see, this doctor, that there's a difference between grieving and hankering. 'You've got to grieve,' she said, 'but hankering is just self-destructive.'"

S IMON PAUSED and drank some wine. "Anyway, that was the turning point for me. It didn't happen overnight, but letting go turned out to be much less painful than hanging on. Gradually things started slotting into place and I began to feel like a whole person again. And it didn't destroy what I'd had with Sarah; it made it more real, a good memory instead of a fantasy." Simon drained his glass. "I've talked too much, I'm afraid."

"No, you haven't. It's helped me to understand a lot of things."

"It's funny. I've been wanting to tell you about it for quite a while, but it never seemed to be the right moment. But it was in the way, somehow."

"In the way?"

"Of getting to know you better. I've been wanting to ever since you first walked into the shop."

"Really?"

"Yes, really. Don't look so surprised! You are worth getting to know better, you know."

At that moment Sue didn't feel worth very much. All the fuss she'd been making over — what was Gilly's phrase? — a stupid, arrogant male who'd ditched her! Of course it had hurt, but when Simon spoke of hanging on to a load of self-pity, she knew exactly what he meant. Simon had had good cause to feel sorry for himself. She wasn't sure now that she had.

"I've had a few things in the way, too," she said.

"I rather thought you had," said Simon. "D'you want to talk about them?"

She shook her head. "Just now I feel a bit confused. But I think I can work it out on my own."

"Take your time." He stood up. "Come on, I'll walk you home."

S UE STOOD on top of Windy Hill. The whole scene had changed since that snowstorm. The green downs rolled away to a sunlit sea; there was blossom in the hedgerows. Without the snow, she thought, it would be less easy for tigers to follow one's trail. 'Tiger! tiger! burning bright. . .'

Alan was a sort of tiger, beautiful but predatory. Memory was a sort of tiger, too; it padded after you, nibbling, gnawing, teasing you into believing that you'd lost more than you had.

What she'd had with Alan had been precisely what he'd offered; a brief, uncommitted fling, exciting while it lasted. It could never have been anything more. Alan would always step away from involvement; would never give away anything that mattered. Had she really loved him?

Simon had really loved Sarah, and she'd been taken away. But Sue could no longer think, 'Poor Simon.' Simon had depths she'd been quite unaware of, and the courage to let go.

And Simon valued her, it seemed, enough to give her time. No sweeping her off her feet Alan-fashion, dizzying her so that she couldn't see the flaws in their relationship.

She wouldn't keep him waiting any longer. She might not be sure what love was, but she was prepared to find out. She turned and faced the way she'd come. "Goodbye, Alan," she said. "And get lost, tigers!" she added for good measure. A gust of wind caught her words and blew them away.

She began to walk quickly down the hill, towards the town and the shop — towards Simon. With each step, her heart grew lighter. The only fly in the ointment, she thought, was that Gilly was bound to say, "I told you so!" But she felt too happy to care.

THE END

© *Thea Ride, 1983*

Christmas in other places

The celebration of Christ's birthday
by Christians all over the world follows an intriguing
variety of much-loved tradition

THE WORLD'S favourite Christmas song, *Silent Night*, came to us from AUSTRIA, where Christmas is the most important holiday of the year. Fried carp is often eaten for Christmas Eve dinner, after which the presents spread round the tree are opened. Centre of attraction is the replica of the manger scene, its figures carefully preserved from year to year and often handed on from one generation to another. In the mountains, the villagers come to midnight mass carrying lighted torches and singing carols. Christmas Day brings the main feasting, with the best food the family can afford served — roast goose is popular.

On Christmas Eve, the thoughts of Christians throughout the world turn inevitably towards BETHLEHEM. On December 24 the Protestant Mission provides the customary carol-singing in Manger Square and midnight mass is held by the Roman Catholics in the Church of the Nativity, built over the exact place where Jesus is supposed to have been born. On Shepherds' Fields, a mile or two outside the town, many people gather to remember the Christmas story and the star that guided Shepherds and Wise Men to the stable. Greek Catholics remain faithful to the old date of January 6 for their celebration of Christ's birthday, while the Armenian Christians hold their Christmas mass on January 18. To be in Bethlehem at Christmas-time is indeed a moving experience.

In FINLAND, preparations for Christmas start early. On the first Sunday of Advent, called Little Christmas, the first of four candles is lit on a special candlestick, children are given Advent calendars and the whole family helps to make the *pepparkakor*, or gingerbread biscuits, made in the shapes of stars, the moon, pigs or houses. The main feasting takes place in the late afternoon of Christmas Eve — dried salt cod in a white sauce, a huge ham, pickled and marinated herrings, salads, rice pudding with hidden almonds — find one and marriage within the year is promised — and everyone gathers round the tree to toast each other in *glogg*, a heady concoction of red wine, raisins and spices.

The celebration of Christmas is much looked forward to in FRANCE — fantastic shop window displays, trees decorated with lights and tinsel and, in churches and homes, the dressing of the *crèche*, or crib. The figures of the Holy Family, Wise Men, Shepherds and animals are often augmented by models of local public figures like the priest, the mayor, the policeman, butcher and baker. Three masses are held during Christmas Eve, after which families return home

to a feast called *le réveillon* — roast fowl, ham, salads, cake, fruit, cheese. Children put out wooden clogs or shoes in the hearth before they go to bed, confident that Père Noel will fill them with gifts by morning. Christmas Day brings the exchange of presents and further feasting.

Christmas preparations in NORWAY are marked by a great baking session of seven different kinds of biscuit. The sudden thaw that follows the first of the winter's heavy snows before Christmas is known as "the biscuit thaw", reputed to be caused by the heat of all those Norwegian ovens. Christmas trees appear in every window — and on every ship, large or small, in Norwegian harbours. Christmas Eve is the time of the main feasting — usually in mid-afternoon. Codfish and dried mutton can be expected on the menu — both far more delicious than they sound. Presents are exchanged round the tree the same evening and time-honoured songs sung and stories told. The superstitious leave bowls of porridge out for the gnome called Nisse.

Since the Revolution, there has been an official attempt in RUSSIA to replace the religious feast of Christmas with the secular Festival of Winter. Father Christmas has been encouraged to change his name to Grandfather Frost. The attempt has not been totally successful and the old customs persist. Christmas trees, though now called New Year trees, are quite common. Presents and greetings are exchanged between families and friends. On Christmas Eve it is customary to fast until after the first service in the churches — usually Eastern Orthodox — and priests' blessings of homes still take place, with family worship, followed by a special meal shared with friends — the highlight of the festivities.

St. Lucia's Day, December 13, opens the Christmas season in SWEDEN. Christian Vikings brought home the story of the virgin martyred in 4th century Syracuse for bringing food each night to fellow Christians hiding in the catacombs. She carried lights in her hair in order to have her hands free. Now, early in the morning, a young daughter of the family, dressed in white and with lighted candles on a head wreath, serves coffee and St. Lucia cakes, singing the old melody *Santa Lucia*. Between then and Christmas Eve, Swedish housewives must make their homes spotless. Then the feasting begins — a special Smörg–asbord, or Cold Table, with all kinds of marinated herring, meat balls, salads, roast pork with prunes and apple sauce and rice porridge is the traditional fare.

A Father Christmas of generous girth and friendly expression welcomes passers-by to his castle from the window of the famous Au Printemps department store in Paris — a city of special enchantment as Christmas-time draws near and festive excitement fills the air.

153

Young at heart—little girl's charming suit comprising raglan sleeve sweater with three colour pattern band, plus matching skirt and beret. (Instructions on page 163.) *Left:* Party spread for Twelfth Night includes Spicy Cheese Dip, Paprika Pork or kebabs, the special cake and a choice of hot punches. Recipes begin on page 142.

*W*hen wintry winds blow you have to work harder to keep looking beautiful —
lots of helpful hints on page 168. *Left:* Knit a doll with a difference. This is an
upside-down doll (at one end she's wide awake; at the other, she becomes a sleepy
head). For knitting instructions see page 166.

Needlepoint (embroidery in wools or cotton threads on canvas) is one of the
simplest and most satisfying crafts. To learn more, see page 176. *Left:*
Brightly does it, with this striking geometric design mohair mix sweater knitted in
simple stocking stitch in three bold colours. (For instructions turn to page 180.)

*P*lants that bloom outdoors in winter are particularly worth growing. Iris stylosa *(inset)* is a sweetly scented beauty that does well in full sun and poor soil. The Winter Jasmine bears a succession of bright yellow flowers on bare green branches from November to February *(photo: Hillier Nurseries (Winchester) Ltd.).*

YOUR GARDEN IN WINTER

JOY SIMMONS considers the various jobs to be done
as the year draws to its close

FLOWER GARDEN

FORK OVER herbaceous borders, cutting down spent perennial tops and removing old plant stakes. Where necessary, roots may be lifted and divided. Prise the sections apart with two forks and replant the new outer growth.

Rake up leaves from deciduous shrubs and put them on the compost heap. Any dead wood should also be removed.

Complete the lifting of summer bedding plants by the end of November and replant with spring-flowering subjects—Wallflowers, Polyanthus and bulbs.

Clear debris from the lawn and rockery. Then scatter a few stone chips round the necks of rock plants as a precaution against rotting. Protect any soft-leaved alpines with an open-ended cloche.

If moss has been a problem in the lawn, aerate the grass roots by "spiking"—driving a fork into the surface 4 in. deep at 6 in. intervals. Fill holes with sand or compost.

Protect crowns of Paeony plants, preferably with a thick mulch of dry rotted manure.

Finish putting in bulbs. Tulips may be planted well into November and clumps of Narcissi should be planted round shrubs, for naturalising.

Cover Christmas Roses with a cloche to ensure that the opening blooms are completely protected from mud splashes.

Finish digging up Dahlias, Gladioli and Begonias by the end of November and store them in a cool, frostproof place for replanting in spring.

Late Chrysanthemums can be lifted and planted in a frame, top-dressing with a little peat or silver sand to encourage growth for cuttings.

Seedling perennials may be transplanted to their final quarters where they are to flower.

Prepare the ground for Sweet Pea planting in spring by digging and manuring.

Shorten long growth of Roses to prevent damage from wind-rock later. After clearing

Continued overleaf

Forced bulbs can brighten the greenhouse and home.

the beds of fallen leaves, prick over the soil with a fork.

Towards the middle of February, given a mild spell, stems of established Hybrid Tea Roses may be shortened by about half. Floribundas or cluster Roses need slightly different treatment; some of the old stems should be cut back to within a few inches of the ground, pruning new shoots only lightly.

Blackcurrants and Gooseberries can be propagated by cuttings taken in November. Prune Gooseberries, removing crossing branches and cutting out overcrowded ones from the centre.

Finish picking late Apples and Pears before hard frosts, storing them in trays in a frostproof place. Prune Apple and Pear trees, then spray them with tar oil wash to control overwintering pests.

KITCHEN GARDEN

Lift Runner and French Beans and burn to avoid risk of overwintering disease. Finish lifting Carrots and Beetroot for storing in boxes of damp sand in a frostproof shed.

Parsnips, which are usually better flavoured after frost, can be left in the ground and dug as required. The same applies to Kohl Rabi and Salsify, if space permits.

Cut Winter Cabbage and Winter Spinach, and pick Sprouts and Kale as required.

In warmer districts, Broad Beans can be sown in November, for early crops next year.

Continue digging and manuring vacant ground. On soil that is acid, apply lime.

In frosty weather, barrow and stack manure where required for use.

Cover Rhubarb roots with boxes filled with straw, to force young shoots that can be pulled from January onwards.

GREEN HOUSE

Wash down the woodwork and glass. Wash seed trays and pots ready for sowings.

Sow seeds of Antirrhinum, Lobelia, Begonia, Ageratum, Petunia and annual Carnations in gentle warmth in January/February.

Lily bulbs—varieties *Lilium auratum* and *L. regale*—can be potted up, three to an 8 in. pot, in John Innes Potting Compost No. 3 mixed with peat. Leave tops showing.

When Chrysanthemums finish flowering, cut back the stems and top-dress with fresh soil. Cuttings may be taken from December onwards, given a temperature of 10-13°C (50-55°F). Remove new shoots 2-3 in. long, strip off the lower leaves, and plant firmly in boxes or pots of cuttings compost.

Mustard and Cress can be sown under glass for winter salads.

EARLY BLOOMERS

WHY NOT brighten up your garden with some of those invaluable plants that flower in the bleaker months?

If you have plenty of room to spare, consider a border of winter- and spring-flowering Heathers (*Erica*), such as *Erica carnea December Red, E. C. Springwood Pink* (January/March) and *E. c. aurea,* with one or two dwarf conifers.

People with small gardens may be more interested in winter-flowering and berried shrubs, or perennials that bloom in winter. Most popular of these perennials are the deliciously scented *Iris stylosa* (or *Iris unguicularis,* as it's called today), which bears lovely lavender-blue flowers, and the *Hellebores*—the white Christmas Rose (*Helleborus niger*), the Lenten Rose (*H. orientalis,* November/April) with plum-purple flowers and *H. foetidus* (February/April) with clusters of pale citron-yellow bells edged maroon. *Iris stylosa* does best in full sun in poor soil, whereas the Hellebores prefer part shade and rich, moist, loamy soil.

Favourites among the shrubs for winter bloom are *Viburnum farreri* with pink-budded, white flowers, the yellow Chinese Witch Hazel (*Hamamelis mollis*) and the purplish-red *Daphne mezereum,* all sweetly scented. The *Cotoneasters* and *Pyracanthas* are good berry-bearing shrubs. So, too, is the red-berried *Stranvaesia.*

No garden should be without Winter Jasmine (*Jasminum nudiflorum*), which bears a succession of dainty yellow flowers on its bare stems from November to January.

MERRY-GO-ROUND!

Add a touch of variety to her wardrobe with this enchanting stocking stitch suit with its colourful three-colour bands of patterning on raglan-sleeved sweater, skirt and beret

Instructions in 3 sizes

Colour photo on page 155

MATERIALS: *Allow the following quantities in 50 g balls of Sirdar Majestic Double Knitting: 8 white for 56 cm size; 9 for 61 cm size; 11 for 66 cm size. For any one size: 1 ball of the same yarn in each of green, red and blue; a pair each of No. 8 (4 mm) and No. 10 (3¼ mm) knitting needles.*

TENSION: *Work at a tension of 24 stitches and 30 rows, to measure 10 x 10 cm, over the plain stocking stitch, using No. 8 (4 mm) needles, to obtain the measurements given overleaf.*

ABBREVIATIONS: To be read before working: *K., knit plain; p., purl; st., stitch; tog., together; inc., increase (by working twice into same st.); dec., decrease (by taking 2 sts. tog.); single rib is k.1 and p.1 alternately; s.s., stocking st. (k. on the right side and p. on the wrong side); s.k.p.o., (slip 1, k.1, pass slipped st. over); w., white; r., red; g., green; bl., blue.*

NOTE: *The instructions are given for the 56 cm (22 inch) chest size. Where they vary, work the figures within the first brackets for the 61 cm (24 inch) chest size; work the figures within the second brackets for the 66 cm (26 inch) size.*

THE SWEATER

THE BACK: With No. 10 (3¼ mm) needles and w. cast on 72 (78) (84) sts. and work 32 rows in single rib increasing 1 st. at the end of the last row — 73 (79) (85) sts.

Change to No. 8 (4 mm) needles and work the 3-colour pattern, which is worked entirely in s.s. beginning with a k. row, so only the colour details are given.

1st and 2nd rows: All w.

3rd row: 1 g., * 2 w., 1 g.; repeat from * to end.

4th row: 2 w., * 3 g., 3 w.; repeat from * ending last repeat with 2 w.

Continued overleaf

5th row: 1 w., * 5 g., 1 w.; repeat from * to end.

6th row: 3 g., * 1 w., 5 g.; repeat from * ending last repeat with 3 g.

7th to 11th rows: As 5th row back to 1st row in that reverse order.

12th row: 1 r., * 2 w., 1 r.; repeat from * to end.

13th row: 2 r., * 3 w., 3 r.; repeat from * ending last repeat with 2 r.

14th row: As 12th row.

15th and 16th rows: As 1st and 2nd rows.

17th and 18th rows: 1 bl., * 2 w., 1 bl.; repeat from * to end.

19th row: 2 w., * 3 bl., 3 w.; repeat from * ending last repeat with 2 w.

20th row: 1 w., * 2 bl., 1 w.; repeat from * to end.

21st row: 2 bl., * 3 w., 3 bl.; repeat from * ending last repeat with 2 bl.

22nd and 23rd rows: As 17th and 18th rows.

24th and 25th rows: As 1st and 2nd rows.

26th to 28th rows: As 12th to 14th rows.

These 28 rows form the border pattern.

Break off g., bl. and r.

With w., s.s. 10 (14) (18) rows.

To shape the raglan armholes: 1st and 2nd rows: Cast off 6 sts., work to end of row.

3rd row: K.1, s.k.p.o., k. until 3 sts. remain, k.2 tog., k.1.

4th row: All p. **

Repeat 3rd and 4th rows, 16 (18) (20) times.

Leave 27 (29) (31) sts. on a spare needle.

THE FRONT: Work as given for back to **.

Repeat 3rd and 4th rows, 8 (10) (12) times, then the 3rd row again—41 (43) (45) sts.

Divide sts. for front neck: Next row: P.12 and leave these sts. on a spare needle for right front shoulder, p. the next 17 (19) (21) and leave these sts. on a st. holder for neckband, p. to end and work on these 12 sts. for left front shoulder.

The left front shoulder: To shape the neck and continue shaping raglan armhole: Dec. 1 st. at neck edge on the next row and the 2 following alternate rows, *at the same time*, dec. 1 st. at armhole edge as before on the next row and the 6 following right side rows—2 sts.

Next row: P.2.

Take remaining 2 sts. tog. and fasten off.

The right front shoulder: With right side of work facing, rejoin w. yarn to inner end of sts. on spare needle and work as given for left front shoulder to end.

THE SLEEVES (both alike): With No. 10 (3¼ mm) needles and w. cast on 34 (38) (42) sts. and work 32 rows in rib as given for back.

Next (inc.) row: K.2, * inc., k.1; repeat from * until 2 sts. remain, k.2 more—49 (55) (61) sts.

Change to No. 8 (4 mm) needles and p.1 row, then k.1 row.

Work 12th to 14th rows of border pattern as given on back. Break off r.

With w. only, s.s. 2 rows.

Continue in s.s., inc. 1 st. at each end of the next row and the 2 following 10th rows—55 (61) (67) sts.

S.s. 41 (45) (49) rows.

To shape the raglan sleeve top: Work exactly as given for raglan shaping on back when 9 (11) (13) sts. will remain. Leave sts.

THE NECKBAND: First set in right raglan sleeve, then left sleeve to front only. With right side of work facing and using No. 10 (3¼ mm) needles and w., k. across the 9 (11) (13) sts. at top of left sleeve, pick up and k. 12 sts. down left front neck edge, k. across the 17 (19) (21) sts. at centre front, pick up and k. 12 sts. up right front neck edge, k. across the 9 (11) (13) sts. at top of right sleeve, then finally k. across the 27 (29) (31) sts. at back neck—86 (94) (102) sts.

Work 32 rows in single rib. Cast off loosely in rib.

TO MAKE UP THE SWEATER: Press work lightly on the wrong side, using a warm iron over a damp cloth. Join remaining raglan seam, continuing seam across neck band. Join sleeve and side seams. Fold neckband in half to wrong side and slip st. in place on the inside.

THE SKIRT

BACK AND FRONT (both alike): With No. 10 (3¼ mm) needles and w. cast on 91 (103) (109) sts. and beginning with a k. row, s.s. 9 rows.

Next row: All k. on the wrong side to mark fold line.

Change to No. 8 (4 mm) needles and work the 28-row border pattern as given for jersey.

Break off g., bl. and r.

With w., s.s. 2 (2) (6) rows.

Colours with little-girl-appeal include: eucalyptus, festive scarlet, and adonis blue on white; white, banana and caramel on lupin; claret, pink dawn and Balmoral grey on adonis blue.

MEASUREMENTS *in centimetres (and inches, in brackets)*

To fit chest sizes	56	(22)	61	(24)	66	(26)
JERSEY						
All round at underarms	61	(24)	66	(26)	71	(28)
Side seam	22.5	(8¾)	23.5	(9¼)	25	(9¾)
Length	34.5	(13½)	37	(14½)	39.5	(15½)
Sleeve seam	33.5	(13¼)	34.5	(13½)	36	(14¼)
SKIRT						
Length, including waistband	24.5	(9½)	30.5	(12)	36	(14¼)
BERET will fit average head sizes						

Tights from Mothercare

To shape the skirt: 1st (dec.) row: K.2 tog., k. 30 (34) (36), k.2 tog., k.23 (27) (29), s.k.p.o., k.30 (34) (36), s.k.p.o. — 87 (99) (105) sts.

S.s. 7 (7) (9) rows.

2nd (dec.) row: K.2 tog., k.28 (32) (34), k.2 tog., k.23 (27) (29), s.k.p.o., k.28 (32) (34), s.k.p.o. — 83 (95) (101) sts.

S.s. 7 (7) (9) rows.

Continue to dec. in this way on every 8th (8th) (10th) row, working 2 sts. less at beginning and end between the decreases on each successive repeat of the dec. row, until 5 (7) (7) dec. rows in all have been completed — 71 (75) (81) sts.

S.s. 3 rows.

Change to No. 10 (3¼ mm) needles and beginning odd-numbered rows with k.1 and even numbered rows with p.1, work 8 rows in single rib for waistband. Cast off in rib.

TO MAKE UP THE SKIRT: Press as for jersey. Join side seams. Turn hem under at fold line and slip st. in place on the wrong side. Sew elastic into a circle and secure to wrong side of waist ribbing with a herringbone st. casing.

THE BERET

TO MAKE: With No. 10 (3¼ mm) needles and w., cast on 114 (118) (122) sts. and work 8 rows in single rib.

Next (inc.) row: K.2, * inc., k.1; repeat from * until 2 sts. remain, k.2 — 169 (175) (181) sts.

Change to No. 8 (4 mm) needles and beginning with a p. row, s.s. 10 rows.

Work the 12th to 16th rows of border pattern as given for jersey.

To shape the crown: 1st (dec.) row: K.1, * k.2 tog., k.4; repeat from * to end — 141 (146) (151) sts.

S.s. 3 (5) (7) rows.

2nd (dec.) row. K.1, * k.2 tog., k.3; repeat from * to end — 113 (117) (121) sts.

S.s. 3 (5) (7) rows.

3rd (dec.) row: K.1, * k.2 tog., k.2; repeat from * to end — 85 (88) (91) sts.

S.s. 3 (5) (5) rows.

4th (dec.) row: K.1, * k.2 tog., k.1; repeat from * to end — 57 (59) (61) sts.

S.s. 3 (5) (5) rows.

5th (dec.) row: K.1, * k.2 tog.; repeat from * to end — 29 (30) (31) sts.

S.s. 3 rows.

6th (dec.) row: K.1 (2) (1), * k.2 tog.; repeat from * to end — 15 (16) (16) sts.

P.1 row.

7th (dec.) row: K.1 (2) (2), * k.2 tog.; repeat from * to end — 8 (9) (9) sts.

Break off yarn, leaving a long end, thread yarn through remaining sts., draw up tightly and fasten off securely.

TO MAKE UP THE BERET: Press as for jersey. Join seam.

KNIT A TOPSY TURVY DOLL

She sleeps — turn her upside down, reverse the skirt and she's smiling wide-awake! Little girls love her (see her on our cover and also in colour on page 156). All in double knitting, she sells and sells at fêtes and bazaars

MATERIALS: *Allow the following quantities in 20 g balls of double knitting: 2 light pink (a.); 3 dark pink (b.); 4 turquoise (c.); 1-20 g ball of 4-ply in brown for hair; oddments of double knitting in purple (d.); red (e.); white (w.) and black for trimmings; a pair of No. 11 (3 mm) knitting needles; washable filling for stuffing; scrap of dark blue felt; red pencil for cheeks; short length of tape or bias binding.*

TENSION AND SIZE: *Worked at a tension of 24 stitches and 32 rows, to measure 10 x 10 cm, over the stocking stitch, using No. 11 (3 mm) needles the doll will measure 37 cm (14½ inches) from top of head to lower edge of skirt.*

ABBREVIATIONS: To be read before working: *K., knit plain; p., purl; st., stitch; tog., together; dec., decrease (by working 2 sts. tog.); inc., increase (by working twice into same st.); s.s., stocking st. (k. on the right side and p. on the wrong side); g.st., garter st. (k. plain on every row); y.fwd., yarn forward to make a st.; a., light pink; b., dark pink; c., turquoise; d., purple; e., red; w., white.*

NOTE: *The directions in brackets are to be worked the number of times stated after the last bracket.*

THE SLEEPING BODY AND HEAD: Beginning at waist edge of one body, using No. 11 (3 mm) needles and b. cast on 48 sts. and beginning with a k. row, s.s. 14 rows.
   Next (dec.) row: K.10, (k.2 tog.) twice, k.20, (k.2 tog.) twice, k.10 — 44 sts.
   S.s. 5 rows, then break off b. and join in a.
   S.s. 2 rows.
   Next (inc.) row: K.10, inc. in each of next 2 sts., k.20, inc. in each of next 2 sts., k.10 — 48 sts. S.s. 27 rows

Child's dress from a selection at Mothercare.

To shape for top of head: Next row: * K.1, k.2 tog.; repeat from * to end — 32 sts.
Next row: All p.
Next row: * K.2 tog.; repeat from * to end — 16 sts.
** Break off yarn, leaving a long end, thread this loosely through remaining sts.
Make wide-awake body and head in the same way, but using c. for body instead of b.

THE SLEEPING ARMS WITH SHORT SLEEVES (2 alike); Beginning at top of arms, using No. 11 (3 mm) needles and b. cast on 16 sts. — read using c. cast on 16 sts. here when working arms with long sleeves.
1st row: K. across row, increasing in every st. — 32 sts.
Beginning with a p. row, s.s. 11 rows — s.s. 23 rows here when working arms with long sleeves.
Next (dec.) row: * K.2 tog.; repeat from * to end — 16 sts.
Break off b. and join in d. — read break off b. and join in e. here when working arms with long sleeves.
G.st. 5 rows.

Break off d., join in a. — read break off e., and join in a. here when working arms with long sleeves.
Beginning with a k. row, s.s. 22 rows — read s.s. 10 rows here when working arms with long sleeves.
Next (dec.) row: * K.2 tog.; repeat from * to end — 8 sts.
Complete as given for sleeping body and head from **.

THE WIDE-AWAKE ARMS WITH LONG SLEEVES (2 alike): Work as given for arms with short sleeves, noting variations.

THE WIDE-AWAKE SKIRT: Beginning at lower edge, using No. 11 (3 mm) needles and w. for lace edging, cast on 145 sts.
1st row: * K.1, y.fwd., k.2 tog.; repeat from * until 1 st. remains, k.1.
2nd row: All k.
3rd row: K.1, * k.1, y.fwd., k.2 tog.; repeat from * to end.
4th row: All k.
5th row: As 1st row. **
G.st. 3 rows.
Break off w., join in e. — read join in d. here when working sleeping skirt.
G.st. 4 rows.
Break off e., join in c. — read join in b. here when working sleeping skirt.
P.2 rows, then beginning with a k. row, s.s. 62 rows.
To dec. for waist: Next row: K.1, * k.1, k.2 tog.; repeat from * to end — 97 sts.
Next row: All P.
Next row: K.1, * k.2 tog.; repeat from * to end — 49 sts.
Cast off k. wise.

THE SLEEPING SKIRT: Work as given for wide awake skirt, noting variations.

THE LACE COLLARS (2 alike): With No. 11 (3 mm) needles and w. cast on 73 sts. and work in lace pattern as given for wide-awake skirt to **.
Next row: All k.
Next row: * K.1, k.2 tog.; repeat from * until 1 st. remains, k.1 — 49 sts. Cast off.

TO MAKE UP THE DOLL: Join body pieces at cast on edges, oversewing them neatly tog. Now join row ends of work on both bodies leaving tops of heads open. Turn right side out having seam at back, stuff firmly, then draw up sts. at top of each head and fasten off. Tie a strand of a. tightly round each neck to shape it, then sew ends of yarn into necks. For nose, use b. and work a small straight st. across centre of each face 4 cm (1½ inch) up from neck.
For mouth on sleeping face, work a straight st. in b. a bit longer than nose, 2 cm (¾ inch) below

Continued overleaf

KNIT A TOPSY TURVY DOLL *Continued*

nose, then work a small vertical stitch in b. at centre of mouth.

For mouth on wide-awake face, work a V-shape in b. below nose. Cut wide-awake eyes in felt from pattern; sew to face with ordinary sewing thread on each side of nose, about 2 cm (¾ inch) apart.

For sleeping eyes work small shallow v-shapes with black yarn about 2 cm (¾ inch) apart on either side of nose.

Colour cheeks with pencil. To make hair for both heads, wind the ball of brown 4-ply yarn into a hank measuring about 36 cm (14½ inches) across. Cut through the hank at each looped end to form two groups of 36 cm (14½ inches) lengths of yarn. For a fringe, sew a few loops of yarn to each forehead about 5 cm (2 inches) above nose. Cut a 14 cm (5½ inches) length of tape for each head and machine st. centres of yarn lengths to each tape leaving 1 cm (³/₈ inch) of tape free at each end. Turn under ends of tape and pin one end to each forehead above fringe and other end to head at back above neck. Sew to heads through stitching lines. Gather strands of yarn to sides of each head and sew there in bunches. Trim ends of yarn evenly. Plait if desired.

On each arm, pull up length of yarn threaded through hands sts. and fasten off, then join arm seams. Turn and stuff, but add filling quite lightly at top of arms; over-sew top edges of each arm tog. having arm seam at centre back. Sew top edges to sides of body 1 cm (¾ inch) down from neck.

On each skirt, work flowers as illustrated round lower edge as follows, using d. for sleeping skirt and e. for wide awake skirt: work four lazy daisy sts. for each flower, then work 2 w. sts. at centre. Space flowers about 4 cm (1½ inch) apart measuring between centres. Now join skirts to each other at cast on edges, oversewing edges neatly tog. Join row ends of both skirts. Turn skirts right side out and bring waist edges tog.

Put skirts on doll having seams at centre back of doll. Pin, then sew waist edge of one skirt just above centre body seam. Sew second skirt in place in same way. Place one collar round one neck and join ends at centre back. Sew cast off edge of collar to back of neck, then to front of body as illustrated to form a square neckline. Sew cast on edge of collar to front and back of body but leave collar free where it passes over each arm. For belt, make a twisted cord from a 2.5 metre (2¾ yard) length of d. for sleeping skirt and e. for wide-awake skirt, folding length in half before twisting. Knot ends of twisted cord and trim close to knots. Tie belt round waist in a bow at back, then sew to waist. Using d. for sleeping doll and e. for wide-awake doll, make a twisted cord from single yarn, tie in a bow and sew to neck of dress at front.

EYE

You may have to try extra hard to look serene and lovely, but it can be done!

Colour photo page 157

OUR LOOKS have four big problems to face in winter—harsh winds, poor circulation, central heating and lowered vitality.

Take each one in turn and you'll find that with knowledge and a little care you can deal with it, with the result that you can look as delectable in winter as under blue summer skies.

HARSH WINDS tend to dry up the skin almost as quickly as blotting-paper dries ink! They have a drying effect on hair, too, cheating it of its natural oils.

Let's deal with skin first. Never go out on a winter's day with a face unprotected by moisturiser and make-up. Moisturiser, as more and more women are finding, really does help skin to stay softer and more dewy. It replaces the moisture which is continually being lost from the skin cells below the surface. The loss is imperceptible but it does go on all the time and conditions which tend to dry the skin just speed it up, making tiny lines and wrinkles come sooner. So always remember to apply a little moisturiser underneath your make-up. You don't need much, just a speck on cheeks, chin and forehead. Blend it in well and wait for a minute to let the skin absorb it before proceeding with your foundation and then the rest of your make-up.

Use a very bland and gentle soap for cleansing and follow it up with cleansing milk or lotion, or a rich cream if the skin is dry. In cold weather it is more vital than ever to keep your skin supple and well-nourished by using a night cream.

COLD

As for hair which has become dry and flyaway, consider switching to a gentle shampoo, even a baby shampoo, which will not strip away the natural oils. Hairspray becomes even more of a necessity in windy weather and two light applications of a fine spray are better than one over-enthusiastic spraying with just any type of lacquer. Hats can make hair a little greasy, so more frequent shampooing may be needed. In that case, apply the minimum of shampoo and use a conditioner more often than usual.

POOR CIRCULATION results in a pale or bluish complexion, red hands and a tendency to chilblains.

Try to improve your circulation by taking more exercise. Nothing strenuous, just a good walk every day—but remember to wrap up well.

Consult your doctor about chilblains and always ensure that shoes and gloves are roomy

WEATHER BEAUTY

enough, so that circulation is not further restricted.

Clever make-up can make an enormous difference. Choose a beigey foundation and steer away from blue-toned lipstick or blusher. Instead, pick a tawny or coral blusher with a tomato-red or geranium lipstick. The vivid lipstick will draw attention away from watery eyes. You can use tearproof mascara if you don't mind using that more indelible type.

Don't forget to be lavish with handcream. If hands get very red, smooth a little tinted liquid foundation on the backs.

CENTRAL HEATING, blessing though it is, does steal away moisture from the skin. Deal with this problem as with harsh winds. If you work in a centrally heated office or live in a centrally heated house, be especially careful to use a moisturiser under your make-up.

LOWERED VITALITY is something which affects most of us at some stage in the winter and results in colds or 'flu and a general lack of sparkle. Even a beautiful make-up can seldom conceal it completely, so try to keep yourself fit by eating enough of the right kinds of food, getting plenty of exercise and dressing sensibly (preferably with several layers of clothing which can be adapted to suit changing temperatures).

It's important to start the day with a really good breakfast and your daily intake should include adequate protein foods, like fish, meat, eggs, nuts, milk, cheese—plus fresh vegetables and fruit.

A Kind of Hope

By Louise Collins

Looking into Thomas's set little face,
I thought how wrong it was for a child to be sad at Christmas.
But I was on Edward's side, too. It was hard to
understand how this warm, gentle man could ever have
become so estranged from his son

AT FOUR in the afternoon, everyone in the office got edgy. This was the time when the pace began to accelerate. A daily paper was a daily paper, after all, and deadlines had to be met. Only today Emma did not think she was going to make it.

"You've got forty minutes," Sam, the editor, had told her. "Write it clearly and simply."

Emma propped her chin on her hand and sighed. Outside in the square a band was playing. She almost wished that it wasn't. Christmas carols were distracting.

"Anything interesting today, Sam?" That was old Mr. Hotchkiss shambling in through the door for his afternoon chat. Officially, Sam had taken over the job about a year ago, but his predecessor found it hard to keep away from the office.

"As flat as old ale," Sam grumbled. He was crusty today.

"What you need is a pretty girl on the front page." Mr. Hotchkiss threw Emma a wink. "Or a nice little tug-at-the-heartstrings story — with a happy ending timed for Christmas Eve."

"I know what I need," Sam growled. "Finding it is something else. Emma, get on with it, lass. Papers won't wait, you know!"

NEITHER WOULD buses. Emma sighed, watching the one she had planned to catch pulling away into the sleety darkness. Now she would have to wait at Rachel's for an hour until the next one came. Having your car out of action when you shared a cottage five miles out of town was not at all convenient, she was rapidly discovering.

"Emma! Come in out of the cold." Rachel, Emma's older sister, had the baby straddled over one hip, and her face was alight with relief. "You're just in time to keep an eye on the boys while I finish the marzipan. Things are just a tiny bit chaotic at the moment."

"So tell me something new," Emma said with a grin. "All right, I'll see to the boys — provided I get a cup of tea for my pains."

"Five minutes," Rachel promised. Then, "By the way, it's not just our boys. There's Thomas as well."

"Thomas?"

"Thomas Henderson." Rachel shook back her fine, reddish hair and shifted the baby. "Thomas has been staying with us for a few days, since his grandmother died. He lived with her, you see. Poor little Thomas! He's rather a dear. I don't think he quite knows what's hit him, yet."

"How old is he?" Emma asked.

"Six."

"What happened to his parents? I mean, why was he living with his grandmother?"

"His mother was killed in a car crash when he was a baby. And then Thomas's father went abroad to work for a spell and the boy stayed with his grandmother. She was a funny old stick, but Thomas seemed fond of her. She died very suddenly. A heart attack, it seems. Thomas's father — Edward Henderson — got home just in time for the funeral and, as I'd been looking after Thomas in the meantime, I offered to keep him for a day or two more while everything got sorted out. Edward Henderson's a vet. He'd been in the middle of buying a practice up in the Dales when the old lady died. It's just as well he's home, I suppose. For Thomas's sake, anyway."

Continued overleaf

THOMAS HENDERSON had thick brown hair and alert hazel eyes and was pretending to be colouring in a fort he had drawn, but Emma knew that he was watching her instead — warily, as if she might have brought bad news.

"So you've got a new friend to play with, Dom?" she said to her nephew, deeming it better to ignore Thomas for the moment. She sank into a chair by the roaring fire.

"Yes. His name's Thomas," Dominic told her. "He doesn't like beefburgers, so he has sausages instead."

"Really?" Emma solemnly digested this piece of news. "That's a wonderful fort that you've drawn, Thomas. Can I have a closer look?"

"If you like." Thomas casually delivered a rather wet painting. He stood there by her chair, in a rumpled fawn sweater and cord jeans, and Emma knew that it was important to find the right words. "That look-out tower is quite something! You must like painting, Thomas."

"Yes, I do."

"Mind the jar of water, Tabby!" Dom's voice broke shrilly into their conversation. In the small commotion by the coffee table, Emma saw that Tabby, the giant tortoiseshell cat, was making herself something of a hazard among the paint pots.

"Give her to me, Dom," she said. When Tabby had been deposited, purring, in her lap, Emma said, "Isn't she beautiful, Thomas? But she's a bit of a nuisance sometimes. Aren't you, Tabby?"

Thomas's hand came out, lovingly but experimentally, to touch Tabby's fur. "I couldn't have a cat," he said. "Gran said they leave hairs all over everything."

"I don't think they worry about that here." With a rueful grin, Emma surveyed her sister's cheerful but untidy sitting-room. "Perhaps your father will let you have a cat like Tabby. Vets love animals," she added.

"I'd better finish the tower." Thomas took the painting back to the table. It was his face that Emma remembered later. At the mention of his father's name, the shutters came down over the boy's expression, and no amount of coaxing could change things.

"That boy is scared of meeting his father," Emma said, closing the kitchen door behind her.

"I'm not surprised," Rachel replied. "He's scarcely ever seen him. I've got the feeling that Mrs. Fowles didn't exactly encourage Edward Henderson's visits. There was some sort of rift. It's a strange sort of situation, isn't it? For both Thomas and his father, I mean."

"It's worse for Thomas," Emma said. "He's only a child." She dipped her finger into the trifle topping. She wasn't at all sure that she approved of fathers who deserted their infant sons. "So when is he coming to fetch Thomas?"

"Actually, that's what I wanted to see you about." Rachel found her most appealing smile. "Edward Henderson's new practice is in Tarnley, as it happens. And as we'd be driving up there to spend Christmas with Mother, I said we'd drop Thomas off on the way. Only John's got a rush on at the office and now we can't get away until Christmas Eve, so I thought that Thomas could travel up with you."

THE JOURNEY was only an hour by train, up through the bare, sheep-strewn landscape of the upper Dales. Thomas sat in the seat opposite, next to the window. Today Emma found him hard to reach, as if he had shut his true self away in the tower of his fort.

"You'll be able to go out to all the farms with your father, Thomas." She was determined to cheer him up. "And see all the animals. Won't that be fun?"

"Yes," he said, but his solemn brown eyes said something else.

"I can't imagine anything nicer at Christmas." The words evoked a memory from somewhere far back in her own childhood. "I remember having to learn a poem once about the oxen kneeling to the Christ child on Christmas Eve. In my head I always saw it happening in one of those windswept little stables up in the Dales."

"What are oxen?" Thomas asked.

Emma struggled for a definition and wished he hadn't asked. "They're a sort of old-fashioned cow," she told him at last.

Thomas stared back at her. "I don't believe that cows would kneel," he said. "Do you believe it?"

"I did when I was your age. I'd like to now. It's a lovely old story. And at Christmas you believe all sorts of things you wouldn't believe otherwise. That's what it's all about."

"I still don't believe it," Thomas persisted.

"That's because you're a boy," Emma told him. "Boys have to pretend they don't believe in magic. They get called cissies otherwise."

Thomas grinned at last. Rachel was right, Emma decided. Thomas really was rather a dear.

IT WAS good to be home at last. Home was a rambling cottage on the edge of the moors, all twisting stairs and beams that cracked your head, and a great stone fireplace that took up half of the wall. Today, the fire was half-way up the chimney.

Thomas's father was due to pick him up at five o'clock. At six-thirty, Emma heard the phone jangle. It was Edward Henderson. He had been held up with a difficult calving and couldn't get away for at least an hour. Emma tried not to show her disapproval. She supposed it couldn't be helped. "Thomas is quite happy," she said. "He's watching the television. Come when you can."

"I don't know how to thank you." His voice was attractive, she thought reluctantly, husky and friendly.

Edward Henderson arrived at eight o'clock. He had his son's dark eyes and wore a tweed jacket, stout Wellington boots and a harassed expression. "I'm terribly sorry about this," he exclaimed. He ducked his dark head to avoid a beam and spotted his son in a dark corner of the hall. "Well, Thomas, have you been having a good time?"

"Yes, thank you."

There was a short, awkward pause.

"Good. Well, fetch your coat, then. It's starting to sleet, so we shall have to hurry."

Thomas had edged himself back into the doorway. Emma, trying to help, said, "I left it on the kitchen chair, Thomas. Shall we go and fetch it?"

"I don't want to go. I want to stay with you." Without any warning, he was suddenly across the room and clinging to her skirt.

"Thomas, you've got to go." She bent to take him by the shoulders. The panic in the boy's eyes went straight to her heart. "Listen, I'll come and see you."

"When will you come? Will you come tomorrow?"

"Thomas — are you ready?" Edward Henderson's voice was quiet but firm.

"I'll see. I'll try. Come and fetch your coat." Emma saw the expression in Thomas's father's eyes and, in spite of her emotions, she knew he was right. The quicker the goodbyes, the better.

WHEN EMMA returned from a shopping expedition the following day, her mother met her with a strange expression on her face. "You've got a visitor," she said.

"A visitor?" Emma was not expecting anyone. When she found Thomas standing by the stove in the kitchen, she said, "Thomas, what are you doing here?"

Thomas fixed his gaze guiltily on the floor. "I ran away," he said. "I wanted to talk to you."

"But how did you get here? It's three miles from town!"

"He — Dad took me up to this farm. And it was cold and I got fed up of waiting in the barn, and I knew that if I followed the path down over the moor I'd get to your house."

"But Thomas —" consternation filled Emma's voice — "he'll be looking for you! He'll be worried sick."

"I don't suppose he will," Thomas said stubbornly.

"Oh, Thomas, don't be silly!" It was necessary to say it with conviction. "Of course he'll worry!"

"He didn't worry when my mother went out driving on an icy road." Thomas was glaring back at her defiantly now. "So why should he worry about me?"

"Who told you that?" Emma asked, shocked. "That he didn't worry about your mother, I mean?"

"Gran. She said we could get along without him very well. That we were better off on our own."

"I'm sure she didn't mean it, Thomas," Emma said quietly.

When Edward Henderson came hammering on the door, Emma made a decision. "Come in," she said. "Yes, Thomas is here and he's fine. But before you get too cross with him, I want to talk to you." With the sitting-room door closed behind them, she told him what Thomas had said. "Would his grandmother tell him such things?" she asked.

"It's not impossible." His dark gaze was grim.

Emma hesitated. "I take it that you and Mrs. Fowles didn't get on?"

His mouth quirked. "You could say that. In fact, it would be a considerable understatement." He turned suddenly to stare down at the fire. "Perhaps I ought to tell you that my marriage wasn't exactly a happy one. Jill and I . . . well, we were very young. And Mrs. Fowles didn't approve of her only daughter marrying a penniless vet."

"How old was Thomas when your wife died?"

"He was three months old. It was all pretty awful." He moved suddenly, passing a hand through dark hair still ruffled from the icy wind. "Perhaps Mrs. Fowles was right to hate me after Jill's accident. I don't know. It's true that I shouldn't have let her take the car out in that weather. But it was Christmas and she was frantic to go shopping, and we'd had a bit of a quarrel about something her mother had said. The car skidded on black ice. Mrs. Fowles probably wished it had been me instead of her daughter."

Continued overleaf

"Oh, surely not," Emma murmured.

"You didn't know Mrs. Fowles," he said abruptly. Then, "So Thomas thinks I don't care about him?"

"I'm sorry." Now that some of the background had been shaded in, Emma could put the picture into perspective. A possessive grandmother clinging on to Thomas for comfort, biasing him against his father. "I shouldn't have told you."

"Why not? I knew it anyway." The dark eyes met hers for a moment. "That was the hardest thing of all, you see. I knew what she was doing to him. That he was too young to see it all as it was."

E MMA HAD to ask it. "So why did you leave Thomas with her?" she asked quietly
  "A good question," he answered carefully. "I often asked myself that. At first, it was out of a kind of panic. I didn't know how to look after a three-month-old baby, and I couldn't face staying on in the same place. I applied for the job in Sweden on the spur of the moment. It was all too quick, too instinctive. I wanted to get right away for a while. She offered to have Thomas and I thought it was some kind of solution. It wasn't."

Emma said, "He looks like you." It sounded ridiculously inconsequential. The truth was that she wanted somehow to help, but did not know how.

He smiled. 'When he does that,' she thought, 'his face softens, becomes younger.'

"That's something," he said. "It doesn't solve any problems, though."

Thomas went home with his father, but Emma kept remembering his face; set tight when she had kissed him goodbye, his brown eyes veiling what they felt. It wasn't right for a child to look like that at Christmas. Something had to be done. She did not want to think that there was only this terrible ache of compassion and nothing practical to be done. And yet what could anyone do?

The decision to visit Thomas on Christmas Eve was purely a selfish one. She could not fully enjoy her own family gathering until she knew that Thomas had settled.

Edward's house was a small Regency one at the far end of town. Thomas opened the door himself. There was a huge fir tree in the hall behind him and Emma began by admiring it.

"Why, Thomas, what a beautiful tree! Did you decorate it yourself?"

"Mrs. Goodman helped me." Thomas's brown eyes had lit up at the sight of Emma. "She makes the beds and looks after me. I didn't think you'd come."

Emma shut the door behind her. "Well, how silly of you!" She bent to whisper conspiratorially, "Is your Mrs. Goodman nice?"

"She's all right." Thomas scuffed the toe of his shoe. "She keeps asking me what I want for Christmas — every five minutes. She's gone home now."

"I don't expect she's used to small boys. And I won't ask you what you want for Christmas. It ought to be a secret, anyhow. So what have you been doing with yourself?"

T HOMAS WAS about to answer her when a door opened behind them and she heard Edward's voice. "Emma!" Judging by the warmth in his dark eyes, his delight at seeing her was as great as his son's. Today he wore a battered old porridge-coloured sweater, and seemed enormously tall.

"I hope you don't mind," she said. All of a sudden, she felt ridiculously shy. "I wanted to say hello to Thomas."

"Why should I mind? Thomas — see if you can find some mince pies in the kitchen," he suggested lightly. "I'll pour Emma a drink."

Thomas did as he was told, but Emma did not miss a gleam of mutiny in the boy's eyes. He went through the kitchen door half-reluctantly, as if he resented being sent away. In the pretty little sitting-room, with its long, elegant windows, she sank into an easy chair. "So how are things?" she asked.

"Things are excessively polite." Edward reached for a glass and smiled wryly. "Thomas edges his way around me as if I'll bite." He poured the sherry and brought it over to her. "Didn't you notice?"

"Have you talked to him?"

"I've tried." He sank down in the chair opposite. "I wish it wasn't Christmas. Not just yet. We need more time to adjust. I listen to myself sounding all loud and jolly, and it doesn't convince Thomas in the least. It's just awkward. I don't know how to reach him. I can't talk naturally to him, like you can."

"I'm not involved," Emma said. "It's easier for me."

Thomas came in, balancing a plate of mince pies.

All at once there was tension between them. Thomas would not chatter as before. His father's presence had changed the rules of the game. "Aren't you going to have a mince pie?" Emma asked.

"No," Thomas said. "Thank you," he added politely. And he went and sat with a book in the chair by the window, looking as if he was inhabiting some private world of his own, and listening to the conversation of strangers in a railway waiting room. To try to force him out of his mood would be foolish, as well as cruel. Emma did not even bother to try.

"Had a nice afternoon?" her mother asked when she got home. "How was Thomas?"

"Fine," Emma lied. She did not want to talk about it.

T HE NOTION came out of her sleep. Long before even the earliest child was downstairs, she was making a surreptitious cup of coffee and scribbling a hurried note for her mother before shrugging herself into her coat and reaching for the keys of the family car.

Three-quarters of an hour later, she was struggling awkwardly to reach Edward's front door bell without dropping the enormous cardboard box that she held in her arms. Already some of the charm of the idea was beginning to fade. It was the corny sort of solution that Sam would love to see plastered all over his front page. And what on earth was she going to say when the front door finally opened?

What she did say came out in a rush. "Happy Christmas, Edward, I'm sorry I'm so early. I had this sudden idea. I've brought Thomas a present."

Edward's hair was rumpled from pulling on his sweater. There was a grin in his dark eyes. "Happy Christmas," he said, bemused.

Once inside, she said, "He'd better open it in the kitchen." There was a fine rose colour in her cheeks that was not entirely caused by the cold.

"Open what?" Thomas's clear tones rang out from the stairs.

"Come and see," was all that Emma would say.

In the kitchen she manoeuvred the box on to the table. She stamped the cold out of her feet and took off her gloves. Thomas was already scrabbling at the lid, his pyjama collar awry.

"Take care!" she warned. Then, as Thomas lifted out a tiny, furry bundle mewing weakly in the unexpected warmth, "It's a kitten," she explained unnecessarily. "A tortoiseshell kitten, Thomas, just like Tabby."

Only now did she risk a glance at Edward. "I ought to have checked with you first," she said in a guilt-ridden voice. Did his silence mean that he was angry with her? "I know you shouldn't give kittens or puppies on impulse. I expect you have to deal with all those abandoned strays."

"Is he mine?" Thomas shouted.

"She," Emma corrected. "It's a she. Yes, she's yours. If your father doesn't mind, that is."

Thomas stopped the kitten from scrambling over the hump of his shoulder. He shot a quick, guarded look at his father, then away again. "She wants something to eat," he said in a queer, tight little voice. "What does she have?"

"Your father will have to tell you that," Emma said. "He's the expert. I'm absolutely hopeless with animals." She added this last whopping fib, said a little prayer of contrition, and waited.

Thomas stood there, eyes fixed on the kitten. His voice was enormously casual. "Do you know what she eats?" he asked Edward. "And can I keep her?"

"Try half a saucer of milk for a start," Edward told him. "You'll have to make a bit of a fuss of her for a day or two, she'll feel strange in a new house. And of course you can keep her."

A FTERWARDS, EDWARD said, "Emma, you're an angel! He's a different child. We actually had a friendly chat!"

"I didn't know if it would work," Emma said. "I just hoped."

"How long can you stay?"

"Not long. I ought to be at home."

"I'm glad you're not," was all that he said, but the expression in his eyes made her feel suddenly breathless.

Outside, in the solemn hush of the morning, a bell began to clang. "Perhaps you might like to bring Thomas over to tea this afternoon," she said quickly. "If you've no other plans, that is."

"We've no other plans." He just stood there, looking down at her.

"That's all right, then," Emma said. There was this extraordinary, joyful feeling around her heart. She told herself that it was purely because Thomas was so happy, but she knew better than that. "We'll be waiting for you," she said quietly.

THE END

©*Louise Collins, 1983*

STAR QUALITY

What better pastime for a winter evening than embroidering this canvaswork cushion in rich shades of blue and gold? Colour photo on page 159

You will need: Coats Anchor Tapisserie Wool in the following amounts—6 skeins of Tangerine 0311; 5 skeins each of Jade 0185 and 0187; 4 skeins each of Kingfisher 0162 and Powder Blue 0564; 3 skeins each of Peacock Blue 0170 and Amber Gold 0565; 2 skeins each of Chestnut 0350 and Gold 0501; 1 skein of Ecru 0388. A piece of single thread canvas with 18 holes (19 threads) to 2.5 cm (1 in.), measuring 68 x 50 cm (27 x 19½ in.); 40 cm (½ yd.) of matching backing fabric 91 cm (36 in.) wide; a Milward International Range tapestry needle no. 18; a 30 cm zip; matching machine thread; a 35 cm cushion pad.

Notes: Although you can work the cushion without the aid of a tapesty frame, you will achieve a much neater finish if you use one. A hand-held frame is not too expensive and you will find it a worthwhile investment if you enjoy canvaswork. The frame stops the work from pulling out of shape as you stitch and also makes it easier to handle.

The finished size of the cushion is approximately 35 cm (14 in.) square.

KEY		
1a – 0170	⎫	
1b – 0185		
1c – 0187	⎬ GOBELIN STITCH VARIATION	
1d – 0311		
1e – 0388		
1f – 0565	⎭	
2a – 0170	⎫ SATIN STITCH VARIATION	
2b – 0565	⎭	
3a – 0162	⎫ DOUBLE CROSS STITCH	
3b – 0501	⎭	
4a – 0311	⎫ RICE STITCH	
4b – 0350	⎭	
5a ⊡ 0170	⎫ PETIT POINT STITCH	
5b ⧄ 0311	⎭	
6 – 0162 , 0185, 0187, 0564 HUNGARIAN STITCH		
⊟ 0565	CROSS STITCH	

The embroidery: Mark the centre of the canvas both ways with lines of tacking stitches. Mount the canvas on the frame or, if you are not using a frame, tape the edges of the canvas with masking tape to prevent them fraying.

The chart below shows one quarter of the design. The centre is indicated by the black arrows which should match up with the centre of the canvas (where the two lines of tacking stitches cross). *Each background square on the chart represents two threads of the canvas.*

The area marked '6' on the chart (Hungarian Stitch) is worked in 4 colours—0162, 0185, 0187 and 0564 (see Stitch Details). The Gobelin Stitch Variation on the upper and lower points of each star motif is worked horizontally; the stitches on the side points are worked vertically.

Referring to the chart and key, and to the Stitch Details overleaf, begin working the design centrally and work the lower left-hand quarter first. To start embroidering, thread the needle with about 46 cm (18 in.) of wool—anything longer than this will wear thin from being drawn through the canvas too often. Bring the needle through to the right side of the canvas in the correct position for the first stitch, leaving a short length of wool on the wrong side. Hold this end while you work the first stitch, then catch it into the back of the embroidery as you work more stitches. Never knot the wool as you would with a piece of sewing

Continued overleaf

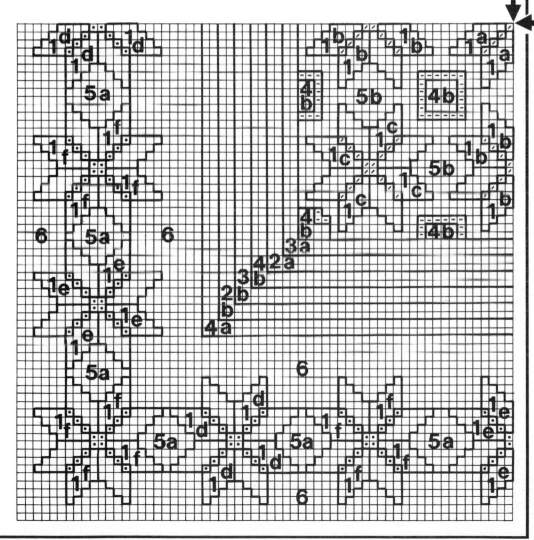

thread, and when you start a new piece of wool, weave it into the back of the stitches on the wrong side.

When you have completed the first quarter, work the other three quarters turning the chart a quarter turn each time so that the pattern matches up.

To make up the cushion: When the embroidery is complete, trim the edges of the canvas to within 2 cm (¾ in.) of the stitches. Cut a piece of backing fabric to the same size as the canvas and place them together, right sides facing. Tack together along one edge taking a 2 cm (¾ in.) seam allowance. Machine along the tacked seam 4.5 cm (1¾ in.) from each end. Press the seam open. Tack, then machine the closed zip, face down, along the tacked seam. Undo the tacking and open the zip.

With front and back of cushion cover right sides facing, machine round the other three sides as close to the embroidery as possible. Trim corners, turn cover through to the right side and insert the pad.

STITCH DETAILS

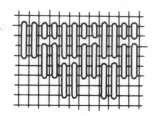

GOBELIN STITCH VARIATION
Work pairs of straight stitches over 4 threads of the canvas with a 2 thread gap between each pair. Fill the gaps with pairs of straight stitches over 2 threads of the canvas as shown. Start the second row of long stitches 2 threads down from the first row and underneath the pairs of short stitches.

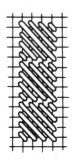

SATIN STITCH VARIATION
Work straight stitches diagonally across 1, 2, 3, 4, 3, 2 and 1 intersections of the canvas threads as shown. Make sure the stitches lie flat and even.

CROSS STITCH
Step 1 Bring the needle through at the arrow, insert the needle at A (2 threads up and 2 to the left) and bring it out at B (2 threads down), thus forming a half cross. *Step 2* Insert the needle at C (2 threads up and 2 to the right) and bring it out again at B, thus completing the stitch. *Step 3* shows the needle in position for the next stitch. Always complete one stitch before starting the next and make sure that the upper stitches of each cross all lie in the same direction.

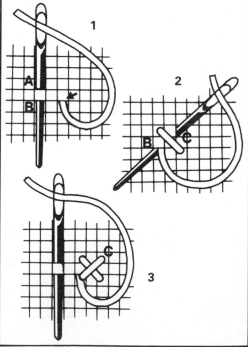

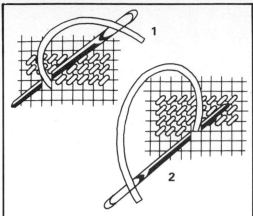

DOUBLE CROSS STITCH

This stitch forms a square over 4 horizontal and 4 vertical threads of the canvas. *Step 1* Work a cross stitch as shown, bringing the needle through 4 threads down and 2 threads to the left. *Step 2* Insert the needle 4 threads up and bring through 2 threads to the left and 2 threads down. *Step 3* Insert the needle 4 threads to the right and bring through 2 threads down and 4 threads to the left, ready to begin the next stitch. Make sure when working an area of this stitch that the last upper stitch of each one lies in the same direction.

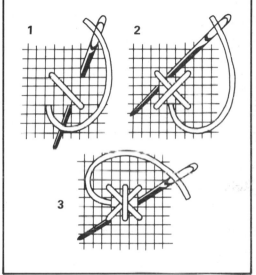

PETIT POINT STITCH

Work rows from right to left then left to right alternately. *Step 1* Bring the needle out at the right-hand side, work a stitch diagonally upwards over 1 canvas thread intersection; pass the needle diagonally downwards behind 1 horizontal and 2 vertical canvas threads and bring through ready for the next stitch. *Step 2* Work the second row from left to right. The direction of the stitches is the same but the needle is passed diagonally upwards. The stitches on the reverse side are longer and slope more than on the right side.

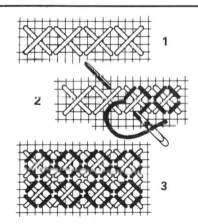

RICE STITCH

Step 1 First cover the required area with cross stitch worked over 4 threads of the canvas each way. *Step 2* Over the corners of each cross stitch, work small diagonal back stitches at right angles, over 2 threads of the canvas each way, so that the small stitches also form a cross. *Step 3* shows a completed area of rice stitch.

HUNGARIAN STITCH

This stitch is worked in 4 colours, following the same sequence in blocks of 4 rows. Work groups of vertical straight stitches over 2, 4 and 2 horizontal threads of the canvas, leaving 2 vertical threads between each group of stitches. Each subsequent row is set alternately into the preceding row as shown.

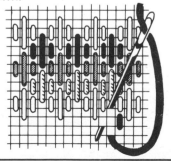

ALL A-GLOW!

Treat yourself to something bold and bright for dull winter days.
Our cheerful three-colour sweater with its bold geometric
design in softest mohair looks stunning with skirts or trousers

Instructions in 3 sizes

Colour photo on page 158

MATERIALS: *Allow the following quantities in 25 g balls of Wendy Mohair: 11 scarlet, 4 navy and 2 white for 81 cm size; 12 scarlet, 5 navy and 2 white for 86 to 91 cm size; 13 scarlet, 5 navy and 2 white for 97 cm size. For any one size: A pair each of No. 5 (5½ mm) and No. 7 (4½ mm) knitting needles.*

TENSION: *Work at a tension of 17 stitches and 17 rows to measures 10 x 10 cm, over the pattern, using No. 5 (5½ mm) needles, to obtain measurements given below.*

ABBREVIATIONS: To be read before working; *K., knit plain; p., purl; st., stitch; tog., together; inc., increase (by working twice into next st.); dec., decrease (by taking 2 sts. tog.); up 1, pick up loop lying between needles and k. or p. into back of it; s.s., stocking st. (k. on right side and p. on wrong side); nil, meaning nothing is worked here on this size; s., scarlet; n., navy; w., white; single rib is k.1 and p. alternately.*

NOTE: *The instructions are given for the 81 cm (32 inch) bust size. Where they vary, work figures within first brackets for the 86 to 91 cm (34 to 36 inch) bust size; work figures within second brackets for the 97 cm (38 inch) bust size.*

THE BACK: With No. 7 (4½ mm) needles and s. cast on 74 (80) (86) sts. and work 10 rows in single rib, increasing 1 st. at end of last row — 75 (81) (87) sts.

Change to No. 5 (5½ mm) needles and beginning with a k. row, s.s. 2 rows.

Joining and breaking colours as required,

You'll have fun thinking up other colour combinations in this mohair-mix yarn—why not try pink tu-tu/heather mist/silver cobweb, smoke cloud/heather mist/honeycomb or orchid silk/blue angel/blue chiffon.

MEASUREMENTS *in centimetres (and inches, in brackets)*

To fit bust sizes	81	(32)	86-91	(34-36)	97	(38)
All round at underarms	88	(34½)	95	(37½)	102	(40)
Side seam	39	(15¼)	39	(15¼)	39	(15¼)
Length	65.5	(24½)	64	(25¼)	65	(25½)
Sleeve seam	45	(17¾)	45	(17¾)	45	(17¾)

work pattern as follows, beginning with a k. row so only the colour details are given.

1st row: 1 (nil) (1) w., 2 s., * 2 w., 2 s.; repeat from * ending last repeat with 2 (1) (2) s.

2nd row: 2 (1) (2) w., * 2 s., 2 w.; repeat from * until 1 (nil) (1) st. remains, 1 (nil) (1) s.

3rd row: All in s.

4th and 5th rows: 2 s. (4 n., 1 s.) (2 s.), * 5 n., 1 s.; repeat from * until 1 (4) (1) st(s). remain(s), 1 s. (4 n.) (1 s.).

6th row: 2 s. (3 n., 2 s.) (2 s.), * 4 n., 2 s.; repeat from * until 1 (4) (1) st(s). remain(s), 1 s. (4 n.) (1 s.).

7th row: 3 s. (4 n., 2 s.) (3 s.), * 4 n., 2 s.; repeat from * to end (until 3 sts. remain, 3 n.) (to end).

8th row: 2 s. (2 n., 3 s.) (2 s.), * 3 n., 3 s.; repeat from * until 1 (4) (1) st(s). remain(s), 1 s. (3 n., 1 s.) (1 s).

9th row: 4 (1) (4) s., 3 n., * 3 s., 3 n.; repeat from * until 2 (5) (2) sts. remain, 2 s. (3 s., 2 n.) (2 s.).

10th row: 2 s. (1 n., 4 s.) (2 s.), * 2 n., 4 s.; repeat from * until 1 (4) (1) st(s). remain(s), 1 s. (2 n., 2 s.) (1 s.).

11th row: 5 (2) (5) s., 2 n., * 4 s., 2 n.; repeat from * until 2 (5) (2) sts. remain, 2 s. (4 s., 1 n.) (2 s.).

12th row: 2 (5) (2) s., * 1 n., 5 s.; repeat from * ending last repeat with 6 (3) (6) s.

13th row: 6 (3) (6) s., * 1 n., 5 s.; repeat from * ending last repeat with 2 (5) (2) s.

14th row: All in s.

15th and 16th rows: As 1st and 2nd rows.

17th row: All in s.

18th row: 2 (1) (2) s., * 3 n., 1 s.; repeat from * ending last repeat with 2 (1) (2) s.

19th row: 3 (2) (3) s., * 2 n., 2 s.; repeat from * ending last repeat with 2 (1) (2) s.

20th and 21st rows: 2 (1) (2) s., * 1 n., 3 s.; repeat from * ending last repeat with 4 (3) (4) s.

22nd and 23 rows: As 19th, then 18th row.

24th row: All in s.

25th to 27th rows: As 1st to 3rd rows.

28th and 29th rows: 2 s. (2 n., 3 s.) (2 s.), * 3 n., 5 s., 3 n., 1 s.; repeat from * until 5 (8) (5) sts. remain, 3 n., 2 (5) (2) s.

30th and 31st rows: Nil (3) (nil) n., * 3 s., 3 n.; repeat from * until 3 (nil) (3) sts. remain, 3 (nil) (3) s.

32nd and 33rd rows: 4 s. (2 n., 5 s.) (4 s.), * 3 n., 1 s., 3 n., 5 s.; repeat from * ending last repeat with 4 s. (5 s., 2 n.) (4 s.).

34th and 35th rows: 1 s. (1 n., 3 s.) (1 s.), 1 n., * 3 s., 5 n., 3 s., 1 n.; repeat from * until 1 (4) (1) st(s). remain(s), 1 s. (3 s., 1 n.) (1 s.).

36th and 37th rows: Nil (3) (nil) s., 3 n., * 3 s., 3 n.; repeat from * until nil (3) (nil) sts. remain, nil (3) (nil) s.

38th and 39th rows: 4 n. (2 s., 5 n.) (4 n.), * 3 s., 1 n., 3 s., 5 n.; repeat from * ending last repeat with 4 n. (4 n., 2 s.) (4 n.).

40th row: All in s.

41st and 42nd rows: As 1st and 2nd rows.

43rd row: All in s.

44th row: As 18th row.

45th row: 2 (1) (2) s., * 2 n., 2 s.; repeat from * until 1 (nil) (1) st. remains, 1 (nil) (1) s.

46th and 47th rows: 4 (3) (4) s., * 1 n., 3 s.; repeat from * ending last repeat with 2 (1) (2) s.

48th row: As 45th row.

49th row: As 18th row.

50th row: All in s.

These 50 rows form the pattern. Pattern a further 6 rows.

To shape armholes: Keeping continuity of the pattern, cast off 4 (5) (6) sts. at beginning of next 2 rows then dec. 1 st. each end of the following 6 rows — 55 (59) (63) sts. **

Pattern 26 (28) (30) rows.

To slope shoulders: Cast off 4 (5) (6) sts. at beginning of next 2 rows and 5 sts. on the following 4 rows.

Break yarn and leave remaining 27 (29) (31) sts.

THE FRONT: Work as back to **.

Pattern 17 (19) (21) rows.

To divide for neck: Next row: Pattern 22 (23) (24) and leave on a spare needle for right front neck, pattern 11 (13) (15) and leave on a st. holder, pattern to end and work on these last 22 (23) (24) sts. for left front neck.

The left front neck: Dec. 1 st. at end of next row then cast off 3 sts. at beginning of the following row.

Repeat last 2 rows, once — 14 (15) (16) sts.

*** Pattern 4 rows — read 5 rows here when working right front neck.

To slope the shoulder: Cast off 4 (5) (6) sts. at beginning of next row, then 5 sts. on the following alternate row.

Work 1 row, then cast off remaining 5 sts.

The right front neck: With right side facing, rejoin yarns to inner end of sts. on spare needle.

Cast off 3 sts. at beginning of next row then dec. 1 st. at end of following row.

Repeat last 2 rows, once — 14 (15) (16) sts.

Work as left front neck from *** to end, noting variation.

THE SLEEVES (2 alike): With No. 7 (4½ mm) needles and s. cast on 30 (34) (38) sts. and work 9 rows in single rib.

Increase row: Rib 3 (2) (1), up 1, * rib 3, up 1; repeat from * until 3 (2) (1) st(s). remain(s), rib to end — 39 (45) (51) sts.

Change to No. 5 (5½ mm) needles, and s.s. 2 rows.

Joining in colours as required, beginning with a k. row, continue in s.s. and work 41st to 50th, then 1st to 4th pattern rows of back.

These 14 rows set the position of the pattern.

Keeping continuity of pattern, and working extra sts. into pattern as they occur, inc. 1 st. each end of next row and the 7 following 6th rows — 55 (61) (67) sts.

Pattern 9 rows.

To shape sleeve top. Cast off 4 (5) (6) sts. at beginning of next 2 rows, then dec 1 st. each end of next row and the 10 following alternate rows — 25 (29) (33) sts.

Work 1 row, then dec. 1 st. each end of the next 6 (8) (10) rows. Cast off 13 sts.

THE NECK RIBBING: First join right shoulder seam.

With right side facing, rejoin s. and using No. 7 (4½ mm) needles, pick up and k. 20 sts. from left front neck shaping, k. across sts. at front neck, pick up and k. 20 sts. from right front neck shaping, then k. across sts. at back neck — 78 (82) (86) sts.

Work 17 rows in single rib. Cast off loosely.

TO MAKE UP THE SWEATER: Press lightly with a warm iron over a dry cloth. Join left shoulder seam, continuing across neck ribbing. Set in sleeves, then join side and sleeve seams. Fold neck ribbing in half to wrong side and catch in place.

Secrets of a Smile

By Jean Buchanan

Warm-hearted, funny, a lover of good food
and gaudy pantomimes, Tania was all that Alex could wish for
in a woman. Dare he risk ruining everything by
revealing the dread secret he had instinctively
decided she had better not know?

183

A LEX FARRELL—twenty-nine, unmarried, brown-haired and six foot three—had a
problem; it was a permanent problem, and it manifested itself particularly at parties.
He was a dentist; a worthy, not to say honourable, profession which combined skill of
hand and eye, patience, tact, and immensely detailed knowledge. But it put people off like nothing
else. Alex's answer to the question he dreaded most, 'What do you do?', frequently caused
involuntary shudders and made people either back away from him or else talk incessantly about their
teeth, and neither of these reactions appealed to him. He understood that doctors had similar
problems at parties. Consequently, in social situations, Alex was loth to divulge his true vocation and
invented other occupations for himself.

'What shall I be tonight?' he thought as he stepped over the threshold of Oliver and Gillie's house,
returning their greeting and commenting on the weather. There was a light powdering of snow on the
ground and the air was freezing—he hoped that it wouldn't snow again. Oliver took Alex's sheepskin
coat and the gaily wrapped present he had brought; Gillie pressed a glass of hot punch into his hand
and led him into the enormous drawing-room, where the party had already begun.

"I don't suppose you'll know anyone here, since you're new to the area," said Gillie.

"No, I don't think I do," said Alex, casting his eye round the room.

"In that case I'll introduce you to . . . Oh, hang, there's the doorbell again. Excuse me. Back in a
minute." She hurried away, and Alex was left contemplating the scene in front of him—about thirty
people standing in tight conversational knots with, over in the far corner, a small breakaway group
dancing to loud music. He supposed that they would almost all be accountants, since Oliver was a
chartered accountant and Gillie, before their marriage, had been his secretary.

'What shall I be tonight?' he thought again. 'Shall I say I'm a tax inspector? Film director? Tax
exile?' He looked doubtfully at the glass of hot punch which Gillie had given him—red and murky,
with half a fruit salad in it. He took a small sip. The punch tasted like paintstripper.

There was a lull as the music was changed, and he could hear fragments of conversation from the
hall where Gillie and Oliver were welcoming a newly-arrived guest. "You haven't got . . . er . . .
what's-his-name with you?" Gillie was asking.

"No," replied a female voice, "he went off with a big blonde Swede."

"I never liked him," said Gillie. "Come and meet people."

A LEX TURNED interestedly towards the door, and then he saw her, chatting animatedly to
Oliver. She was wearing a sea-green dress; her hair was long and dark, and held in place by two
gold combs which sparkled. She couldn't have been more then twenty-five.

"Alex!" called Oliver. "Come and be introduced. Tania, may I present Alex Farrell? Tania
Davies. Used to share a flat with Gillie's sister. Hold on, I'll get you some punch."

"How do you do?" he said, with the slight bow that worked wonders with his older female patients.
Tania smiled at him. 'Marvellous teeth,' he thought. 'Perfect. *Blast.* Why do dentists always notice
people's teeth?'

Oliver wafted back with a glass of punch and gave it to Tania. Once he was out of the way she
sniffed it suspiciously. "Have you tasted Gillie's punch?" she asked.

"Just a sip," Alex admitted.

"I notice you're not exactly knocking it back," said Tania, and tried a little of it, very tentatively.
"Tastes like old socks," she muttered, and then smiled broadly and raised the glass as she caught
their hostess's eye.

"I must confess," said Alex, feeling obliged to take a few sips in sympathy, "that I was looking
round for a pot plant in need of a little extra nourishment. Always assuming it wouldn't kill it."

"That would put hairs on an African violet," said Tania, taking another mouthful.

"Give me your glass," said Alex, "and come and dance. I can't bear to see a lady suffer." He took
her glass and headed for the nearest windowsill. Interpreting his thoughts correctly, Tania pulled the
brown velvet curtain back slightly, but there was already a cache of half-empty glasses on the
windowsill. They both started to laugh.

"Never say die," said Alex, making for the fireplace. He managed to conceal the two glasses behind
the coal scuttle. "It might look," he said kindly, "as though we've put them on the hearth so that they
won't get knocked off the mantelpiece."

"Mmm," said Tania doubtfully, as they joined the other dancers. The music, thankfully, had
become slower and quieter, so that they could talk.

"Do you know many people here?" asked Tania.

"Not many," Alex admitted. "I moved here a couple of months ago. I'm only just getting my house
straight." 'Please don't ask me what my job is,' he prayed.

"What do you do?" asked Tania, and then, without waiting for an answer, she added as she looked
around, "I suppose you're a chartered accountant—almost everyone else at this party is."

Alex nodded vaguely, taking advantage of the supposition. "Awfully boring, I'm afraid," he said quickly. "You're an accountant, too, are you?" he asked, hoping she wasn't.

"No, I'm not," she said, and he heaved a small sigh of relief.

AFTER a slight pause, he asked, intrigued, "Then what *do* you do?" He found himself smiling, though he wasn't sure why.

"I design ladies' underwear," she admitted in a very quiet voice.

"Oh," said Alex, rather nonplussed. "How — er — interesting." He felt mildly embarrassed, and changed the subject. They found themselves talking about the weather, and about the possibility of snowdrifts and frozen ponds. The music changed from slow and romantic to something upbeat and vigorous. Several aspiring John Travoltas began hurling themselves around in attempts to impress.

"Do you suppose they're really chartered accountants?" Tania whispered.

"Certainly," said Alex. "Limbering up for spring when a chartered accountant's fancy lightly turns to thoughts of the end of the financial year. Maybe they've had a bad week at the office. Or maybe it's the economic equivalent of a rain-dance."

"You mean, to improve the British position on the world market?"

"Exactly."

"Looks more like the Wall Street Crash to me," said Tania, as she narrowly missed being struck by an attitude assumed by one of the dancers.

"Shall we go and get something to eat?" suggested Alex, guiding her away.

There was a large buffet set out in the dining-room, and they helped themselves to a selection of quiches and salads, and found some wine to go with it. They discovered that they were both tasting their food with extreme caution.

"It's not bad," Tania said, mostly to herself, with considerable surprise. She caught Alex's eye, and looked vaguely guilty. "Never look a gift horse, etcetera," she said. "I must tell Gillie how nice the food is."

Alex contrived to spend the rest of the evening with Tania, who seemed entirely happy in his company. They chatted to some of the other guests, and Alex listened attentively to the financial parts of the conversation, in the hope of picking up a few tips.

He had the occasional uneasy moment when someone asked him which firm he worked for, but he contrived, with great politeness, to give the impression that he didn't believe in talking shop at parties. Tania seemed quite ready to follow this line, and they found themselves talking about films and the theatre.

Tania confessed that she loved pantomimes, but that she felt too old to go to them by herself. Alex, who remembered seeing hoardings announcing *The Sleeping Beauty* outside their local theatre, made a mental note to ask her to go to the pantomime with him.

Sleeping Beauty. He wondered idly how Tania looked when she was asleep, with her long dark hair streaming across the pillow . . . He kicked himself mentally several times, and made himself contribute several telling remarks on the state of the Italian cinema, to which the conversation had turned.

The evening wore on. People started drifting away. A few of the more energetic guests were heard muttering things about all-night discos. Tania looked at her watch. "Good heavens," she said, "it's half-past one! I thought it was about eleven o'clock."

"Don't worry about that," said Oliver, their host, swanning up. "All the best parties end after midnight. One should take it as a compliment if one's guests stay that long. Gillie's just in the kitchen now, making some more punch in case people would like it before they go."

"It's getting awfully late," said Tania.

"Shall I take you home?" said Alex, almost at the same time.

Tania smiled at him, and then at Oliver. "It's been a very good party," she said. "Lovely food."

"Marvellous party," said Alex. "Thank you. Please thank Gillie for me. I don't want to disturb her if she's making punch."

"Yes," said Tania.

"We'd better get you home before it starts snowing again," said Alex pointedly.

"I'll fetch my coat," said Tania, disappearing into the hall.

"Good night, Oliver," said Alex, following her.

"Hot punch, everyone," they heard Oliver announce loudly. "Or, if you're driving, there's coffee."

"We're driving," a group in the corner chorused rapidly.

ALEX AND Tania got themselves out of the house as quickly as possible, pulled the front door shut behind them, and leaned against the wall under the porch light to laugh silently.

"I'm afraid it was the prospect of more punch that did it," whispered Tania, gasping faintly with

Continued overleaf

suppressed laughter, her face close to Alex's ear.

He could see her breath curling upwards in the chill air, and she was wearing her collar turned up to keep out the cold. 'Irresistible,' he thought.

"Come on," he said. "Let me take you home before you catch cold. We don't want Oliver and Gillie to find us frozen to the porch tomorrow morning. They might try to revive us with punch."

Tania giggled. "It would be like *Babes in the Wood*—they could find us curled up on the doormat, covered with dead leaves by kind little robins."

"I suspect robins only work daylight hours, and all the dead leaves are probably on Oliver and Gillie's compost heap by now."

One thought struck them both at the same time: "Or in that punch!"

"Come *along*," said Alex. He took her arm and helped her to his car across the new inch of snow which had fallen. She skated slightly in her high-heeled shoes, and he felt her weight push against his shoulder and then move away quickly as she regained her balance. He took a firmer grip on her.

"I don't want you breaking a leg," he said, smiling down at her. "I'm not a doctor." 'Not quite,' he thought. 'Do you a lovely set of dentures, though — not that you'll ever need them, of course,' as she smiled back at him.

They reached his car unscathed and he settled Tania in the passenger seat. She looked in wonder at the snow-covered scene around them, with everything—grass, trees, sundial, the house itself—outlined and defined by the snow, which deadened all sound but their voices. "It's like fairyland," she said. "Sorry. I get like this about snow."

"You're going to have to direct me," Alex said, moving off cautiously.

"I do dislike driving in this weather," said Tania. "I'm glad I didn't bring my car."

'So am I,' thought Alex, negotiating the end of the drive. "I'm used to it, actually," he said. "My last job was in the Scottish Highlands. I used to drive a Land-Rover. I've still got it, in fact—I couldn't bear to sell it. I wish I'd brought it this evening, but I didn't realise it would snow again."

"Whatever made you leave the Highlands?" asked Tania. "How marvellous to live there—all that air, those mountains, the clear water."

"I'm afraid it's called professional advancement," said Alex. 'That, and a broken heart,' he added, to himself. "Maybe I'll go back there one day." Some rather painful memories started stirring. He concentrated hard on the road ahead so as to push them to the back of his mind.

He realised that they were passing the new dental hospital which incorporated the dental school. "What's this building we're passing now?" he asked innocently, knowing full well what it was because he lectured there once a week.

"That?" said Tania. "It's the new dental hospital. I've been there a few times, to see people. Not at all bad, really—you know, light, airy, and not too hospitalised. There's a dental school there, too. I'm told it's rather good. This area used to be a wasteland before they built the new hospital. Have you seen the new shopping parade and that rather select development of houses over there?"

ALEX HAD to confess, honestly, that he hadn't. "For living in, I must say that I prefer older houses. My house is Edwardian. Very small. Needs a bit of redecoration. Actually," he added as the thought struck him, "if you're in — er — design and artistic things like that, you must come and see it and advise me about décor and paint and wallpaper. All I know is that there's a limit to how long I can go on living with cabbage roses and blue ribbons all over the walls. 'Structurally sound but would benefit from redecoration,' as the estate agent put it. I need help with the curtains, too."

"I'd like to help," said Tania. "Oh, left here. I live just round this corner. That block of flats by the holly tree with the postbox outside." Alex left the egine running, and helped her to the door of her flat. "Would you like some coffee?" she asked. "After all, you didn't get any at Oliver and Gillie's."

Alex declined regretfully. "I'd better get back," he said. "I don't give much for my chances of starting that engine again if it gets cold. Let me take you to the pantomime on Monday instead."

Tania's face blossomed into a smile. "I'd love that," she said, "if you really wouldn't mind. Pantomimes aren't the same if you go by yourself," she added, with the air of one who had. Alex wrote her telephone number down on a pound note, which was all he had in his pocket, and promised to ring her about it the following afternoon. He drove back home with a faint feeling of exultation, had a hot toddy to warm himself up, and went to bed.

On Sunday afternoon he rang the theatre to book tickets and tussled briefly with their answering machine. Then he rang Tania to report, and arranged to pick her up at six-thirty the following evening. They found themselves talking about interior decorating and gardens and the weather; he told her about Highland winters, and she told him about the local do-it-yourself discount store and the best place to have curtains made. They talked for over an hour without even noticing the time. Eventually Tania said she would have to go because she'd promised to feed next-door's cat while its owners were away, and it was mewing pathetically.

THE ROBIN FAMILY

SNOW FOR CHRISTMAS

On the last day of term, snowflakes begin to fall in the Woodlands

THE LAST DAY of term at Miss Owl's School had finally arrived, making all her little pupils especially happy because that meant that Christmas was only just around the corner!

"Have you got your presents wrapped yet?" Sam Sparrow asked his friend Roley Robin.

"Yes," Roley answered, "and Rosemary and I are going to deliver them tomorrow."

"That is just what we are going to do," chirruped Sally Sparrow, who had just come scampering over. "And I do hope it snows, then we can use our sledge."

Roley said that he hoped it would snow too. Snow made Christmas even more exciting.

As the day wore on, it grew colder and colder and the sky grew greyer and greyer, and when it was time for Miss Owl's pupils to go home, the first snowflakes were beginning to fall like tiny white feathers. Everyone was *so* pleased.

"Now mind how you go," called Miss Owl, as she stood at the door waving her little pupils goodbye. "And have a very happy Christmas!"

At home at The Old Well House, little Rowena Robin stood at the window.

"Look at the snowflakes," she chirruped. "Aren't they pretty? And they mean that Christmas is really here, at last!"

Alex practically counted the minutes until six-thirty on Monday evening. Tania looked stunning in a fine wool dress of deep rose-pink, with a burgundy bag and shoes, and a furry coat. Alex was wearing a chalk-striped suit which he hoped would make him look like a chartered accountant.

Tania climbed into the Land-Rover. "I feel rather like a polar explorer," she said.

"I'm afraid it's not exactly a coach and four," Alex replied apologetically. "I have carried sheep in it, though. Oh, don't worry, it's been cleaned out since then."

"Suits me fine," said Tania cheerfully. "Four-wheel-drive and absolutely no chance of it turning into a pumpkin."

THE PANTOMIME started on time. The audience, who were mostly between the ages of five and fifteen, fell silent — or more or less silent. The court glittered with unrestrained magnificence; the King and Queen were good, conscientious and deeply incompetent parents; the Wicked Fairy cackled evilly; the Dame, who was also Princess Aurora's nurse, wore a false bosom, lots of petticoats and striped drawers, and was rude about the Wicked Fairy.

During the interval, Tania and Alex made their way to the bar. "My one concession to being grown-up," said Tania as she followed in his wake. "A concession aided by the size of the queues for ice-cream," she added, looking back at them.

"Would you rather have a choc-ice or something?" asked Alex. "I'll go and queue."

"No, really, thank you," said Tania, realising that any man who was prepared to go and queue for ice-cream for her at a pantomime was clearly a man to be reckoned with. "I'll be very happy with a drink. When I was a little girl I thought it would be the most sophisticated thing in the world to be able to go into the bar at the theatre. . . A glass of white wine, please," she said in answer to his raised eyebrow.

As Alex returned with their wine, he noticed a number of children's faces peering around the entrance to the bar, eating ice lollies and drinking orange squash from cartons through straws. Their gazes appeared fixed on Tania, but she was unaware of them because her back was to them. She half-turned to gesture in the direction of the stage while discussing the design of the sets with Alex, and saw the children looking at her.

"Hello, Miss Davies," they chorused.

Continued overleaf

"Hello," said Tania, smiling at them. "They live in my road," she explained.

"All of them?" asked Alex.

"It's a big road," she said. "Local school."

The children continued to observed Tania closely until their parents, who had been drinking coffee, came up and told them that it was rude to stare.

"I like you better with long hair," said one of the little girls in a parting shot as she was whisked off back to her seat.

In answer to the quizzical expression which had crossed Alex's face Tania said, "I put my hair up for work to keep it out of the way. They're used to seeing me like that. Usually I pin it up in a plait. I have this ambition to look like one of the beauty consultants that one sees in department stores. You know — cool, gracious, and faintly glamorous."

Alex tried to imagine her with her hair up. "You look glamorous to me, already," he said.

THE FIVE-MINUTE bell rang. Alex's heart sank as, with the bar clearing, he caught sight of a face he recognised. A patient who, given half a chance, would reveal his true identity to the world.

"Hello, Mr. Farrell," the man bellowed as he got nearer. "Fancy seeing you here. I didn't realise you'd come to anything so innocuous as the panto."

"Hello, Mr. James," Alex shouted back, mostly to stop him before he could say anything more. "Enjoying it?" Mr. James nodded enthusiastically and waved a hand in the direction of his wife and family who were waiting patiently outside the bar.

"One of my clients," Alex muttered, just stopping himself in time from saying 'patients'. Another bell rang. Alex took Tania's arm and guided her back to their seats.

It all ended satisfactorily: the handsome Prince woke Aurora with a kiss, the Wicked Fairy exploded with rage and disappeared through a trap door, and everyone else was invited to the Royal Wedding.

Alex took Tania home and accepted her invitation to stay for coffee and chocolate cake. He sat in a large, throne-like wing chair while Tania rushed about fetching cups and saucers and putting the coffee machine on.

"No, thank you," she said, "you can't help me — look at the size of the kitchen." Alex saw her point: the kitchen was really what brochures call a 'kitchen area', the basic essentials concealed behind folding louvre doors. "Not designed by anyone who cooked seriously," she said.

"Talking about kitchens," said Alex, "would you come and look at mine? I want to get it completely revamped and I don't know where to start. The same goes for the rest of the house. I feel that my possessions are rattling around in it like peas in a pod."

"At least you've got *space*," said Tania. "I've more or less filled this place."

Alex cast his eye over the room — it was furnished with some very good pieces, beautifully upholstered.

"I got the furniture at sales," Tania said, "and I know someone who upholsters very well. I love going round salerooms. It's something I do at lunchtimes."

At half-past eleven, very reluctantly, he decided that he ought to go home. "I've got a lot to do tomorrow," he told Tania, "and, anyway, I might turn into a pumpkin if I stay after midnight. How will you get to work tomorrow? I could give you a lift in the Land-Rover." Tania thanked him, but said that there was a very good bus service, and she would wear her fell boots. Alex insisted on giving her his phone number. "Let me know if you need a lift," he said. "I get up very early."

HE WENT home, half-hoping that she would call him in the morning and ask for a lift, but she didn't. The snow continued for the whole of the next day. He rang up to ask how she had got on. He invited her to his house the following Saturday afternoon, ostensibly to advise on décor, and asked her to stay for dinner as well. She said that she would like that very much, and promised to look out for good pieces of furniture for him on the viewing days of the next sale of antique furniture at the local auctioneer's. She would probably look in on Thursday lunchtime and let him know if there was anything worth having, so that he could bid for it at the sale on Friday.

Alex made sure he was in the auctioneer's saleroom on Thursday lunchtime by five-past one.

At quarter-past one, Tania came bustling in, in a pine-green coat and dark brown boots. Alex almost didn't recognise her for a moment because her hair was pinned up in a plait, as she had said. Her dark eyes looked enormous, and her face was revealed as a perfect heart-shape. Alex couldn't decide whether he preferred her hair up or down. She looked around the saleroom and he waved to her. She smiled and crossed the room to him.

"Hello," she said, "at least it's warm in here. Seen anything you like?"

'You,' he could have said. 'You.' "I've only just got here myself," he said instead, offering her the catalogue. "Have you had any lunch?"

"I just had a quick sandwich in the office. How about you?"

"I've got until three o'clock to get something."

They agreed to look around the saleroom first, and then see whether there was enough time left for coffee. Tania studied the catalogue intently, and began to examine various pieces of furniture, pulling out drawers and banging them, prodding chairs and sofas, and getting Alex to upend them so that she could look at the webbing underneath.

"Hello, hello," said a voice behind them just as Alex was righting a chaise-longue. "I see you two have got together, then." Alex turned round. It was Ted Lucas, who had a dental surgery a few doors along from his in one of the medical quarters of the town.

"Hello, Ted," said Alex, none too enthusiastically, hoping that he could prevent him from launching into shop talk. He turned to Tania. "Do you know Ted Lucas?" he began.

Tania smiled. "Yes, I know Ted. Hello. We've known each other for years . . . It's quite a small town," she added, for Alex's benefit. Alex looked frostily at Ted and wished he would go away, but Ted appeared completely oblivious, and said, "By the way, Alex, I wanted to ask you about . . ."

Alex managed to stem this potentially disastrous flow of words by saying, "Would you ring me about it later? We haven't got all that much time." Ted nodded understandingly and wandered off to look at a tallboy.

ACROSS THE road they found a pretty little coffee shop with scrubbed pine tables and gingham curtains, and over a pot of coffee they discussed the better items in the sale. "I did like that chaise-longue, with the crimson velvet upholstery," said Tania, "I've always wanted to have a chaise-longue, but my flat's too small. It really is quite a nice piece, not too heavy although it's Victorian."

Alex decided to take her advice and bid for the chaise-longue, and she told him about the system by which saleroom staff would bid up to a given limit on behalf of an absent customer. Then she had to rush back to work, and Alex arranged to bid for the chaise-longue and for a chest of drawers that Tania had rather liked. He looked around the saleroom for Ted Lucas but discovered that he had left, then drove off to the dental school.

Alex rang Tania on Friday evening, first of all to arrange to pick her up on Saturday afternoon, and secondly to tell her that he had succeeded in acquiring both the chaise-longue and the chest of drawers. She sounded pleased, and promised to bring all sorts of colour charts and fabric samples with her.

In the time between then and the following afternoon, Alex tidied up the house assiduously, carefully collecting up copies of *The British Dental Journal* and stowing them under his bed, along with everything else that was lying about downstairs that might arouse Tania's suspicions, such as free samples of toothpaste, literature advertising assorted bits of dental equipment, and his lecture notes.

On Saturday morning he got up early, went out shopping, and bought some wine and the ingredients for dinner. Next, on a sudden thought, he went into the newsagent and bought the *Financial Times* and a selection of accountancy journals. When he got home, he distributed these casually around the sitting-room, and roughed the pages up a bit so that they would look as though they'd been read. He stood back to survey his handiwork, and thought it looked very convincing.

He told the roses-and-ribbons wallpaper, with considerable glee, that its days were numbered, and tried to imagine the room, uncluttered and elegant, as he hoped Tania would help him to redesign it. He had a very quick lunch, prepared a casserole and a pudding for dinner, and went to fetch Tania. He was on time, and she was ready.

She was wearing a hyacinth-blue cord dress, and her hair was loose, flowing around her shoulders. He commented on that, and she laughed. "When my hair's down, I know I'm not working." He carried a large bag of bits and pieces for her, and when they got to his house she unpacked it on the floor of the sitting-room, producing shade cards, scraps of velvet, a paint brush, a fruit cake and a bottle of white wine.

These last two she gave to him. "House-warming present," she said. Then, "Wow," she added, as she noticed the wallpaper. Alex felt quite overcome, realising even as he thanked her that here was a woman who could cook and select a decent bottle of wine, *and* share his taste in wallpaper.

He took her on a tour of the house, then they had tea and ate some fruit cake, and discussed colours and furnishings, and where to put the chaise-longue and the chest of drawers. For Alex the afternoon passed in a few minutes.

Tania chatted to him in the kitchen, miraculously not getting in the way as he cooked vegetables, chopped parsley and put the finishing touches to the casserole. He asked her to check the table which he had set in the tiny dining-room, and to light the candles which he had put out in the hope of keeping the illumination low enough to conceal the waterlilies-on-ponds wallpaper.

Tania looked just as beautiful by candlelight, smiling at him across the flame. They took their time

Continued overleaf

over dinner, and then moved back to the dimly-lit sitting-room for coffee.

"That was a marvellous dinner," said Tania, leaning back on the chaise-longue sybaritically. "You must be a man of many talents."

'If you only knew,' thought Alex, smiling brightly at her.

"I could sleep for a hundred years on this," said Tania, patting the chaise-longue.

"Have some coffee first," said Alex, passing her a cup.

TANIA LOOKED around the room. "You know," she said, "this is a lovely house. It has a very friendly atmosphere. It needs to be looked after, and loved . . ."

"So does its owner," said Alex, and took her hand. He caught the smile in her eyes, and kissed her gently.

From that moment, they were out of each other's company as little as possible. They met almost every evening, and Tania spent most Saturdays and Sundays helping Alex to sort his house out. When she was not there, Alex felt that his house was large and lonely without her. He sat in his bedroom dealing with the correspondence, papers and journals that he did not dare leave downstairs in case she saw them. 'It's no good,' he thought finally, 'I'm going to have to tell her. What will she say when she knows I'm a dentist? Still, a rose by any other name . . .'

His gaze strayed to the phone, and he looked at his watch. It wasn't too late in the evening to telephone her. He picked up the receiver, and then put it down again. He had to see her. He rushed down the stairs, grabbed his jacket, and ran for the Land-Rover. Quarter-of-an-hour later he was hammering at her door. "Who is it?" she called.

"Me, Alex."

"Just a minute."

There was a few seconds' pause and then the door opened. "Is anything the matter?" asked Tania. "I thought you were going to spend this evening writing letters. Would you like some tea?"

"No. Yes. There's something I've got to tell you." There was a note of urgency in his voice.

"Don't tell me," said Tania lightly, leading the way to her sitting-room. "Wife and six children in Birmingham."

"Don't be ridiculous."

"Just a wife then?" Her voice was a little shaky.

"Of course not. I'm not married. I want to marry *you*. How could you possibly imagine I'm married? It's about my job. I've lied to you shamelessly. I'm *not* a chartered accountant . . ."

"You're an *un*chartered accountant, then?"

"No, nothing like that."

"You're not an inspector of taxes, are you?"

"Good heavens, no." The conversation was defeating Alex. "I'm a dentist," he said lamely.

TANIA LOOKED utterly surprised. Her face went blank for a moment, and then she started to laugh. She laughed so much that she had to sit down on her elderly, cushion-covered sofa.

"You're not angry?" said Alex, but she just went on laughing. He sat down next to her and put his arm round her. "What is it?" he said. "What's so funny about that? I only told you that I'm a dentist."

"So am I," said Tania, in between gasps, and buried her face in his jersey. When she finally stopped laughing, she said, "I'd learned to conceal my profession in exactly the same way you did. You picked accountancy because everyone else at that party was an accountant, and anyway people tend to think accountancy's either very boring or too complicated for them to understand. And I picked underwear design because — well — the nicer sort of a man feels that he shouldn't really ask any questions about it."

"You'd better marry me so that we can end all this deceit," said Alex, and kissed her.

"Yes, please," she said, shifting so that she could put her arms around him. The sofa creaked in protest at the sudden movement and, from underneath the cushion at her elbow, several copies of *The British Dental Journal* slid gracefully to the floor.

THE END

© *Jean Buchanan, 1983*